ELEMENTS

of

ATOMIC PHYSICS

PRENTICE-HALL PHYSICS SERIES

ELEMENTS

of

ATOMIC PHYSICS

BY

D. C. Peaslee

**Associate Professor of Physics
Purdue University**

EDITED BY

H. Mueller

**Professor of Physics
Massachusetts Institute of Technology**

Englewood Cliffs, N. J.

PRENTICE-HALL, INC.

Library of Congress Card Catalog Number: 55:7572.

First printing .... *March, 1955*
Second printing .. *March, 1956*
Third printing ...... *July, 1958*

26259

FOREWORD

The undergraduate student usually begins his study of atomic physics with great interest and anticipation but soon encounters two difficulties. The first is due to the fact that he must learn to deal confidently with numerical quantities whose significance is beyond the reach of anyone's imagination, with immense numbers of small particles which move at tremendous speeds, with waves of a nature and frequency never encountered in daily life, and with physical concepts which defy description in space or time. He can learn to convince himself about the reality of these numbers and concepts only by using them for the solution of a large number of numerical problems which establish their correlation with measurable quantities. The problems at the end of each chapter of this book and the illustrative examples of solutions should prove valuable to him for this purpose.

The student's second difficulty derives from the wide scope of the atomic theory, which embraces almost all problems of matter. It relates to the mechanical, thermal, caloric, electric, magnetic, optical, and chemical properties of matter, reviewed in the introductory chapters of this book, but the empirical foundation of atomic physics was developed mainly from information supplied by research in newer fields: electronics, gas discharges, photoelectricity, spectroscopy, X-rays, and radioactivity. In an introductory text it is impossible to give an adequate account of these investigations and their techniques; this must be supplied by a laboratory course—but to profit properly from it the student must know beforehand what he is to look for in each experiment. A summary of this information is presented in the later chapters of Part I of this book, which present what might be called "the facts of life" concerning the isolated atom. The failure of classical theories and earlier atomic models to account for these facts supplies the motivation for the theoretical development in Part II.

H. MUELLER

PREFACE

The purpose of this book is to provide the reader with an explanation of those concepts which are fundamental to an understanding of modern physics as well as a knowledge of the detailed application of such concepts to the specific field of atomic physics.

The subject of atomic physics provides an ideal introduction to modern physics. Logically, atomic physics begins with the physical-chemical view of atoms as classical hard spheres and extends through a study of atomic spectra to the wave-mechanical theory of a diffuse cloud of electrons surrounding a tiny central nucleus and described by various quantum numbers. This is also, roughly, the historical pattern of development in atomic physics. Where deviation from the historical sequence offered pedagogical advantage, the author has rearranged the topics accordingly. For example, the subject of black body radiation, although it preceded the quantum historically, is deferred until it can be treated by modern methods.

Although the author's basic objective has been to present a thorough and logical explanation of atomic physics, the book also includes descriptions of the extension of the techniques of atomic physics to developing fields of contemporary interest, such as nuclear physics. The guiding principle throughout has been to impart to the reader an understanding of the problems of atomic physics and their solutions in a minimum of space and without losing sight of the logical unity of the subject. Wherever feasible each argument is introduced by appeal to the experimental facts which forced the adoption of new and at first unfamiliar concepts. Illustrative problems which clarify the application of these ideas are given at the ends of the chapters and are followed by actual problems in which the reader can himself apply them. The problems frequently include important applications that complement the text material.

The author extends his thanks to M. Walker, who drew the illustrations, and to V. P. Close, who typed the manuscript.

D. C. Peaslee

CONTENTS

Part III: FURTHUR APPLICATIONS OF THE THEORY

Part I

THE FACTS OF ATOMIC STRUCTURE

The first part (Chapters 1–7) of our discussion deals with the factual information of atomic physics. This information is the basis for the rather abstract concepts of modern atomic physics. Some of this information—e.g., measurements of atomic size and of certain electric and magnetic properties of matter—can be at least partially interpreted by simple classical models. Unfortunately, the classical explanations are generally incomplete, involve *ad hoc* assumptions, or are mutually inconsistent. For example, although classical mechanics is sufficient to establish the nuclear model of the atom, most atomic phenomena are not comprehensible on a classical basis. An improved theory is required. The data of Part I provide a testing ground for the improved theory, which will be satisfactory only if it can explain all of the facts in a consistent fashion.

Part I includes the evidence establishing the dual nature of light, which is the key to development of an adequate atomic theory. Discussion of the photoelectric effect in metals and ionization by X-rays leads to the conclusion that light consists of particles called photons or light quanta. At the same time, it is emphasized that diffraction of X-rays by crystals requires for its explanation a wave picture rather than a corpuscular picture of light. This is a primary example of the duality between particles and waves. Extension of the duality principle to the "particles" of classical mechanics, particularly electrons, will lead in Part II to the discussion of modern quantum (wave) mechanics.

Chapter 1

ATOMS AND ELEMENTARY CHEMISTRY

The atom, by its original definition, is the smallest unit of a chemical element that still displays all the chemical properties of the element. From the point of view of chemistry atoms are the primary components of all macroscopic matter as we know it.

In such a chemical approach we first glimpse the atoms only from the outside, so to speak. A great deal of essential, quantitative information is already available from this external position. We should start by surveying this information, just as an explorer entering an unknown jungle might first try to find out its size, density, and other characteristics. Such a survey provides the proper orientation for our subsequent study of the details of internal atomic structure. Much of the subject matter in this and the next chapter comes under the general heading of physical chemistry. The difference is that in physical chemistry the atom is the smallest unit under consideration, while in our discussion of atomic physics it will be the largest.

1.1. The elementary laws of chemistry

The elementary laws of chemistry gave birth to the concept of the atom. We may state the first three of these laws as follows:
  (i) There exist chemical *elements*, which cannot be resolved into simpler components by chemical means;
 (ii) Elements combine chemically in fixed mass ratios (Dalton's law of constant proportions);
(iii) When two elements combine in more than one mass ratio, the relation of these ratios is always that of small whole numbers (law of multiple proportions).

There is some logical sequence among these laws. The rules (ii) and (iii) of constant and multiple proportions cannot exist without the prior recognition (i) of the existence of chemical elements.

To arrive at a simple formulation of (i) and (ii) we introduce the concept of the *atom*. The atoms are the chemically indivisible units that make up a substance. All the atoms of a given element are identical in size, mass, and all other properties;* they are different from the atoms

---

* This is not strictly true in a physical sense, although it is accurate enough for most chemical purposes. Actually, different atoms of the same element may have slightly different masses; such atoms with the same chemical properties but dif-

of any other element. The law of constant proportions then states that in a chemical compound containing N_A atoms of element A, N_B atoms of element B, N_C atoms of element C, etc., the successive ratios $N_A:N_B:N_C:$ ... are constant.

By expressing the law of constant proportion in terms of masses and in terms of atoms, we can obtain a scale of relative atomic masses. For example, we observe that 2 grams of hydrogen combine chemically with 16 grams of oxygen to form water. If we decide from additional evidence that the correct formula for water is H_2O, then we know that the masses of individual hydrogen and oxygen atoms are in the ratio 1:16. By proceeding in this way through many compounds, we can build up a table of relative masses for the atoms of all elements. The masses in this table are not absolute but merely relative to some fixed standard, which we are free to choose for convenience. The conventional chemical standard is to define the *atomic mass unit* (amu) to be precisely $\frac{1}{16}$ the mass of an oxygen atom;* we can then specify the masses of all other atoms in terms of amu.

To account for the rule (iii) of multiple proportions, it is convenient to introduce the concept of *valence*. The valence of an atom A can be positive or negative: it is the number of hydrogen atoms that A can replace in a chemical compound (positive) or the number of hydrogen atoms that will combine with A in a chemical compound (negative). Multiple proportions will occur if an atom can have two or more valences. For example, O has the valence -2, while C has the valences 2 and 4, so that the compounds CO and CO_2 are both possible. The valences are all small whole numbers, since the law of multiple proportions also involves only small whole numbers.

The atomic mass unit is not defined directly in terms of macroscopic mass units, such as grams. A combined unit is the *gram atomic weight*: if the atoms of an element have mass A amu, then one gram atomic weight of that element weighs A grams. For a chemical compound the gram molecular weight has a similar definition: if the molecule has a total mass of M amu, then one gram molecular weight of the compound weighs M grams. Another name for gram molecular weight is the *mole*.

---

ferent masses are called *isotopes*. For most of our discussion it will be sufficient to neglect the differences between isotopes. The "mass" of an atom is then the average mass of all the naturally occurring isotopes of that element. The value given in chemical tables of atomic mass corresponds to this average mass.

* The *chemical scale* of amu is based on the average mixture of oxygen isotopes occurring in nature; the *physical scale* is based solely on the most abundant oxygen isotope. In Chapter 3 we see that 1 amu (chemical) = 1.00028 amu (physical). This difference is generally negligible for the purposes of atomic physics.

In terms of the gram atomic weight we can state Avogadro's hypothesis:

(iv) One gram atomic weight of any element contains the same number of atoms; this number is *Avogadro's* number, $N_0 = 6.03 \times 10^{23}$ atoms/g at wt.

The numerical value of N_0 was unknown at the time of Avogadro's original hypothesis. Section 1.4 discusses methods of measuring N_0. A knowledge of N_0 allows us to assign an absolute mass value for the amu. From the definition of the gram atomic weight it follows that

$$1 \text{ amu} = 1/N_0 \text{ g} = 1.66 \times 10^{-24} \text{ g} \qquad (1.1)$$

A single oxygen atom, for example, weighs $16 \times 1.66 \times 10^{-24} = 2.66 \times 10^{-23}$ g.

In our discussion of elementary chemical laws we should include the periodic table of elements, originally devised by Mendeléeff. This table classifies elements of similar properties into groups. We shall ultimately find an explanation of the periodic table in terms of the modern theory of atomic structure (Chapter 12).

Some 90 elements exist in nature. To organize them into the periodic table, we classify them according to their atomic mass, their valences, and their chemical similarities to other elements. The best organization according to present knowledge is that of Fig. 1.1, which differs slightly from Mendeléeff's original scheme. We arrive at this organization empirically in the following way. In an arrangement of the elements according to increasing atomic mass, we note that the inert noble gases Ne, A, Kr, Xe, Rn (He is an exception) come directly after five elements that resemble each other in chemical properties. These are the halogens F, Cl, Br, I, At. They in turn come directly after the set of chemically similar elements O, S, Se, Te, Po. The succession continues through three more groups of five elements, ending with the group B, Al, Ge, In, Tl.

A shorter succession of this sort consists of the alkali earths Be, Mg, Ca, Sr, Ba, Ra, which come directly after the alkalis Li, Na, K, Rb, Cs. To this succession of two groups we may add the pair He, H.

The remaining elements constitute three sequences of 10 and one of 14. The group of 14 consists exclusively of the rare earth elements. The three groups of 10 do not show perfect correspondence in the chemical properties of equivalent members; *e.g.*, Fe, Ru, and Os have different valences.

The sequences of 2, 6, 10, 14 combine as indicated in Fig. 1.1 to form a table of elements that follow generally the order of increasing atomic mass. There are a few exceptions to this rule, however. For instance, all

							Valence
$_1$H$^{1.008}$	$_3$Li$^{6.94}$	$_{11}$Na$^{23.00}$	$_{19}$K$^{39.10}$	$_{37}$Rb$^{85.48}$	$_{55}$Cs$^{132.9}$	$_{87}$Fr^{223}	1
	$_4$Be$^{9.02}$	$_{12}$Mg$^{24.32}$	$_{20}$Ca$^{40.08}$	$_{38}$Sr$^{87.63}$	$_{56}$Ba$^{137.4}$	$_{88}$Ra$^{226.1}$	2
	$_5$B$^{10.82}$	$_{13}$Al$^{26.97}$	$_{31}$Ga$^{69.72}$	$_{49}$In$^{114.8}$	$_{81}$Tl$^{204.4}$		1,3
	$_6$C$^{12.01}$	$_{14}$Si$^{28.06}$	$_{32}$Ge$^{72.60}$	$_{50}$Sn$^{118.7}$	$_{82}$Pb$^{207.2}$		2,4
	$_7$N$^{14.01}$	$_{15}$P$^{30.98}$	$_{33}$As$^{74.91}$	$_{51}$Sb$^{121.8}$	$_{83}$Bi$^{209.0}$		3,5
	$_8$O$^{16.00}$	$_{16}$S$^{32.06}$	$_{34}$Se$^{78.96}$	$_{52}$Te$^{127.6}$	$_{84}$Po^{210}		2,4,6
	$_9$F$^{19.00}$	$_{17}$Cl$^{35.46}$	$_{35}$Br$^{79.92}$	$_{53}$I$^{126.9}$	$_{85}$At^{211}		1,3,5,7
$_2$He$^{4.003}$	$_{10}$Ne$^{20.18}$	$_{18}$A$^{39.94}$	$_{36}$Kr$^{83.7}$	$_{54}$Xe$^{131.3}$	$_{86}$Rn$^{222.0}$		0

				Valence
$_{21}$Sc$^{45.10}$	$_{39}$Y$^{88.92}$	$_{57}$La$^{138.9}$	$_{89}$Ac^{227}	3
$_{22}$Ti$^{47.9}$	$_{40}$Zr$^{91.22}$	$_{72}$Hf$^{178.6}$		4 (2,3)
$_{23}$V$^{50.95}$	$_{41}$Nb$^{92.91}$	$_{73}$Ta$^{180.9}$		3,5 (2,4)
$_{24}$Cr$^{52.01}$	$_{42}$Mo$^{95.95}$	$_{74}$W$^{183.9}$		3,6 (2,4)
$_{25}$Mn$^{54.93}$	$_{43}$Tc^{99}	$_{75}$Re$^{186.3}$		2,4,7 (3,6)
$_{26}$Fe$^{55.85}$	$_{44}$Ru$^{101.7}$	$_{76}$Os$^{190.2}$		2,3,4,8 (6)
$_{27}$Co$^{58.94}$	$_{45}$Rh$^{102.9}$	$_{77}$Ir$^{193.1}$		3,4 (2,6)
$_{28}$Ni$^{58.69}$	$_{46}$Pd$^{106.7}$	$_{78}$Pt$^{195.2}$		2,4 (3,6)
$_{29}$Cu$^{63.57}$	$_{47}$Ag$^{107.9}$	$_{79}$Au$^{197.2}$		1 (2,3)
$_{30}$Zn$^{65.38}$	$_{48}$Cd$^{112.4}$	$_{80}$Hg$^{200.6}$		2 (1)

$_{58}$Ce$^{140.1}$	$_{90}$Th$^{232.1}$
$_{59}$Pr$^{140.9}$	$_{91}$Pa^{231}
$_{60}$Nd$^{144.3}$	$_{92}$U^{238}
$_{61}$Pm^{147}	$_{93}$Np^{237}
$_{62}$Sm$^{150.4}$	$_{94}$Pu^{239}
$_{63}$Eu$^{152.0}$	$_{95}$Am^{243}
$_{64}$Gd$^{156.9}$	$_{96}$Cm^{244}
$_{65}$Tb$^{159.2}$	
$_{66}$Dy$^{162.5}$	
$_{67}$Ho$^{164.9}$	
$_{68}$Er$^{167.2}$	
$_{69}$Tm$^{169.4}$	
$_{70}$Yb$^{173.0}$	
$_{71}$Lu$^{175.0}$	

Fig. 1.1. Periodic table of elements. The order number Z is at the lower left, the atomic weight A at the upper right. The valences of the rare earth groups are very complex.

the evidence from chemical properties indicates that argon A should precede potassium K, although A is a little heavier. The deviations from increasing atomic mass are relatively slight and do not cause any uncertainty in the order of the elements. It is possible, therefore, to assign to each element in the table a definite *atomic number* (or *order number*) Z. This number is an integer running consecutively from $Z = 1$ for hydrogen up through $Z = 92$ for uranium, the heaviest element occurring in nature.

In general the atomic number is about one-half the atomic mass A in amu: for the lightest elements $Z/A = 0.5$; this ratio diminishes and becomes $Z/A \approx 0.4$ as we approach the heaviest elements. The value of Z is of great significance in relation to the internal structure of the atom.

Appendix II lists some physical properties of the elements.

1.2. Boltzmann principle of statistical mechanics

To relate the observed properties of large-scale matter to those of the atoms composing it, some statistical method is necessary because of the enormous numbers of atoms involved (on the order of 10^{23}). The basis for such a statistical procedure is Boltzmann's principle. We give here an elementary discussion of the principle; for a complete derivation the reader is referred to standard texts on statistical mechanics or theoretical physics.

Consider the example of a gas enclosed in a container. We divide the container mathematically into a large number of small, equal boxes. At any instant we can describe the gas by specifying how many molecules are in each box, regarding all the molecules in a given box as indistinguishable. Each such distribution of the molecules among the boxes is called a *configuration*. Since the boxes are a mathematical artifice, the individual molecules have no preference for any of the boxes. It is a straightforward matter to compute the probability of occurrence of a specific configuration according to the laws of chance. In particular, there is one configuration that has a maximum probability. For the simple case of a gas in a container, the most probable configuration corresponds to uniform density of the gas. That is, the most probable configuration is just the one expected when the system is in thermal equilibrium.

This principle is quite general: any system in thermal equilibrium assumes the configuration of maximum probability. Let this maximum probability be p. The description of the system in terms of configurations is a microscopic one, in which we count the individual molecules (or even atoms). We wish to find a way of relating this microscopic definition to a macroscopic (i.e., thermodynamic) one. According to thermodynamics a system in thermal equilibrium has a maximum value of the entropy S. The key to the relation between the two descriptions is the observation that at thermal equilibrium p is a maximum in the microscopic description, while S is a maximum in the macroscopic description. This suggests a direct connection between S and p.

We can immediately see that the relation between S and p is logarithmic. Suppose that we have two independent systems 1 and 2, both in thermal equilibrium, and we consider the total system formed by 1 plus 2. The total entropy is $S = S_1 + S_2$, while the total probability is $p = p_1 p_2$. To satisfy both these relations, we can only have

$$S = -k \ln p \qquad (1.2)$$

The minus sign is necessary because S is a positive quantity, and the probability can always be normalized so that $p \leq 1$.

In (1.2) k is a universal constant, which must be independent of the system under consideration. Its value can therefore be established by considering a simple example.

Consider a mole of a monatomic gas at constant temperature, which contains N_0 molecules. Compare two states: (1) the gas occupies a section of volume $V/2$ in a box of total volume V; (2) it occupies the entire box. The probability that one of the N_0 molecules in the box is in the section $V/2$ is $\frac{1}{2}$; and the chance that all the molecules are in this section is $p_1 = (\frac{1}{2})^{N_0}$. The probability that all the molecules are in the total volume V is just $p_2 = 1$. Thus

$$\ln p_1 - \ln p_2 = N_0 \ln \tfrac{1}{2} \qquad (1.3)$$

State 1 can be transformed into state 2 by an isothermal expansion. During this revisible change the work output is equal to the heat input $-dQ$. For a small change of volume, using $PV = RT$, we have

$$dW = P \, dV = RT \, dV/V = -dQ \qquad (1.4)$$

Since entropy is defined by

$$dS = dQ/T \qquad (1.5)$$

the entropy difference of the states is

$$\begin{aligned} S_2 - S_1 &= \int_{V/2}^{V} dQ/T = -R \int_{V/2}^{V} dV/V \\ &= R \ln \tfrac{1}{2}V - R \ln V = R \ln \tfrac{1}{2} \end{aligned} \qquad (1.6)$$

The identification $S = -k \ln p$ therefore requires

$$k = R/N_0 = 1.36 \times 10^{-16} \ \text{erg/}^\circ\text{K} \qquad (1.7)$$

where k is called Boltzmann's constant. Since it is the ratio of the universal gas constant R and Avogadro's number, it is also a universal constant.

For any system or subsystem we can write for the integral of (1.5) as

$$S = S_0 + E/T \qquad (1.8)$$

where E is the total energy of the (sub)system, and S_0 does not depend on the energy. With (1.2) this becomes

$$p = e^{-S_0/k} e^{-E/kT} = C e^{-E/kT} \qquad (1.9)$$

Equation (1.9) states that for a system in thermal equilibrium, the probability for a subsystem to have energy E is proportional to the *Boltzmann factor*, $e^{-E/kT}$. The constant C depends on the total system; for many applications of (1.9) it is not necessary to have an explicit expression for C. The subsystem to which (1.9) applies can be as small as a single molecule in a gas (see illustrative problem 1). Equation (1.9) or its quantum-mechanical modifications (Chapter 14) are fundamental to considerations of statistical mechanics.

In practice (1.7) has proved most useful for the determination of N_0. The value of the constant R results from macroscopic experiments, and certain other experiments provide values of k (section 1.4). Avogadro's number, on the other hand, is difficult to determine directly in spite of its great practical importance, so that (1.7) has frequently been helpful for this purpose.

The Boltzmann relation (1.9) has many other applications. The sedimentation of particles in solution also follows the law of atmospheres (illustrative problem 1). The Maxwell distribution of molecular velocities in a gas follows from inserting $E = \frac{1}{2}mv^2$ in (1.9). The Boltzmann factor also applies to the energy of rotation and of internal vibration of the gas molecules, and to the vibrational energy of atoms in a crystal.

The great usefulness of the Boltzmann principle in the form (1.9) is its ability to express measurable, macroscopic properties in terms of atomic behavior. The relation (1.7) between the macroscopic constant R and the microscopic constant k is an example of this usefulness.

1.3. Ions and electric charge

It is not always necessary to invoke Boltzmann's principle in order to learn the properties of atoms from macroscopic measurements. Atoms contain electric charges which can be detected by laboratory techniques. The conductivity of electrolytic solutions, for instance, gives us direct information about some electrical properties of atoms. When a salt like NaCl is dissolved in water, the solution becomes a relatively good conductor of electricity. As current passes through the solution, chlorine gas appears at the positive electrode (anode) and sodium is released at the negative electrode (cathode).

The electrolysis of any such solution follows a definite, quantitative law originally established by Faraday: to deposit one gram atomic weight of a z-valent element, a total charge zF must pass through the solution, where the faraday $F = 9.65 \times 10^4$ coulombs. The dependence of this law upon valence, as well as the fact that the original compound deposits out as separate elements, indicates that individual atoms are involved in electrolytic conduction. We can understand all the features of electrolytic conduction by supposing that the NaCl molecules in solution decompose into electrically charged units called *ions*, Na^+ and Cl^-. The ions do not have the same chemical properties as the corresponding atoms. For example, Na atoms will react with water to form NaOH, while Na^+ ions are able to move through water without reacting, as electrolysis reveals.

Ions also differ electrically from atoms, which are electrically neutral. The sign of the charge on a particular ion is readily determined from the electrode at which it deposits. Positively (negatively) charged ions are call *cations* (*anions*) because they deposit at the cathode (anode) in electrolysis. Elements just before the inert gases in the periodic table form anions. The strict proportionality of Faraday's law with valence indicates that the charges on ions are all multiples of a basic unit. There exist uni-, di-, tri-, etc. valent ions such as Li^+, Be^{++}, B^{+++}. The magnitude of this basic unit of ionic charge is $e = F/N_0 = 1.60 \times 10^{-19}$ coulomb. Thus chemical valence and the chemical forces holding atoms together to form molecules appear to be basically electrical in character.

To account for the atomistic behavior of ionic charge, which varies only in multiples of a basic unit, the simplest hypothesis is that this charge is carried by some kind of indivisible, subatomic particle. This particle is known as the *electron*. J. J. Thomson first definitely established the existence of these particles shortly before 1900. The thermionic radio tube, in which electrons are emitted by a hot filament or cathode, has made the electron almost a modern household item. The electron proves to be the basic building block of the atom, and atomic physics is mainly the study of how electrons behave in atoms.

In proceeding from the observed fact of electrolytic conduction to the eventual concept of the electron, we included as an essential step the hypothesis of ionic conduction in electrolytes. This hypothesis cannot be considered valid until we have shown that it can account for the major features of electrolytic conduction. Consider an electrolyte like NaCl in which both positive and negative ions have valence 1 (a 1-1 valent electrolyte) with n ions of each kind per cm^3. An electric field E subjects a positive ion to a force Ee. Since the ion is in a viscous medium (water), it will not perform an accelerated motion but will move with a constant average velocity v_1, given by Stokes' law for the motion of a sphere in a viscous medium.

$$v_1 = eE/6\pi\eta R_1 \tag{1.10a}$$

Here R_1 is the radius of the positive ions, assumed to be spherical in shape, and η is the coefficient of viscosity of the medium. Similarly, if R_2 is the radius of the negative ions, they will move with a velocity

$$v_2 = -eE/6\pi\eta R_2 \tag{1.10b}$$

The ratio v/E is called the *mobility* of the ions; it is numerically equal to the velocity of the ion in a unit field. Certain ions such as those of chromium are colored and allow direct observation of their motion: one observes the motion of the color boundary in a cell containing a colored and an uncolored electrolyte.

The current density J is the current passing through one square centimeter of area perpendicular to the current. Both positive and negative ions contribute to this current density, which is

$$J = nev_1 - nev_2 \qquad (1.11)$$

where n is the number of ions per unit volume. The number of positive and negative ions is equal for a 1-1 valent electrolyte, and the charges are $+e$ and $-e$, respectively. The specific conductivity is defined by $\sigma = J/E$, whence

$$\sigma = \frac{ne^2}{6\pi\eta}\left(\frac{1}{R_1} + \frac{1}{R_2}\right) \qquad (1.12)$$

The conductivity of electrolytes is observed to increase rapidly with temperature, which (1.12) ascribes to the decrease of viscosity with increasing temperature.

According to (1.12) the conductivity should be proportional to the ion concentration n. Experiments show, however, that the conductivity is not proportional to the amount of dissolved salt. Another disturbing experimental fact is the dependence of ionic mobility on concentration, although (1.10) does not contain the factor n. This does not mean that the basic idea of ionic conduction is incorrect, but rather that the considerations presented above are oversimplified. The theory of Debye and Hueckel gives a satisfactory explanation of the properties of electrolytes by taking into account the Coulomb forces of attraction between the positive and negative ions. In ionic conduction the positive ions move opposite to the negative ions. Because of the Coulomb forces, the stream of positive ions tries to pull the negative ions along with it, and vice versa. This effect is called *electrophoresis*, or *electric friction*. The net effect of electrophoresis is to increase the viscosity, and the electrophoretic effect naturally increases with concentration of the ions. Thus electrophoresis causes the effective value of η in (1.10) and (1.12) to increase with n, which accounts for the experimental observations just mentioned.

The theory of Debye and Hueckel assumes the salt to be totally dissociated into ions in the solution. Since NaCl molecules are stable in the solid state and in fact combine to form macroscopic crystals, we may ask how it is that these molecules dissociate so completely in aqueous solution. The answer lies in the exceptionally high dielectric constant $\epsilon = 80$ for water. This reduces the electrostatic forces between two point charges by a factor 80 from what they would be in vacuum. The fact that the NaCl molecule completely dissociates under such a force reduction again indicates that its cohesive forces are primarily electrostatic in nature.

1.4. Avogadro's number

The laws of chemistry, of ideal gases, and of solutions offer no absolute proof of the existence of atoms and the validity of Avogadro's hypothesis. A number of prominent nineteenth-century physicists were, indeed, reluctant to admit the atom as an established scientific fact. The atomic theory gained general acceptance only after several different determinations of N_0 led to the same value (within experimental errors), even though the methods of measurement were based on different physical principles. The value of N_0 also is of great practical importance in relating macroscopic measurements to atomic constants. It is therefore worth while to consider some of the independent ways of determining N_0.

We possess today a dozen or more methods that furnish N_0 to an accuracy of better than 10 %. The paragraphs below discuss some of these methods, which fall into four main categories: (1.4a) determination of Boltzmann's constant k, which allows the calculation $N_0 = R/k$; (1.4b) direct measurement of the electronic charge e, which allows the calculation $N_0 = F/e$; (1.4c) direct counting procedures; (1.4d) miscellaneous.

1.4a. Determination of Boltzmann's constant k

(a) *Sedimentation Equilibrium.* A suspension of fine oil droplets in water obeys the law of atmospheres, except that here m is replaced by $m' = m - m_0$, where m is the mass of the oil droplet, m_0 is the mass of the same volume of water, and m' is the effective mass with allowance for the buoyant effect of the water. If the density of the oil is not much greater than that of water, the particle size can be chosen large enough to be directly measured with a microscope. After the suspension has remained at constant temperature for several days to establish thermal equilibrium, particles of a fixed size are counted at two different heights h_1 and h_2. Then by (1.32),

$$k = m'g(h_1 - h_2)/T \ln (n_2/n_1) \qquad (1.13)$$

where n_1 and n_2 are the densities of particles at h_1 and h_2. Within an experimental error of about 3 % such measurements give $k = 1.36 \times 10^{-16}$ erg/°C. Thus at room temperature $kT \approx 4 \times 10^{-14}$ erg.

The inaccuracy of this determination arises chiefly in the measurements of n_1 and n_2. They are obtained by counting the number of particles appearing in a definite range of view in the microscope. This number is subject to fluctuations and will vary considerably in successive observations. The error in the average of a large number of observations Q decreases only as $1/\sqrt{Q}$, so that several thousand observations are necessary to attain an accuracy of 1 %.

With k a known quantity, sedimentation equilibrium represents an important technique for determining the molecular weight of large organic molecules typical of biological systems, such as proteins, rubber, and cellulose. In the study of these systems, an ultracentrifuge replaces gravity, producing an acceleration of $10^7 g$ or more. The absorption of light by the protein molecules determines the relative numbers n_1 and n_2 at two different heights. Such studies have revealed the important fact that protein molecules can have definite molecular weights on the order of 10^4–10^5 amu.

(b) *Brownian Motion.* A small particle suspended in a solution executes a random zigzag motion under the impacts of the solution molecules, which are continually colliding with and bouncing off the particle. Although the colliding solution molecules are too small to be seen, the resulting (Brownian) motion of the small particles can be observed in an ultramicroscope. The displacements of the particle in the x direction at equal time intervals t are observed over a large number of such intervals. The mean-square value of these displacements $\bar{x}^2$ is computed, and the value of k follows from the diffusion-theory formula

$$k = \frac{3\pi\eta R}{T}\frac{\bar{x}^2}{t} \tag{1.14}$$

Here η is the viscosity of the solution and R is the radius of the particle, which must be independently determined.

(c) *Coagulation Measurements.* The addition of electrolyte to a colloidal solution will cause it to curdle. During this process two colloidal particles that collide are likely to stick together; and if the electrolyte is sufficiently concentrated, the likelihood of sticking together is practically unity. The detailed theory of this coagulation process, developed by M. v. Smoluchowski, leads to the result that the number of separate colloidal particles present at a time t after addition of the electrolyte is

$$n(t) = \frac{n_0}{1 + t/\tau} \tag{1.15}$$

Here n_0 is the original number of particles present at time $t = 0$, and τ is a constant called the coagulation time, which is the time after which the original number of particles is reduced by one-half. Then $n(t)$ and hence τ can be measured, either by counting the particles in a microscope (using samples in which the coagulation has been stopped with "protective colloids," such as tannic acid) or by measuring color changes of the colloid. The measurements provide excellent verification of (1.15).

The theory of Smoluchowski further shows that

$$1/\tau = \tfrac{4}{3}n_0 kT/\eta \tag{1.15a}$$

where η is the viscosity coefficient of the solution. The coagulation time is thus independent of the particle size and type. Measurements indeed show that different colloids, such as milk or colloidal gold and silver, coagulate at the same rate regardless of particle size, provided that the original number of particles is the same. For any colloid with 10^{10} particles per cm^3 the coagulation time is 18 sec in water at 18°C. Introducing this result and the corresponding values $T \approx 300$, $\eta = 0.01$ into (1.15) gives nearly the right value for k. Extensive measurements indicate that this method is accurate to better than 2%.

(d) *Black Body Radiation.* A "black body" is one from which the emission of radiation is independent of the material constituting the body and depends only on the absolute temperature T of the material. The total energy radiated per second per cm^2 is given by the Stefan-Boltzmann law,

$$W = \sigma T^4, \quad \sigma = 5.67 \times 10^{-5} \text{ erg/cm}^2 \text{ sec } (°K)^4 \tag{1.16a}$$

If the radiation is plotted as a function of wavelength λ, the maximum intensity occurs at a wavelength λ_0 given by Wien's displacement law,

$$\lambda_0 T = b = 0.290 \text{ cm °K} \tag{1.16b}$$

The first satisfactory explanation of these phenomena came from the work of Max Planck, who introduced the concept of the quantum in formulating his explanation. This entailed introduction of a new constant h, in terms of which

$$\sigma = 2\pi^5 k^4/15 h^3 c^2, \quad b = hc/4.965k \tag{1.17}$$

where $c = 3 \times 10^{10}$ cm/sec is the velocity of light. Elimination of h from the two equations (1.17) yields

$$k = \tfrac{1}{2}(4.965)^3 \sigma b^3/c\pi^5 \tag{1.18}$$

Substitution of the experimentally determined values for σ, b, and c leads to $k = 1.38 \times 10^{-16}$ erg/°K.

1.4b. Direct measurement of the electronic charge e

To measure an electric charge, we determine the force exerted on it by an electric field of known intensity E. The instrument generally used for this purpose is an electrometer, or electroscope. A common type of instrument is one in which the electric force is determined by balancing it against gravity (gold leaf electroscope) or against an elastic force, as in the string or quadrant electrometer. The smallest charge measurable with these instruments is about 10^{-15} coulomb, or at least 10^4 elementary charges e. The limit of the sensitivity is set by the Brownian motion of the gold leaf or string. Thus if we can count the number of elementary charges e, we can use an ordinary electrometer to determine e; otherwise a more sensitive electrometer based on a different principle will be necessary. Both procedures are in fact feasible.

(e) *Counting of Alpha Particles.* A number of so-called radioactive substances have been found to emit charged particles. Examples of such substances are radium, thorium, and uranium. These naturally produced particles are of two types called α and β, with respective charges $+2e$ and $-e$. A magnetic field will separate positive and negative particles in motion, so that an experiment can use α particles alone. The rate of emission of α particles from a natural source remains constant over a period of many years and is determined by counting the particles with a Geiger-Mueller counter, which produces an electric discharge for each α particle entering the counter chamber. If the α particles are used to charge an electrometer, it is possible to attain a charge of $10,000e$ or more on the electrometer with a known number s of α particles. The electrometer measures this total charge q directly, and the elementary charge is then $e = q/2s$. It is evident that s must be large, usually on the order of 10^5.

(f) *The Millikan Oil Drop Experiment.* This determination of e followed the invention of an improved electrometer, which consists of a capacitor with horizontal parallel plates. Through a battery and short-circuiting switch the potential difference across the plates can be made a fixed value V or zero. The space between the plates contains a fine mist of oil droplets. The capacitor volume is in the field of view of a horizontally mounted microscope with illumination coming from the side. The droplets appear in the telescope as "stars," whose vertical progress can be accurately measured by means of horizontal crosshairs in the eyepiece. An ionizing radiation from an X-ray tube or from radium irradiates the capacitor volume to provide plenty of charged particles.

The droplets move under two vertical forces: that of gravity, which is always downward, and that of the electric field, which is downward or upward according to the sign of the charge on the drop and the polarity of the capacitor plates. A few of the droplets have the right relation between mass and charge to stand nearly stationary under equal and opposite gravitational and electric forces. The vertical velocities of these droplets with and without the electric field can be determined through the telescope and crosshairs.

The motion of the droplets follows Stokes' law for a sphere in a viscous medium,

$$F = 6\pi\eta Rv \tag{1.19}$$

Here F is the applied force, η is the coefficient of viscosity, R is the radius of the sphere, and v is the final velocity of the drop, at which the applied force is just balanced by the viscous drag. Thus for a constant applied force the final velocity is a constant, and the final acceleration is zero. The value of R is not known but can be determined from the free fall under gravity, for which

$$6\pi\eta Rv_1 = F_1 = mg = (\tfrac{4}{3}\pi R^3)(\rho - \rho_0)g \tag{1.20}$$

Here ρ and ρ_0 are the densities of the droplet material and of the air, respectively, the difference accounting for the buoyant effect of the air on the droplet. All factors in (1.20) except R are known or measured in the experiment, and hence R is determined. With the electric field the equation corresponding to (1.20) is

$$6\pi\eta Rv_2 = F_2 = mg - (V/d)q \tag{1.21}$$

Here V and d are the potential difference between the capacitor plates and q is the total charge on the droplet. In (1.20) and (1.21) the downward direction has the positive algebraic sign for forces and velocities.

These equations yield

$$
\begin{aligned}
q &= \frac{d}{V}\, 6\pi\eta(v_1 - v_2)R \\[2mm]
&= \frac{d}{V}\, 6\pi\eta(v_1 - v_2)\left[\frac{9\eta v_1}{2(\rho - \rho_0)g}\right]^{1/2}
\end{aligned}
\tag{1.22}
$$

The values of q determined in this way are found, within the experimental error, always to be a small integral multiple of $e = 4.8 \times 10^{-10}$ esu.

A variation of this experiment shows the atomicity of electric charge even more directly. In the electric field a drop will often abruptly change its velocity from v_2 to v_2'. This must be due to a gain or loss of electric charge, given by

$$q' - q = \Delta q = (d/V)6\pi\eta(v_2 - v_2')R \tag{1.23}$$

Equation (1.23) may be used relatively or absolutely. If R is not determined, then when the drop is followed through several successive velocity changes in a constant field, Δq is in constant proportion to Δv. It is found that Δv is always equal to a constant magnitude or sometimes a small multiple of that magnitude, which implies the same about Δq. If R is determined from the free-fall velocity v_1 of the same drop, the absolute Δq may be obtained. It is always e, or a small multiple thereof. Thus not only is the droplet charge a simple multiple of e, but the process of losing or gaining charge always occurs in units of e and never gradually. This is the most direct evidence we have that the basic unit of charge is e.

1.4c. Determination of N_0 by counting

(g) *Counting of α Particles.* This method uses the same particles and Geiger-Mueller counter as method (e) above, but is based on Rutherford's observation that an α particle in coming to rest loses its charge and becomes a helium atom. The α particles emitted by a radioactive source collect in an evacuated container, and the amount of helium resulting is determined by spectroscopic analysis. Such measurements show that 1 g of radium emits in one year enough particles to form 0.156 cm^3 of He gas at 0°C and 1 atm pressure. Counting experiments show that 1 g of radium emits 1.36×10^{11} particles per second. The numbers of atoms in 1 mole of He is therefore

$$N_0 = 1.36 \times 10^{11} \times 60 \times 60 \times 24 \times 365 \times 22414/0.156$$

$$= 6.16 \times 10^{23}$$

(h) *X-Ray Investigations of Simple Crystals.* This method is today considered to give the most accurate determination of N_0, because of the precision of X-ray measurements. Chapter 5 contains a more complete discussion of X-ray diffraction, but the principle of the method can be sketched here. Suppose that we wish to count the number of lines in an optical grating. Instead of counting the lines with a microscope, we can measure the distance d between the lines by using the grating for diffraction of light of a known wavelength λ. The well-known grating equation then tells us that the diffraction maxima occur at the angles θ_j, for which

$$\sin \theta_j = j(\lambda/d), \qquad j = 1,2,3, \ldots \qquad (1.24)$$

The number of lines in a grating of length L is thus L/d. In an exactly analogous manner, X-rays are diffracted from the three-dimensional lattices formed by the atoms in a crystal. Study of the X-ray diffraction patterns produced by crystal of NaCl shows that the ions are arranged

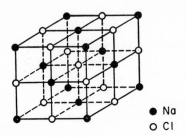

● Na
○ Cl

Fig. 1.2. Simple cubic structure
of NaCl crystal.

in a *simple cubic* lattice, as illustrated in Fig. 1–2. The Na and Cl ions are at alternate corners of unit cubes of side d, and exact measurements show that $d = 2.82 \times 10^{-8}$ cm.

This information on the lattice structure and dimensions of the crystal is sufficient to compute Avogadro's number from the molecular weight $M = 58.45$ of NaCl and the density $\rho = 2.17$ g/cm^3. There are $1/d^3$ ions per cm^3, and one mole of NaCl occupies a volume of M/ρ cm^3. The number of ions per mole is thus

$$M/\rho d^3 = N_0 \,(\text{Cl}) + N_0 \,(\text{Na}) = 2N_0 \qquad (1.25)$$

Equation (1.25) holds only for simple cubic lattices, with one atom at the corner of each unit cell. It is applicable to NaCl, KCl, NaBr, LiF. For other types of regular lattices formulas similar to (1.25) but with different coefficients can be established. An alkali halide like CsCl, for instance, has a body centered lattice in which all the atoms of one kind are at the corners of the cubes, and all the other atoms are at the cube centers. Many metals, such as Ni, Fe, Cu, Ag, and Au, have cubic lattices. Usually they are body centered, but some are face centered with the atoms in the centers of the faces of the unit cell, as well as at the corners.

1.4d. Miscellaneous methods

These methods usually require the measurement of a number of different macroscopic constants, while those described above generally require the measurement of one macroscopic and one microscopic constant.

(i) *The Refractive Index and Light Scattering of Gases.* Elementary considerations show that the refractive index n of a gas at 0°C and 1 atm pressure is related to the electric polarizability α of the atoms or molecules by the equation

$$2\pi L\alpha = (n^2 - 1)/2 \approx n - 1 \qquad (1.26)$$

Here $L = N_0/22414 = 2.69 \times 10^{19}$ is Loschmidt's number, the number of molecules per cm^3 of gas at normal temperature and pressure. The same considerations show that if a parallel light beam of intensity I (erg/cm^2 sec) is incident on a volume V of the gas, the rate dU/dt

(erg/sec) at which luminous energy scatters into a solid angle $d\omega$ at 90° to the incident beam is

$$dU/dt = SVI \, d\omega$$
$$S = \tfrac{1}{2}(2\pi/\lambda)^4 L\alpha^2$$

(1.27)

where S is the *transverse scattering power* and λ is the wavelength of the light. We can determine L and hence N_0 by measuring n and S for a gas with light of a known, constant wavelength. Eliminating α from (1.26) and (1.27), we have

$$L = 2\pi^2(n - 1)^2/S\lambda^4$$

(1.28)

The most careful determination of N_0 by this method, using argon gas, leads to a value $N_0 = 6.6 \times 10^{23}$. This method is subject to some inherent inaccuracy, discussed at the end of Chapter 4.

(j) *The Limiting Law for Electrolytes.* It was pointed out in section 1.3 above that ions in solution exert electrostatic forces on each other These electrostatic forces affect the lowering of the freezing point. For example, the addition to a liter of water of m moles of a 1-1 valent electrolyte like NaCl should ideally lower the freezing point by $\Delta_0 = 3.72 \, m$ °C. Because of the electrostatic interaction between the ions the actual lowering Δ in a solution of finite concentration is somewhat less than Δ_0. The theory of Debye and Hueckel mentioned in section 1.3 leads to the fomula

$$1 - \frac{\Delta}{\Delta_0} = \frac{\sqrt{m}}{2\pi N_0}\left(\frac{\pi F^2}{5\epsilon RT}\right)^{3/2}$$

(1.29)

where F is Faraday's constant and ϵ is the dielectric constant of water. Equation (1.29) is valid only for low concentrations m, where it leads to the same value of N_0 as the other methods described above. This close agreement of many independent procedures for determining N_0 conclusively establishes the validity of the atomic hypothesis.

SUMMARY

The elementary laws of chemistry lead to the concept of atoms as indivisible chemical units of matter. They combine with each other according to strict valence rules. The number of atoms per gram atomic weight, based on $O = 16.000 \ldots$, is Avogadro's number, $N_0 = 6.03 \times 10^{23}$. On this basis one atomic mass unit (amu) equals 1.66×10^{-24} g.

The elements can be unequivocally arranged into groups with similar chemical properties. Such a periodic table indicates a definite atomic number Z for each element. This number will prove to be of cardinal importance for the internal structure of the atom.

The Boltzmann principle of statistical mechanics states that for a system in thermal equilibrium at temperature T, the relative probability for any component of the system to have energy E is $e^{-E/kT}$. Boltzmann's microscopic constant $k = 1.38 \times 10^{-16}$ erg/°K is related to the macroscopic gas constant R through $k = R/N_0$.

Faraday's law of electrolysis states that $F = 9.65 \times 10^4$ coulombs is required to deposit from solution A/z grams of a z-valent element of atomic weight A. This strongly suggests that valences are associated with electric charge, and that electric charge in atoms comes only in multiples of an elementary unit $e = F/N_0 = 4.8 \times 10^{-10}$ esu $= 1.60 \times 10^{-19}$ coulomb. This elementary charge is measured directly in Millikan's oil drop experiment.

The validity of the atomic hypothesis requires that Avogadro's number N_0 be a universal constant. It is therefore of great importance that all independent methods of measuring N_0 lead to the same result, within experimental errors. Several of these different methods are discussed.

REFERENCES

S. Glasstone, *A Textbook of Physical Chemistry*, Van Nostrand, New York (1940).

G. Joss, *Theoretical Physics*, Hafner, New York (1950).

R. A. Millikan, *Electrons* (+ *and* −), *Protons, Photons, Neutrons, Mesotrons, and Cosmic Rays*, University of Chicago Press, Chicago (1947).

J. C. Slater, *Introduction to Chemical Physics*, McGraw-Hill, New York (1939).

ILLUSTRATIVE PROBLEMS

1. Use the Boltzmann relation (1.9) to obtain the density distribution of the atmosphere as a function of height, assuming a constant temperature T. Integrate the resulting equation to obtain (1.7).

Solution. The total energy of each molecule is

$$E = U + K + mgh \qquad (1.30)$$

where U is the internal energy of the molecule, K its kinetic energy, and mgh its potential energy in the gravitational field of the earth. Assuming that U and K are independent of the heights of the molecule in the atmosphere, we have for the relative probability of finding a molecule at heights h_1 and h_2,

$$p_2/p_1 = e^{mg(h_1-h_2)/kT} \tag{1.31}$$

The probability that a molecule will be present at a certain height is directly proportional to n, the average number of molecules per unit volume at that height. Thus in (1.31) we can replace p_2/p_1 by n_2/n_1; or, taking the height $h_1 = 0$ at the earth's surface and calling h_2 a general height h, we have

$$n(h) = n_0 e^{-mgh/kT} \tag{1.32}$$

Here $n(h)$ is the number of molecules per unit volume at height h, n_0 is that at the earth's surface. The relation (1.32) is sometimes called the law of atmospheres.

Equation (1.32) provides a second method for relating k to the macroscopic constants R and N_0. The pressure of the air on the surface of the earth is just the force due to the weight of the molecules above a unit area of the surface. This pressure is

$$P = \int_0^\infty mgn(h) \, dh = n_0 kT \tag{1.33}$$

with the use of (1.32). If V is the volume occupied by one mole of the gas, then $n_0 = N_0/V$, where N_0 is Avogadro's number. Thus (1.33) is equivalent to

$$PV = N_0 kT \tag{1.34}$$

On comparison with the well-known perfect gas law, $PV = RT$, we see that

$$R = N_0 k \tag{1.35}$$

which is identical with (1.7).

2. How many elementary charges are required to deflect the string of an electrometer by 1 cm when its sensitivity is 2×10^{-3} volt/cm deflection? The electrometer has a capacitance of 2 $\mu\mu$f and the charges are collected in an ionization chamber with a capacitance (including leads to the electrometer) of 5 $\mu\mu$f.

Solution. The total capacitance of the system is $2 + 5 = 7$ $\mu\mu$f $= 7 \times 10^{-12} f = 7 \times 10^{-12}$ coulomb/volt. To produce a deflection of 1 cm thus requires a charge of $(2 \times 10^{-3}) (7 \times 10^{-12}) = 1.4 \times 10^{-14}$ coulomb $= (1.4 \times 10^{-14}/1.6 \times 10^{-19}) = 9 \times 10^4$ elementary charges of magnitude $e = 1.60 \times 10^{-19}$ coulomb.

3. It is characteristic of kinetic theory considerations that they give rise to Gaussian probability distributions of the form

$$p(x)\ dx = \sqrt{2/\pi x_0}\ e^{-x^2/2x_0^2}\ dx$$

The mean square value of x is

$$\overline{x^2} = \int_0^{\infty} x^2 p(x)\ dx = x_0^2$$

Such a probability distribution applies to Brownian motion, where x is the displacement of a droplet between two collisions. Using (1.14), determine the maximum radius that an oil droplet can have so that its x-displacements in intervals of 1 second exceed 1 micron ($1\mu = 10^{-4}$ cm) in magnitude at least 50 % of the time. Is the droplet visible in an ordinary microscope, which has a resolution on the order of the wavelength of visible light, $\lambda = 4 \times 10^{-5}$ cm?

Solution. We require the value of $x = x_{1/2}$ such that

$$\int_{x_{1/2}}^{\infty} p(x)\ dx = \tfrac{1}{2}$$

The integral of the Gaussian or error function is given in standard mathematical tables, and we find that the 50 % condition is $x_{1/2} = 0.67x_0$. According to the conditions of the problem, $x_{1/2} = 10^{-4}$ cm, so $x_0 = 1.5 \times 10^{-4}$ cm. Using (1.14) with $kT = 4 \times 10^{-14}$ erg, $\eta = 0.01$, we obtain

$$R = (kT)t/(3\pi \eta x_0^2)$$
$$= 4 \times 10^{-14} \times 1/[3\pi \times 10^{-2} \times (1.5 \times 10^{-4})^2]$$
$$= 1.9 \times 10^{-5}\ cm$$

This droplet is not visible in an ordinary microscope.

PROBLEMS

1. If the water molecules in one gram of water were uniformly distributed over the surface of the earth ($R = 6300$ kilometers), how many molecules would be found in one square centimeter of the earth's surface?

2. (a) If all positive ions in one mole of NaCl could be placed at the north pole of the earth, and all negative ions at the south pole, what force would be necessary to hold an electron at the equator? (b) Find the force between the two charge concentrations themselves; the large magnitude of this force illustrates the enormous quantity of charge contained in one mole of ions.

3. In a modification of Millikan's experiment the plates of the capacitor are vertical and the charged oil droplets, moving under the simultaneous action of gravity (vertical) and electric field (horizontal), move in an inclined straight line. Two different droplets of oil, not necessarily the same size, are observed: droplet A descends along a path at 60° with the vertical, droplet B at an angle of 45° with the vertical. The speed of droplet B is 1.43 times that of droplet A. What are the smallest possible charges on the particles?

4. Alpha particles are doubly positive helium ions (charge $+2e$). When a single alpha particle enters a Geiger counter, it causes an electric discharge of 1 microsecond (10^{-6} sec) duration. To count a rapid succession of particles, the discharge pulses are passed through an electronic device consisting of several stages. Each stage contains two electronic tubes and transmits to the following stage one-half the number of the pulses that it receives from the preceding stage. The final stage operates a mechanical counter. Assume: (1) the Geiger counter records every alpha particle if they enter at a rate not higher than 10^5 particles per second; (2) the mechanical counter has a maximum recording rate of 50 pulses per second. Compute: (a) How many electronic tubes does the device require? (b) If the life of a tube is two years for continuous operation, what fraction of one mole of He can be counted? What is the reading of the mechanical counter at that time? (c) How long would it take, with tube replacements, to count one mole of He by this method?

5. Radium is known to eject α particles, each particle forming after release a helium atom. The rate of ejection remains constant for long periods (decreasing by 50% after about 7×10^4 years). During one year, 1 g of radium is found to produce 0.156 cm^3 of helium gas at NPT (1 atm 0°C). The ejection of a single α particle can be recorded as a single discharge in a Geiger-Mueller counter. How many micrograms will produce ten clicks per second in a counter of 1 cm^2 area placed in a vacuum 10 cm from the Ra source?

6. Compute Avogadro's number from the following sets of data: (a) for light of wavelength $\lambda = 4358$ A in argon at normal temperature and pressure the refractive index is 1.000280 and the transverse scattering power is 1.34×10^{-8}; (b) the density of KCl is 1.984, and its simple cubic lattice spacing is $d = 3.138 \times 10^{-8}$ cm.

7. The Brownian motion of the spherical particles in a gold colloid at room temperature ($T = 300°$, $\eta = 0.01$) is to be studied with an ultramicroscope. The objective of this microscope produces a real image with a magnification of 300 in the plane of the glass scale, which is observed through a 10 power ocular. What must be the radius of the gold particles to observe for a time interval of 16 sec an rms value of the displacement along one direction (a) equal to the diameter of the particle; (b) equal to 5 mm, as seen by an observer with normal vision? (c) What is the sedimentation velocity of the latter particles (apply Stokes' law and the force of gravity)?

8. Protein molecules have a molecular weight of 20,000 and a density of 1.5. A dilute aqueous solution is placed in the cell of an ultracentrifuge. The outer radius of the cell is 3 cm, the inner 2 cm from the axis, and the concentration difference is measured by recording the absorption of light. What must be the number of revolutions per sec and the effective g to observe a concentration ratio of 1.1 between the outer and inner ends of the cell?

9. Two electrodes with a potential difference of 100 volts and a separation of 1 cm are inserted in a dilute solution of NaCl. If the radius of an Na ion is 1.4×10^{-8} cm, how long will it take to travel from the positive to the negative electrode? Assume a viscosity of 0.01 cgs unit and recall that the effective field in the medium is reduced by a factor $1/\epsilon$, where $\epsilon = 80$ for water.

10. Gold particles of radius 10^{-5} cm are observed to migrate under the influence of an electric field with an electric mobility of 4 microns/sec/volt/cm. The direction of the migration indicates that the particles are positively charged in water; and since gold is a conductor, we conclude that a certain fraction f of the gold atoms on the surface of the particles are positive ions of single charge. Assuming that a gold crystal has a simple cubic lattice, compute this fraction f. The viscosity of the water is 0.01 poise (cgs units).

Chapter 2

ATOMS AS COMPONENTS OF MATTER

In this chapter we continue the discussion of Chapter 1, still treating atoms from an external point of view but now emphasizing their physical rather than chemical characteristics. We shall also consider some applications of kinetic theory, which relates the mechanical motions of atoms and molecules to the bulk thermal properties of matter.

2.1. The dimensions of atoms and molecules

We shall see in our later discussions that an atom has no sharply defined boundary, according to our most modern and comprehensive picture of the atom. Nevertheless, many properties of matter can be understood by considering a single atom as a solid sphere of definite radius. The sphere is supposed to be elastic as well as impenetrable; that is, it can absorb no energy into its internal motion or "heating" such as that produced in a macroscopic inelastic sphere. A molecule then consists of a cluster of spheres; although a molecule is not spherical, it is convenient to introduce an average molecular radius. The significance of this radius varies with the problem; for example, it may refer to the radius of the sphere with the same volume as the molecule, or to the radius of a circle that has the same area as the molecule in impact experiments. It is obvious that the various methods of computing molecular sizes cannot give exactly identical results. The same is true for the radii of atoms. The apparent size of an atom in a gas may differ somewhat from the size of the same atom in a liquid or solid. Actually, these differences seldom amount to more than 5–10 % in atoms so that it is reasonable to speak of a definite atomic radius. Although this hard-sphere picture is certainly not correct in detail and has many shortcomings, it provides a useful orientation in the magnitudes of atomic systems. We shall therefore describe some of the numerous methods available for the determination of atomic magnitudes, which generally turn out to be on the order of Angstroms, where $1 \text{ A} = 10^{-8}$ cm.

(a) *The Lattice Constant of Solids.* The high compressibility coefficient of solids indicates that in a crystal the atoms are very closely packed. It is permissible to assume that the spherical atoms are touching each other. Hence we conclude that for a crystal such as NaCl the lattice distance d must be the sum of the radii of the Na and the Cl ions. X-ray investigations of a large number of crystals validate this conclusion. They show that whenever the same two atoms have each other as neighbors in a crystal, they are separated by very nearly the same distance. Thus the distance between a nitrogen atom and an oxygen atom is found to be 1.14 ± 0.02 A in all nitrate crystals. The oxygen-oxygen distance is 1.22 A, and the nitrogen-nitrogen distance is 1.10 A. These data indicate that the radius of the oxygen atom is about 0.6 A and that of nitrogen 0.55 A. Similarly, the distance between O and S atoms is measured with X-rays to be 1.37 A, so that the radius of the S atom must be about 0.8 A. This is verified by the measured S-S distance of 1.60 A. In this manner the approximate radii of atoms and ions in crystals can be ascertained within about 0.02 A. The numerous cross checks agree within this limit. The X-ray method has been extended to measurement of interatomic distances in molecules of gases and liquids, and the results agree with those obtained from crystal data.

(b) *Density of Liquids.* The variations in density ρ of almost all liquids with changes of temperature and pressure are so small that we may assume the molecules to be closely packed. To obtain a rough estimate of the radius R of the molecules, we can assume that they are spheres in the hexagonal close packing, like stacked cannon balls. In this type of packing the empty space between the spheres amounts to 35% of the space occupied by the spheres. Hence the molecules of one mole require a volume $1.35 \times (4\pi/3)R^3 N_0$, which must be equal to M/ρ, or hence

$$R = 0.67\sqrt[3]{M/\rho} \text{ A}, \quad 1 \text{ A} = 10^{-8} \text{ cm} \quad (2.1)$$

While this is a rough approximation, it can be expected to give the correct order of magnitude with an accuracy of better than 30%, because any other type of packing would not change the numerical factor 0.67 by more than this. Within the same accuracy the equation can be expected to hold also for solids, because their density is not much different from that of the liquid form of the same substance.

From the values of M and ρ given in Appendix II it is apparent that the radii of atoms do not cover a large range. Carbon in the crystalline state of diamond has the smallest M/ρ value of 3.4 and Cs has the largest value of 72, indicating a variation of R by a factor 2 to 3. For chemically similar elements such as the alkalies, the alkaline earths, or the halogens, the radius increases with the atomic weight and the atomic number; but a comparison of chemically dissimilar elements shows that a heavy element generally does not have a much larger radius than a light element. For instance, the M/ρ for Li is larger than that of the heavy elements Pt or Hg. A plot of the M/ρ values versus the atomic number Z shows that the alkali atoms are largest, the alka-

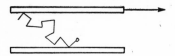

Fig. 2.1. Kinetic theory model
for viscosity.

line earth and halogen atoms come next in size, and for most of the other elements M/ρ is between 5 and 20, with a variation of R of less than 50 %. It follows that the radius of most atoms is less than 2 A, with a lower limit of about 0.5 A.

Although the alkali atoms seem to be exceptionally large, we should remember that these atoms usually occur in the form of positive ions. As ions they have a radius of normal magnitude, as may be inferred from the fact that the lattice constant of the alkali halides is about 3 A.

(c) *Mean Free Path and Viscosity of Gases.* A molecule of radius R, moving along a straight line with a velocity v through an ideal gas would collide with $4\pi R^2 n v$ molecules during each second, where n is the number of gas molecules per cm³. As it travels during this time a distance of v cm the average distance between impacts is $\lambda = 1/4\pi R^2 n$. Actually the molecule follows a zigzag path, which increases the collision probability with the result that the *mean free path* is reduced to

$$\lambda = 1/4\pi\sqrt{2}\, R^2 n \tag{2.2}$$

Suppose that a gas fills the space between two parallel plates, one of which is moving with constant velocity in a direction parallel to the plates, while the other is at rest (see Fig. 2.1). Every molecule hitting the moving plate will gain at the impact an additional momentum due to the motion of the plate. This additional momentum will eventually be imparted to the plate at rest, which will hence feel a force dragging it along in the direction of the moving plate. This is called the force of viscosity. Its determination furnishes the coefficient of viscosity η of the gas. The magnitude of the momentum transferred to the resting plate, and hence the value of η can be computed from kinetic theory, which shows that η is independent of the gas pressure and is proportional to the square root of the absolute temperature. The viscosity η is also proportional to the square root of the molecular weight M and is proportional to the mean free path or hence to $1/R^2$. For 0°C the theory gives the relation

$$\eta(0°C) = 1.14 \times 10^{-20}\sqrt{M}/R^2 \tag{2.2a}$$

Since the viscosities of all gases range between $1–2 \times 10^{-4}$ cgs units, Eq. (2.2a) indicates molecular radii on the order of 10^{-8} cm.

At atmospheric pressure $n = L = 2.69 \times 10^{19}$, and the mean free path computed from the viscosity is

$$\lambda = \eta/(2.06 \times 10^{-19} n\sqrt{M}) = \eta/5.6\sqrt{M} \tag{2.2b}$$

Using $M = 30$ and $\eta = 1.7 \times 10^{-4}$ for air, we have a mean free path at normal temperature and pressure of 5.6×10^{-6} cm. The mean free path lengthens as we reduce the gas pressure; for 1 mm Hg pressure it is roughly 4.3×10^{-3} cm, and to obtain a free path of 1 cm we must reduce the pressure to 4.3×10^{-3} mm Hg.

(d) *Properties of Real Gases.* The ideal gas law is valid only at low pressures where the distance between the molecules is so large that a molecule is effectively a mass point, and the forces acting between molecules can be neglected. To include deviations from the ideal gas behavior, two corrections are necessary to the equation $PV = RT$ for one mole. (1) The volume available to the molecules is not that of the container but is reduced by some volume proportional to that occupied by the spherical molecules. The "proper volume" occupied by the molecules in one mole is $\Omega = N_0(4\pi/3)R^3$. A detailed argument shows that the reduction in V must be $b = 4\Omega$. (2) Neighboring molecules exert forces on each other. Since any molecule inside the gas is surrounded by a large number of neighbors on all sides, the resultant force on any inner molecule averages to zero. This is not true for molecules near the surface, however, because they have neighbors on one side only, which pull them inwards. This pull is equivalent to a pressure from outside, so that P must be replaced by a larger quantity. With these corrections, the equation for an nonideal gas takes the form

$$(V - b)\,(P + a/V^2) = RT \tag{2.3a}$$

which is called the *van der Waals equation.*

The isothermal lines in a PV diagram of Eq. (2.3a) are shown in Fig. 2.2, where $T_1 > T_2 > T_k > T_3 > T_4$. For high temperatures these curves approach hyperbolas, as for an ideal gas. At low temperatures there is a region in which the solution of (2.3a) yields three real values of V corresponding to a particular P. The $P(V)$ curve then has a maximum and a minimum. Between these extremes the volume decreases with decreasing pressure. This is a nonphysical behavior, which must represent a failure of (2.3a). Equation (2.3a) is suitable for a system entirely in the gaseous phase but is not adequate to describe a liquid-gas combination. The anomalous region of Fig. 2.2 corresponds to liquification of the gas. The correct description of liquification is to have a continuous change of volume at constant pressure, as indicated by the horizontal lines in Fig. 2.2. The dotted region in Fig. 2.2 represents the condensation of a gas to form a liquid. Equation (2.3a) predicts such condensation only for temperatures below the critical temperature T_k, determined by the condition that the maximum and minimum of the isothermal $P(V)$ should coincide. Mathematically, we

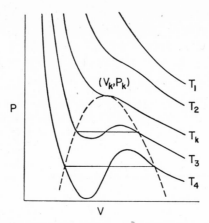

Fig. 2.2. Isotherms PV for the van der Waals Eq. (2.3a): P and V are pressure and volume, and the temperatures $T_1 > T_2 > T_k > T_3 > T_4$. The critical point is at T_k, V_k, P_k.

must require $(dP/dV)_T = (d^2P/dV^2)_T = 0$ in Eq. (2.3a). The corresponding critical volume V_k and critical pressure P_k are

$$V_k = 3b, \qquad P_k = 3RT_k/8V_k \qquad (2.3b)$$

where T_k is the critical temperature below which a gas must be cooled before it can be liquified by compression. The pressure necessary for liquification is always smaller than P_k and approaches this value at the critical temperature. Therefore T_k and P_k are experimentally measurable, and from these values we compute V_k, b, and the radius of the molecule.

(e) *Mobility of Ions and Electrolytic Conductivity.* Equations (1.10) and (1.12) are valid only when the electrophoretic effect can be neglected. This is the case for very dilute electrolytes. By measuring the mobility of one single type of ion as a function of the electrolyte concentration and extrapolating to zero concentration, we can find the radius of such ions from $v/E = e/6\pi\eta R$. The radii of all other types of ions can then be computed from (1.12) and conductivity measurements, which again must be extrapolated to zero concentration.

The results obtained by this method agree with those obtained from X-ray investigations of heteropolar (ionic) crystals only in those cases where the ion is larger than 1 A. For small ions, such as Li or H, the conductivity data lead to radii that are too large. We must therefore assume that small ions are "hydrated." In their migration in the electric field they carry with them a layer of water molecules. Hydration is the result of the extremely strong electric field near the surface of the ion. For an ion of 1 A radius carrying a charge e this field is $e/r^2 = 4.8 \times 10^6$ esu $= 14.4 \times 10^8$ volt/cm and exerts such a strong force on the dipoles of the water molecules that the latter appear to be chemically bound to the ion. In larger ions this effect is greatly reduced.

(f) *Refractive Index of Gases.* Equation (1.26) relates the refractive index n of a gas to the electric polarizability of the gas molecules. If a gas molecule were a perfectly conducting sphere, we should have

$$\alpha = R^3 \tag{2.4}$$

Deviations from ideality will make $\alpha < R^3$, but this method can still be used to give minimum estimates of R.

2.2. Molecular moments of inertia

The moment of inertia I of a molecule has a magnitude of order mR^2, where m is an atomic mass. We know the relation between mass in amu and in grams, 1 amu $= 1.66 \times 10^{-24}$ g. Therefore measurement of I also in principle allows the determination of atomic and molecular radii. Values of I are determined indirectly by measuring the frequencies at which molecules absorb radiation in the microwave and infrared regions.

One important fact about atomic structure is immediately evident from such measurements; namely, that although the atom may behave in some respect like a hard sphere of radius approximately 1 A, its mass appears to be almost entirely concentrated at a point in its center. Consider for example the oxygen atom and O_2 molecule. The radius of the O atom is $R = 0.6$ A, and if the mass of the atom were distributed uniformly throughout this sphere, the moment of inertia would be $I_0 = 2mR^2/5 = 3.8 \times 10^{-40}$ g cm^2. An oxygen molecule would have two moments of inertia: one about the axis joining the centers of the two atoms equal to $I_{11} = 2I_0 = 7.67 \times 10^{-40}$ g cm; the other about an axis passing through the center of mass of the molecule and perpendicular to the line joining the centers of the atoms and itself equal to $I_1 = 2(I_0 + mR^2) = 26.9 \times 10^{-40}$ g cm^2.

These predictions are in direct conflict with the experimental evidence, which shows that the O_2 molecule has only one moment of inertia with the value $I = 19.2 \times 10^{-40}$ g cm^2. This experimental value just equals $2mR^2$, which is the moment of inertia of two mass points m separated by a distance $2R$. Two mass points would have $I_{11} = 0$, which explains the absence of a second measured value for I. Thus the experimental evidence strongly indicates that the mass of an atom is mainly localized in a small region about its center, called the *nucleus* of the atom. By taking this fact into account, we can compute the interatomic distances of simple molecules from their measured moments of inertia. A complex molecule without an unusually high degree of symmetry will have three different moments of inertia. If the geometrical shape of the molecule is known, these moments serve to fix its dimensions. The moments of inertia of molecules vary between wide limits, from 0.47×10^{-40} g cm^2 for H$_2$ to 2750×10^{-40} g cm^2 for HgI$_2$, and to even larger values for complex molecules with heavy atoms. For most common, simple molecules it is on the order of 100×10^{-40} g cm^2.

Table 2.1 contains a summary of some molecular and atomic sizes as determined by various methods. The method called *spectroscopy* for atoms involves measurement of the moment of inertia of a gaseous molecule. Note that the radii of diatomic molecules are approximately

TABLE 2.1. MOLECULAR AND ATOMIC RADII[a]

Molecule	METHOD			Atom	METHOD	
	Gas Viscosity	Critical Point	Liquid Density		X-ray	Spectroscopy
He	0.98 A	1.25 A	2.00 A	He		
Ne	1.17			Ne		
A	1.46	1.45	2.02	A		
Kr	1.6	1.57	2.24	Kr	Molecules	
Xe	1.75	1.63	2.22	Xe	monatomic	
Hg		1.19	1.29	Hg		
H$_2$	1.23	1.33	1.97	H	0.30 A	0.37 A
N$_2$	1.59	1.49	2.12	N	0.70	0.55
O$_2$	1.49	1.35	1.94	O	0.66	0.60
F$_2$				F	0.64	
Cl$_2$	1.85	1.55	1.84	Cl	0.99	0.99
Br$_2$	2.02			Br	1.14	1.14
I$_2$	2.23			I	1.33	1.33
NO	1.5			B	0.88	
CO	1.6	1.52	2.12	C	0.77	
HF			1.42	Si	1.17	
HCl	1.5	1.5	2.09	P	1.10	
HBr	1.56		1.75	S	1.04	
HI	1.7			Ge	1.22	
H$_2$O	1.36	1.44	1.35	As	1.21	
CO$_2$	1.66	1.55	2.3	Se	1.17	
SO$_2$	1.69			Sn	1.40	
CH$_4$	1.67	1.55		Sb	1.41	
CCl$_4$	1.9		2.69	Te	1.37	
C$_6$H$_6$	2.1		2.6			

[a] Data mainly taken from H. A. Stuart, *Molekulstruktur*, Springer, Berlin (1934) and L. Pauling, *Nature of the Chemical Bond*, Cornell, Ithaca (1945).

the sums of the radii of their atoms, but that the molecular radii show larger fluctuations among different methods of measurement than do the atomic radii. This suggests that the hard-sphere approximation is less valid for molecules than for atoms. Note that the heavy atoms do not tend to be much larger than the light ones; for example, the atom of Hg is not much bigger than that of Si.

2.3. Forces between atoms and molecules

Since atoms, ions, and molecules combine to form crystals and larger aggregates of cohesive matter, there must be appreciable attractive forces between them. From the rather limited point of view of this section, which regards atoms, ions, and molecules as hard spheres, we cannot expect to understand the origins of these forces. We must be content merely to describe them phenomenologically. Four types of forces can be catalogued: coulomb, valence, van der Waals, and repulsive.

The coulomb forces are the only interatomic forces that can be well understood without knowledge of internal atomic structure. For ions of valence z_1 and z_2 (positive or negative) separated by a distance r in a medium of dielectric constant ϵ the coulomb force is

$$F = z_1 z_2 e^2 / \epsilon r^2 \tag{2.5}$$

Here F is directed along the line joining the ions and a positive sign means repulsion, negative sign means attraction.

The attractive forces between atoms include valence as well as coulomb force. The hard-sphere model is quite inadequate to explain valence forces. A more complete and detailed model can successfully interpret them as arising from the exchange of electrons between the atoms. The characteristic property of valence forces is their ability to bind a definite number of atoms, no more and no less. Valence forces are also directional, so that an atom with two or more valence links always has definite angles between these valence bonds. For example, in an H_2O molecule, the angle between the two O—H bonds is always 108°. The attractive forces give rise to the *binding energy* of a molecule, which is the energy necessary to dissociate the molecule into separate, neutral atoms. This energy is on the order of 10^{-11} erg for the simplest molecules; for example, the binding energy of H_2 is about 0.7×10^{-11} erg, of N^2 and CO about 1.8×10^{-11} erg, of O_2 about 1.1×10^{-11} erg, of Cl_2 about 0.4×10^{-11} erg.

Van der Waals forces are attractive forces acting between the neutral molecules of a gas. They are responsible for the formation of liquids and the existence of surface tension. They are relatively weak forces and act over a short range, on the order of 1 A or less. For large ranges they fall off very rapidly, having a variation with range roughly as $1/r^7$. They arise from mutual polarization effects of the molecules, which tend to form two electric dipoles and thereby attract each other. The energy required to separate two molecules held together by van der Waals forces can be estimated from the heat of evaporation of liquids. For example, the heat of evaporation of O_2 at its boiling point of 90°K (Kelvin or absolute temperature) is about 1.6×10^3 cal/mole. Because of the short range of the van der Waals forces, we may assume that each molecule is bound by these forces to only two other molecules. Then the number of pairs of molecules per mole is N_0, and the average energy required to separate a pair is on the order of

$$1.6 \times 10^3 \times 4.2 \times 10^7 \text{ erg}/6.0 \times 10^{23} = 10^{-13} \text{ erg}$$

This energy is only about 1 % of the energy required to separate the two atoms of an O_2 molecule.

The forces discussed above are all attractive and would tend to make every molecule collapse into a point. To reproduce the hard-sphere behavior of atoms, we must introduce a strong repulsive force that acts inside the hard-sphere radius and vanishes rapidly outside of it. This is a totally *ad hoc* assumption, and classical physics has nothing to say about the nature of this repulsive force. The form chosen for the force is guided solely by mathematical convenience; it has been customary to take

$$F = A/r^n \tag{2.6}$$

where n is a relatively large number.

As an illustration we apply this phenomenological treatment of inter-atomic forces to the case of an NaCl crystal. For a first approximation we consider only forces between nearest-neighbor ions. Combining (2.5) and (2.6), we have for the force law between ions (using esu, where $\epsilon = 1$)

$$F = -e^2/r^2 + A/r^n \tag{2.7}$$

where A and n are unknown and to be fitted to the empirical data. From X-ray measurements it is known that the spacing of nearest neighbor ions in the NaCl crystal is $d = 2.82$ A. At this point the force F must be zero, since the crystal is in equilibrium. Thus we have

$$F = 0, \qquad e^2 d^{n-2} = A \tag{2.8}$$

A second equation is obtained from the laws of elasticity. By Hooke's law the force S per cm^2 required to stretch a bar of length L an infinitesimal amount ΔL is given by $S = Y \Delta L/L$, where Y is Young's modulus. The crystal can be regarded as composed of long chains of nearest-neighbor atoms. The density of the chains is $1/d^2$ per cm^2. Each pair of atoms in a chain suffers an equal displacement Δd such that $\Delta d/d = \Delta L/L$. The force on each chain is Sd^2 and is transmitted equally throughout the chain, so that $Sd^2 = -\Delta F$, where ΔF is the force due to displacement Δd from the equilibrium position (2.8). Thus

$$Y \frac{\Delta d}{d} = S = \frac{-\Delta F}{d^2} = -\frac{1}{d^2}\left(\frac{dF}{dr}\right)_{r=d} \Delta d = -\left(\frac{2e^2}{d^3} - \frac{nA}{d^{n+1}}\right)\frac{\Delta d}{d^2}$$

$$Y = -\left(\frac{2e^2}{d^4} - \frac{nA}{d^{n+2}}\right) = (n-2)\frac{e^2}{d^4} \qquad (2.9)$$

by substitution of (2.8) Measurement of d and Y permits evaluation of n and A: for NaCl, $Y = 6 \times 10^{11}$ dyne/cm^2, and we find $n \approx 10$, $A \approx 8.2 \times 10^{-83}$.

We next search for phenomena to test this model of the crystal. According to the model, the ions occupy equilibrium positions with an elastic restoring force, given in (2.9) as

$$\Delta F = -Yd \,\Delta d \qquad (2.10)$$

We write $\Delta F = F$, $\Delta d = x$, $(Yd) = f$, where f is the stiffness of the linear restoring force that holds the atom to its equilibrium position. Then (2.10) becomes just the familiar force law for simple harmonic motion with frequency

$$\nu = \omega/2\pi = 1/2\pi\sqrt{f/M} = 1/2\pi\sqrt{Yd/M} \qquad (2.11)$$

Because the harmonic motion consists of two atoms of different masses M_1 and M_2 moving against each other, in (2.11) we must substitute the *reduced mass*,

$$M = M_1M_2/(M_1 + M_2) \qquad (2.12)$$

For NaCl we calculate $\nu = 3 \times 10^{12}$ sec^{-1}.

We can observe this resonance frequency directly. When light is reflected on a succession of NaCl crystals, most of the light passes through the crystals. After several reflections the reflected beam practically vanishes. There is one exceptional case, however. If the light has the resonant frequency (2.11), it strongly excites vibrations of the ions. Since these are charged particles, they reradiate light of the same frequency by their vibration. The net effect is that the NaCl reflects light of the frequency ν selectively. After a number of reflections a beam of light originally containing all frequencies will contain only the frequency ν, which can be measured directly. This light remaining after several reflections is called a *residual ray* (*Reststrahl*). Residual rays were first observed by Rubens at the end of the nineteenth century. Their wavelengths lie in the infrared part of the spectrum. For NaCl the wavelength is 52 μ, where the micron $\mu = 10^{-6}$ meter $= 10^{-4}$ cm. The corresponding frequency is 5.8×10^{12} sec^{-1}, which is of the same order of magnitude as the calculated value. For our phenomenological treatment, order-of-magnitude agreement is all that we can expect.

These classical equations also yield approximately the correct heat of formation of NaCl. From measurement of the heats of solution and of chemical reactions we can determine experimentally the energy required to take a crystal apart into separate, noninteracting ions. For NaCl this heat of formation is 9.8×10^4 cal/mole. This implies that the work necessary to separate a positive from a negative ion is about

$$u = 9.8 \times 10^4 \times 4.2 \times 10^7 / 6.0 \times 10^{23}$$

$$= 6.9 \times 10^{-12} \text{ erg}$$

From the force equation (2.7) the work necessary to separate two ions is

$$u = \int_d^\infty F \, dr = \frac{e^2}{d}\left(1 - \frac{1}{n-1}\right) = 7.2 \times 10^{-12} \text{ erg} \qquad (2.13)$$

Although the value calculated for u in equation (2.13) is almost exactly the same as the measured value, we must regard this as no more than order-of-magnitude agreement on such an oversimplified model.

2.4. *Properties of gases*

Our picture of atoms and molecules as hard spheres should be adequate to interpret at least some of the simplest properties of bulk matter. This proves to be true of gases, especially in their thermal behavior. The thermal equation of state for an ideal gas, which holds for real gases at sufficiently low pressures, is

$$PV = mRT \qquad (2.14)$$

Here m is the number of moles of the gas in the volume V, $R = 8.31 \times 10^7$ erg/mole deg is the universal gas constant, and T is the temperature on the absolute (Kelvin) scale, $0°K = -273.2°C$.

The Maxwell-Boltzmann kinetic theory of gases leads to (2.14) without detailed assumption of molecular structure. Suppose that the molecules of the gas exert no forces on each other and undergo perfectly elastic collisions at the walls of the container. Let a molecule be traveling in the x-direction with the velocity v_x as shown in Fig. 2.3. On making a collision with the wall it returns with velocity $-v_x$. The change of momen-

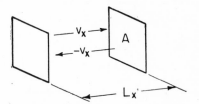

Fig. 2.3. Model for gas pressure.

tum is $\Delta p_x = 2Mv_x$, where M is the mass of the molecule. The interval between successive collisions on one container wall is $t_x = 2L_x/v_x$, where L_x is the distance between parallel walls. The average force exerted on the wall by these collisions is

$$F_x = \Delta p_x/\Delta t_x = Mv_x^2/L_x \tag{2.15}$$

If the area of the wall is A, the pressure on the wall is

$$P = F_x/A = Mv_x^2/AL_x = Mv_x^2/V \tag{2.16}$$

where V is the volume of the rectangular box. The components v_y and v_z of the molecule's velocity make no contribution to the pressure on the area considered.

The molecules are not moving in any preferred direction in space, so that on the average

$$\overline{v_x^2} = \overline{v_y^2} = \overline{v_z^2} = \tfrac{1}{3}(\overline{v_x^2} + \overline{v_y^2} + \overline{v_z^2}) = \tfrac{1}{3}\overline{v^2} \tag{2.17}$$

where $\overline{v^2}$ is the average squared velocity of the molecules. We therefore obtain for m moles of molecules

$$PV = mN_0 M\overline{v_x^2} = mN_0\tfrac{2}{3}(\tfrac{1}{2}M\overline{v^2}) \tag{2.18}$$

where $\tfrac{1}{2}M\overline{v^2} = $ K.E. is the average kinetic energy per molecule.

Equation (2.18) becomes equivalent to (2.14) upon introduction of the classical principle of *equipartition of energy*. This principle states that a system in thermal equilibrium at an absolute temperature T has an average energy $\tfrac{1}{2}kT$ per degree of freedom, where k is Boltzmann's constant. The *degrees of freedom* are just the independent coordinates necessary to specify the system completely in classical mechanics. A monatomic gas molecule has three degrees of freedom: its velocity components v_x, v_y, v_z. More complicated molecules have additional degrees of freedom corresponding to their rotation and internal vibration. Internal degrees of freedom are neglected in deriving (2.18), so that we should substitute

$$\text{K.E.} = \tfrac{1}{2}M\overline{v^2} = 3(\tfrac{1}{2}kT) \tag{2.19}$$

for the kinetic energy of each molecule. The factor 3 comes from the three degrees of freedom for thermal motion.

From (2.19) one obtains the specific heat per mole of a gas of simple, monatomic molecules,

$$C_v = dU/dT = \tfrac{3}{2}N_0 k = \tfrac{3}{2}R \tag{2.20}$$

where $U = N_0$ (K.E.) $= \tfrac{3}{2}N_0 kT$ is the internal energy of the gas. For a diatomic molecule there are in addition two rotational degrees of freedom, since no energy is associated with rotation about the axis joining the two atoms. The law of equipartition of energy assigns an average energy $\frac{1}{2}kT$ to each of these degrees of freedom. Thus, for diatomic atoms that do not vibrate, the specific heat is

$$C_v = \tfrac{3}{2}R + 2(\tfrac{1}{2}R) = \tfrac{5}{2}R \tag{2.21}$$

where $\frac{3}{2}R$ is for translational motion and $2(\frac{1}{2}R)$ for rotation. In a non-collinear molecule of three or more atoms, the rotational contribution is $\frac{3}{2}R$. These conclusions are confirmed by the observation that at ordinary temperatures the specific heat of monatomic gases is $C_v = 3$ cal/mol, and for diatomic gases $C_v = 5$ cal/mol ($R = 2$ cal/mol). At elevated temperatures the specific heat increases because of the contributions of vibrational degrees of freedom. The vibrational specific heat of gas molecules is similar to the specific heat of solids, which we shall discuss in the next section.

The principle of equipartition of energy relates only to the average kinetic energy of the gas molecules. In the 10^{23} molecules of a macroscopic sample there will be large numbers of molecules with considerably more or less energy than this average. To find the distribution of these energies (or velocities), we make use of the Boltzmann principle. According to Eq. (1.9) the relative probability that a molecule in an ideal gas will have energy of translation $\frac{1}{2}Mv^2$ is

$$p(v) = Ce^{-Mv^2/2kT} = Ce^{-Mv_x^2/2kT}e^{-Mv_y^2/2kT}e^{-Mv_z^2/2kT} \tag{2.22}$$

We can regard this as the product of three independent probabilities for the three independent velocity components v_x, v_y, and v_z. The probability that the velocity components will be in the range v_x to $v_x + dv_x$, v_y to $v_y + dv_y$, v_z to $v_z + dv_z$ is then $p(v)\,dv_x\,dv_y\,dv_z$. We define a "velocity" coordinate system with mutually perpendicular axes v_x, v_y, and v_z. In spherical velocity coordinates, where we do not specify the direction of v but only its magnitude, the volume element is $dv_x\,dv_y\,dv_z = 4\pi v^2\,dv$. If we write $P(v)\,dv$ for the probability distribution of the velocity magnitude, we have

$$P(v)\,dv = p(v)4\pi v^2\,dv = C'e^{-Mv^2/2kT}v^2\,dv \tag{2.23}$$

For one mole of gas we must have $\displaystyle\int_0^\infty P(v)\,dv = N_0$, the number of molecules involved, and hence

$$C' = \sqrt{\frac{2}{\pi}}\left(\frac{M}{kT}\right)^{3/2}N_0 \tag{2.23a}$$

The distribution law (2.23) is useful in providing a more detailed description of molecular behavior than is contained in the simple kinetic theory with equipartition of energy. Distributions similar to

(2.23) exist for other types of energy; for example, we obtain the distribution of rotational energies by substituting $\frac{1}{2}I\omega^2$ for $\frac{1}{2}Mv^2$ in the exponent.

2.5. *Properties of solids*

A few properties of solids are interpretable in terms of the simplified atomic and molecular models discussed here. We have described in section 2.3 the relations between intermolecular forces and the elastic constants of solids. The discussion of section 2.4 on the thermal properties of gases also extends to some features of solids.

In a solid conductor the atoms or molecules are more or less fixed in position, and electric current is carried by electrons that move relatively freely from atom to atom. To a first approximation we can regard these conduction electrons as constituting an ideal gas inside the solid. Although these electrons can move freely within the solid, to remove a conduction electron from the solid requires a certain amount of energy W. This energy is characteristic of the material and the condition of its surface; it is generally specified by the *work function* of the surface, $\varphi = W/e$. The work function has the dimensions of an electric potential and is generally a few volts in magnitude (see Table 2.2). The energy W has the same magnitude as φ if expressed in terms of *electron volts*. The electron volt (ev) is the amount of energy that an electron acquires in falling through a potential difference of 1 volt. It is the most convenient unit of energy to use in all atomic problems, and its relation to cgs units is

$$1 \text{ ev} = 1.60 \times 10^{-12} \text{ erg} \qquad (2.24)$$

We can picture the situation at the surface of the metal by means of an energy diagram, as in Fig. 2.4. The energy of an electron is plotted against its position in one dimension. Under ideal-gas conditions the total energy $E = K + V$ of each electron is a constant, represented by a horizontal line on the energy diagram. The potential energy V varies with the position of the electron, and the kinetic energy K must also vary in such a way as to keep the total energy E constant. The potential energy in the metal is represented in Fig. 2.4 by a line that rises sharply by an amount $W = e\varphi$ at the metal surface. This sharp rise is called a "potential barrier." An electron in the metal with $E < W$ can never escape through the surface, because outside the metal it

TABLE 2.2. TYPICAL WORK FUNCTIONS φ OF SOLIDS

C	4.4 volts	Ta	4.2 volts
Ca	3.2	W	4.5
Ni	4.6	Pt	5.3
Mo	4.3	Ba	2.5
Cs	1.8		

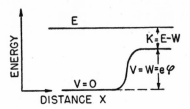

Fig. 2.4. Energy diagram with potential barrier. Potential energy is taken to be $V = 0$ inside barrier.

would have negative kinetic energy, which is impossible in classical physics. Only the electrons with $E \geq W$ inside the metal can escape, and these will have kinetic energy $K = E - W = E - e\varphi$ outside the metal.

If the conduction electrons behave like an ideal gas in the metal, we can use Boltzmann's principle directly to compute the fraction that can escape over the potential barrier. Let the x-direction be perpendicular to the metal surface, so that only the energy $\frac{1}{2}mv_x^2$ associated with the x-component of velocity will be consumed in escaping from the surface. The y- and z-components of velocity remain unaffected and we can accordingly neglect them. The probability of the one-dimensional distribution in v_x is

$$p(v_x) \, dv_x = C e^{-mv_x^2/2kT} \, dv_x \qquad (2.25)$$

If there are n_0 conduction electrons per cm^3,

$$C = \left(\frac{2\pi kT}{m}\right)^{-1/2} n_0$$

The rate at which electrons cross the barrier is proportional to the velocity v_x with which they arrive as well as to $p(v_x)$; thus the rate of emission per second per cm^2 of surface is

$$j = \int_{\sqrt{2W/m}}^{\infty} v_x \, p(v_x) \, dv_x = n_0 \left(\frac{kT}{2\pi m}\right)^{1/2} e^{-e\varphi/kT} \qquad (2.26)$$

The emitted electric current density is $J = \epsilon j$, where here ϵ is the electron charge to distinguish it from the mathematical symbol.

If there is no external field to draw off the emitted electrons, they will eventually be drawn back into the metal by electrostatic attraction, since the metal becomes positively charged through loss of electrons. If, however, fresh electrons continuously flow into the metal to keep it electrically neutral, Eq. (2.26) represents the maximum current density that the metal can produce at a given temperature. This is Richardson's law of thermionic emission, of which the dominant exponential term has been well verified by experiment. More refined arguments using quantum statistics (Chapter 14) indicate the number of conduction electrons available per unit volume should be proportional to $T^{3/2}$, so that the coefficient in (2.26) should vary as T^2 instead of $T^{1/2}$. This difference is not apparent experimentally because of the masking effect of the dominant exponential term.

The specific heat of solids is especially interesting because it illustrates both the success and failure of the simplified models that we have been using. The law of equipartition of energy associates an average of $\frac{1}{2}kT$ of energy with each degree of freedom of an atomic system in thermal equilibrium. In a crystalline solid, the atoms are fixed in position and have no freedom of translational or rotational motion. They can, however, vibrate about their equilibrium positions, performing harmonic oscillations. For each dimension of such an oscillation, two degrees of freedom are involved, one associated with the position (potential energy) and one associated with the velocity (kinetic energy) of the atom. This corresponds to the result of classical mechanics that the motion of a simple harmonic oscillator is completely determined if we know both its position and velocity at a single instant. Since there are three independent directions of oscillation for each atom, the internal energy of oscillation per mole of substance and corresponding specific heat should be

$$U = 3 \times 2(\tfrac{1}{2}kT)N_0 = 3RT \qquad (2.27a)$$

$$C_v = dU/dT = 3R \qquad (2.27b)$$

This equation is the law of Dulong and Petit, according to which all crystalline solids should have a constant specific heat of $3R$ or about 6 cal/mole °C. This law is approached by all crystals at sufficiently high temperatures; but at low temperatures, sometimes considerably below 0°C, C_v falls below the limit $3R$ for all solids and invariably approaches $C_v = 0$ as T approaches 0°K.

The same is true of vibrational specific heats of gas molecules: although the contribution of vibration to the specific heat of a diatomic molecule is $2(\frac{1}{2}k)N_0 = R$ per mole, this specific heat is not observed at low temperatures but is suddenly added over a relatively narrow range at higher temperatures. At sufficiently low temperatures even the rotational specific heats of gasses can be "quenched."

The explanation of these specific heat anomalies is quite outside the scope of our simple models and of classical mechanics itself. A new physical principle—that of quantization—is required. The specific heat problem was historically one of the earliest causes for the introduction of quantum mechanics. We shall nonetheless approach quantum mechanics through a study of atomic spectra and return later to the interpretation of specific heats (Chapter 14).

SUMMARY

As a first approximation we can consider atoms and molecules to behave toward each other as impenetrable spheres of fixed, definite radius. Since they are not really hard spheres, the radius to be used in this approximation depends to some extent on the method of measuring the radius. This fluctuation is particularly apparent for molecules, while for atoms and ions the effective radius remains remarkably constant. The radii of atoms lie almost entirely within the limits 0.5 A to 2.0 A; there is not much general increase in size as we go from light to heavy elements, although mass ratios of 10 or 20 are easily obtained. Thus there is no proportionality between the mass and size of an atom.

Measurements of molecular moments of inertia show that the mass of an atom is almost entirely concentrated in a region at its center called the nucleus. This is inferred from the fact that diatomic molecules exhibit only one moment of inertia instead of two.

Except for the coulomb forces between ions, we can describe the forces between atoms and molecules only in phenomenological terms without detailed understanding, as long as we keep to the oversimplified hard-sphere model. These phenomenological forces are the valence forces, the van der Waals forces between molecules, and a short-range repulsive force to represent the hard sphere. This short-range force is generally written A/r^n. The constants can be adjusted to give order of magnitude agreement with measured binding energies of molecules and crystals.

We can interpret some simple thermal properties of gases and solids without detailed knowledge of atomic or molecular structure. The distribution of molecular velocities in an ideal gas follows from Boltzmann's principle and has application to thermionic emission from solid surfaces. From the law of equipartition of energy the molar specific heat of any substance is $\frac{1}{2}R$ per degree of freedom. This law is in agreement with the translational specific heat of gases, but agrees with vibrational specific heats of solids and gases only at sufficiently high temperatures. As the absolute temperature $T \to 0$, $C_v \to 0$ for all vibrational degrees of freedom. This phenomenon can be explained only on the basis of quantum mechanics, to be discussed in a later chapter.

REFERENCES

S. Glasstone, *A Textbook of Physical Chemistry*, Van Nostrand, New York (1940).

L. Pauling, *Nature of the Chemical Bond*, Cornell University Press, Ithaca, (1945).

J. C. Slater, *Introduction to Chemical Physics*, McGraw-Hill, New York (1939).

H. A. Stuart, *Molekülstruktur*, Springer, Berlin (1934).

ILLUSTRATIVE PROBLEMS

1. Chlorine ($M = 35.5$), argon ($M = 39.9$) and potassium ($M = 39.1$) are expected to have atoms or ions of approximately the same radius. Compute this radius from the information that the refractive index of KCl crystals is $n = 1.49$ for light of wavelength $\lambda = 5890$ A. The density of KCl is $\rho = 1.98$ g/cm^3.

Solution. We must modify (1.26) to apply to a solid by replacing L with $2N_0\rho/M$, the number of ions per cm^3. Here M is the total weight of the diatomic KCl molecule, $M = 64.6$. Substituting (2.4) for α, we obtain

$$R = \left(\frac{n-1}{4\pi}\frac{M}{N_0\rho}\right)^{1/3} = 1.5 \text{ A}$$

2. A crystal of NaCl (molecular weight 58.4, density 2.17 g/cm^3) has a dielectric constant $\epsilon = 6$. Assuming that the dielectric polarization is caused by a displacement of the positive ions in the direction of the applied electric field, and an equal and opposite displacement of the negative ions, compute the distance of these displacements in a field of 100,000 volts/cm (slightly below electric breakdown). This calculation indicates that the ions in the crystal behave like close-packed solid spheres.

Solution. We use the relations (Appendix IV) $D = E + 4\pi P = \epsilon E$, where D is the applied electric displacement and P is the induced dipole moment per unit volume. Eliminating E, we have

$$P = \frac{1}{4\pi}\left(1 - \frac{1}{\epsilon}\right)D$$

The ions Na$^+$ and Cl$^-$ have unit charge e, and displacement of an ion from its equilibrium position by a distance Δx produces a dipole moment $\mu = e\,\Delta x$. Since the displacements of $+$ and $-$ ions are equal and opposite, the moment μ is the same in magnitude and direction at every ion position. Thus $P = (2N_0\rho/M)\,\mu$, or hence

$$\Delta x = \frac{1}{8\pi}\frac{M}{N_0\rho e}\left(1 - \frac{1}{\epsilon}\right)D$$

$$= \frac{1}{8\pi}\frac{58.4}{6.03 \times 10^{23}}\frac{1}{2.17 \times 4.8 \times 10^{-10}}\left(1 - \frac{1}{6}\right)\frac{10^5}{300}$$

$$= 1.0 \times 10^{-12} \text{ cm}$$

The conversion factor of 300 is applied to perform the calculation in esu.

This Δx is less than 10^{-4} times the spacing between ion centers in the NaCl crystal, even though it is about the maximum displacement that can be achieved without electric breakdown in the crystal. Hence the ions behave essentially like incompressible spheres.

3. An HCl molecule can be considered as made up of a Cl monovalent ion of radius 1.27 A, and an H ion which can be considered as a point charge and point mass, located at the surface of the Cl ion.

(a) Compute the moment of inertia of the molecule about its center of mass, assuming that the mass of the Cl ion is concentrated in its center.

(b) Compute the electric dipole moment of HCl, assuming that the Cl ion is not polarizable.

(c) Compute this dipole moment with the assumption that the Cl ion has a polarizability of 3.22×10^{-24} esu. Evaluate the induced moment of the Cl ion by assuming that the electric field acting on it can be considered uniform and equal to that produced at the center of the Cl ion by the charge of the H ion.

Solution. (a) Let the masses of the ions be m and $M = 35.5m$ for H and Cl, respectively. Their centers are separated by the distance d and the distances of the ions from the center of mass are $r = dM/(m + M)$, $R = dm/(m + M)$. The moment of inertia about this center is

$$I = mr^2 + MR^2$$

$$= \left[\frac{mM}{(m + M)} \right] d^2$$

$$= \frac{35.5}{36.5} \times 1.66 \times 10^{-24} \text{g} \times (1.27 \times 10^{-8} \text{ cm})^2$$

$$= 2.6 \times 10^{-40} \text{ g cm}^2$$

(b) $\mu = ed$

$$= 4.80 \times 10^{-10} \text{ esu} \times 1.27 \times 10^{-8} \text{ cm}$$

$$= 6.10 \times 10^{-18} \text{ esu}$$

(c) $\mu = ed - \alpha E$, where $\alpha = 3.22 \times 10^{-24}$,

$$E = e/d^2 = 4.8 \times 10^{-20}/(1.27 \times 10^{-8})^2$$

$$= 2.98 \times 10^6 \text{ esu. Hence } \mu = (6.10 - 9.60) \times 10^{-18}$$

$$= -3.5 \times 10^{-18} \text{ esu.}$$

The polarization is sufficient to change the direction of the dipole moment.

PROBLEMS

1. Chlorine ($M = 35.45$), argon ($M = 39.94$), and potassium ($M = 39.10$) are expected to have atoms or ions of approximately the same radius. Compute this radius from each of the sets of data below:

(a) The mean free path in argon gas at NPT (0°C, 760 mm Hg) is 8.84×10^{-6} cm.

(b) The electric conductivity in reciprocal ohms $\times$ cm (mho $\times$ cm) of aqueous solutions of KCl at 15°C is

Concentration: normal (1 mol/liter) = 0.09252

1/10 normal   = 0.01048

1/100 normal   = 0.001147

Extrapolate to zero concentration. The viscosity of water at 15°C is 0.01140 poise.

(c) The critical data for argon are

$$T_k = -117.4°C, P_k = 52.9 \text{ atm}$$

(d) The density of KCl crystals is $\rho = 1.984$ g/cm^3.

(e) The refractive index of argon for light with $\lambda = 4358$ A at NPT is 1.000280.

(f) The transverse scattering power for natural light with $\lambda = 4358$ A in argon at atmospheric pressure and 27°C is 1.34×10^{-8}.

2. Assume that Na$^+$ and Cl$^-$ ions are of the same size. If all the positive ions in one kilogram of NaCl could be assembled in a square array to form a monatomic layer, with the same interionic spacing as in the crystal,

(a) What would be the area of this monatomic layer?

(b) If the negative ions could be assembled in a similar layer, and the two layers were put together to form a parallel plate capacitor with a plate separation equal to the interionic distance in the crystal, what would be the force between the two layers?

(c) Compare the force per unit area on the capacitor plates with Young's modulus for the NaCl crystal, $Y = 6 \times 10^{11}$ dynes/cm^2.

(d) Compute the electric energy stored in the capacitor and compare it with the heat of formation of the NaCl crystal, 97,900 calories/mole. Comparisons (c) and (d) suggest that as a first approximation we may consider the binding forces of the crystal as due simply to electrostatic attraction between the positive and negative ions.

3. Using Eq. (2.1) and the values of density and molecular (atomic) weight in Appendix II, make a plot of atomic radii against Z.

4. The wavelength of the "residual rays" of KCl is 63.4 microns. Neglecting the difference of mass of the two ions and assuming that both have the atomic weight 37, compute:

(a) the linear restoring force holding the ions at their equilibrium positions in the KCl lattice;

(b) the average amplitude of the thermal vibration of an ion, using the law of equipartition of energy;

(c) what fraction of the normal distance between the ions is represented by this amplitude;

(d) an approximate value of Young's modulus for the crystal. The density of KCl is 1.98 g/cm^3.

5. When NaCl is evaporated, it forms a gas with NaCl molecules in which the distance between ionic centers is 3 A. To increase this by an amount d, a force Kd is required, where K is 4×10^4 dynes/cm. This force can be considered as resulting from the superposition of the coulomb attraction e^2/r^2 of the ionic charges and a repulsive force. If the latter is assumed to depend on the distance r according to an equation A/r^n, what must be the values of A and n? What minimum force is required to separate the two ions? How far must the ions be separated before the average molecule flies apart (recall that equipartition of energy ascribes $\frac{1}{2}kT$ to each rotational degree of freedom)?

6. Consider an O_2 molecule as made up of two spherical O atoms of 1.4 $\times 10^{-8}$ cm radius held together by an "elastic force."

(a) What is the moment of inertia of the molecule at absolute zero temperature?

(b) If the frequency of vibration of the molecule corresponds to that of an infrared absorption line at 100 μ, what is the moment of inertia at 300°K? *Hint:* Find the linear force constant, and note that the O atoms will become separated by centrifugal force.

(c) What is the mean rotational frequency at this temperature?

7. The absorption spectrum of water vapor shows that the H_2O molecule has three moments of inertia about the center of mass: $I_1 = 0.98 \times 10^{-40}$ g cm^2, $I_2 = 2.25 \times 10^{-40}$ g cm^2, $I_3 = 3.23 \times 10^{-40}$ g cm^2. With the assumption that the two valence bonds of the O atom are identical and act at an angle of about 120°, compute the OH distance and the exact angle HOH.

8. A molecule consists of two atoms of weight M_1 and M_2 with a distance d between their centers. For small displacements x the force acting between them is $F = -fx$. Derive an equation for the number of vibrations performed by the atoms while the molecule makes one complete rotation in the gaseous state at the temperature 300°K. Compute this number for the HBr molecule for which $f = 3.6 \times 10^5$ dyne/cm, $d = 1.42$ A.

9. Assuming (1) that the atoms of an element with the atomic weight M have hexagonal close packing in the liquid state, and (2) that they form diatomic molecules in the gaseous state with an effective radius equal to twice the radius of the atoms, derive an equation for the average number g of rotations performed by the molecules in the gas at atmospheric pressure and 0°C between successive impacts. Show that $g = D\rho/M$, where D is a universal constant and ρ is the density of the liquid. Compute the value of D and find g for O_2.

10. If an electron with a speed of 1 meter/sec could pass through a molecule without being deflected or losing speed, through how many molecules of radius 3 A in a gas at NPT would it pass in 1 sec? What is the average distance between impacts? To what pressure in mm Hg must the gas pressure be reduced to obtain a mean free path of 10 cm for the electron?

Chapter 3

PARTICLE BEAMS IN ELECTRIC
AND MAGNETIC FIELDS

Studies made with beams of elementary particles have provided an important part of our information about atomic structure. These studies always involve measurement of the kinematics of the particles under the influence of electric and/or magnetic fields. In this chapter we consider systematically this type of measurement.

It should be remarked that this type of measurement became possible only after the development of high-vacuum techniques, which are essential to the study of isolated atoms. At very low pressure the atoms are far enough apart to have negligible static interactions; moreover, the mean free path becomes so long that we can investigate the dynamics of the motion of a single atom. The development of high-vacuum techniques has also resulted in the discovery of new tools for atomic research, such as the electron and X-rays. These new tools provide examples of a process that constantly repeats itself in all phases of research in physics: upon first discovery a phenomenon undergoes exploration and study for its own sake. As the exploration becomes complete, the phenomenon becomes in its turn a tool for making new discoveries.

3.1. Experimental background

We list the particles involved in experimental atomic physics.

1. Electrons were first discovered as "cathode rays" produced in gas discharge tubes at gas pressures around 10^{-3} mm Hg. At such pressures the mean free path for molecular collisions is much longer than the distance between cathode and anode. The electrons are liberated by ionization of the gas in a narrow space in front of the cathode. More prolific sources of electrons are the metals. They emit electrons when heated (thermionic emission), as in the filament or cathode of a radio tube, or when illuminated with X-rays or other light of sufficiently short wavelength (photoelectric effect).

2. Positive ions of atoms and molecules are produced by electron bombardment of a gas in a discharge tube. Observers first noted them as a colored stream emerging through a hole in the cathode in a direction opposite to the anode. This phenomenon earned for them the early title of canal rays. In applications involving positive ions, the region of production is generally at a much higher pressure (approximately

47

10^{-3} mm Hg) than the region of use (approximately 10^{-5} mm Hg). Differential pumping maintains this pressure difference; an electric field draws the ions from one region to the other and accelerates them to form a beam.

3. Neutral atoms and molecules are produced in streams by heating a gas or evaporating a liquid or solid in a small container in an electrically heated oven. The atoms escape with their thermal velocity through a small hole in the oven into high vacuum. This system needs differential pumping.

4. The α and β particles are components of the radiation emitted by the so-called natural radioactive elements. These comprise all the elements heavier than Bi, such as Ra, Th, U. Methods described below have succeeded in identifying the α particles as doubly charged positive ions of He, the β particles as electrons. These particles have played an important role in the history of atomistics because they have such extremely high speeds as 10^9 to 10^{10} cm/sec. With modern equipment like cyclotrons and betatrons we can produce these and other high-speed particles artificially, so that natural radioactivity is no longer an important source of particles.

We form narrow beams of all these particles by passing them through a set of small circular holes or narrow slits. The high-speed particles are relatively penetrating and can be studied in air at atmospheric pressure but require heavy lead pieces for the stops. For low-speed particles a high vacuum is necessary to produce path lengths of laboratory size.

The methods for detecting beams of charged particles generally rely on the ionizing properties of these particles. In gases at moderate pressure the path of electrically charged particles can be seen directly as a glow. This glow consists of radiation emitted by the gas molecules that have been struck and ionized by the moving particles; the color depends on the gas and is bluish in air, red in hydrogen, etc. A high-speed particle passing through a gas leaves behind it a trail of ionized gas that persists for several seconds after the particle has passed by. We can make the path of a single particle visible by saturating the gas with water vapor and then cooling it by adiabatic expansion just after a particle has passed through. Cooling creates supersaturation and fog formation in the gas. The charged ions along the particle track serve as centers for condensation of this fog. Thus under strong illumination the track appears as a thin line of fog, immediately after expansion of the gas. This is the principle of the Wilson cloud chamber, in which a record is generally made by photographing the track through a window in the chamber.

Beams of electrically charged particles are photochemically active and will "expose" a photographic emulsion at whatever points they pass through the emulsion. Using a microscope to examine the developed emulsion, we can follow tracks of individual particles as in a cloud chamber. Charged particles also produce phosphorescence on glass plates coated with phosphors like ZnS. The phosphorescent light created by a single α particle is sufficiently strong to be seen as a "scintillation" under a low-power microscope.

An ionization chamber detects charged particles by collecting the electrons and positive ions formed by the particles and measuring the extremely small current (down to about 10^{-12} amp) that these ions and electrons produce. The chamber contains two electrodes and has the intervening space filled with gas. A collecting potential of a few hundred volts is placed across the electrodes. Particles entering the chamber release ions and electrons in the gas, and the collecting potential prevents them from combining and draws them to the electrodes. A single fast particle may produce enough current to be observable. If the direct ionization current is too small, we can enhance it by operating the chamber at a somewhat higher collecting potential. In this case the original ions are not only collected but accelerated to the extent that they make secondary collisions in the gas and produce more ions, which are also accelerated towards the electrodes, etc. By the time that an original ion is collected, it is accompanied by a finite number (≤ 100) of secondary ions. This effect is called *gas multiplication*, and essentially amplifies the current pulse produced by each entering charged particle. The chamber operated in this way is a *proportional counter*, because each current pulse is directly proportional to the initial ionization produced by the incident particle. Finally, if we increase the collecting potential still further, each original ion produces so many secondary ions that a self-sustaining, continuous discharge is established in the gas. This is the phenomenon of electrical breakdown: the gas no longer acts as an insulator, and a heavy current passes between the electrodes. At certain potentials this breakdown does not occur spontaneously, but is triggered by the ionization of a charged particle entering the gas. The discharge must be immediately quenched by a special external circuit before the next particle can be counted. When operated in this way, the chamber will give an equal discharge for each incident charged particle, regardless of the initial ionization produced, and is called a (Geiger-Mueller) *counter*.

Neutral particles are rather difficult to detect. We can detect neutral alkali atoms, however, by allowing them to fall on a heated filament, where they turn into positive ions that can be detected by methods applicable to charged particles. The reverse reaction has been observed for neutral chlorine atoms: after falling on a heated filament, they tend to evaporate as negative ions.

The energy of a particle of charge ze that has fallen through a potential difference V volts is zV electron volts (ev). The electron volt is defined in Eq. (2.24). It is also convenient to use units of kilo electron volts (kev), million electron volts (mev), and recently even billion electron volts (bev), where 1 bev $= 10^3$ mev $= 10^6$ kev $= 10^9$ ev. It is often convenient to express neutral particle energies in ev, even though they cannot be accelerated by an electric field, in order to have charged and uncharged particle energies in easily comparable units. In electron volt units the thermal Boltzmann's constant is $k = 0.86 \times 10^{-4}$ ev/°K. At room temperature the average thermal energy per degree of freedom is $\frac{1}{2}kT = 1.25 \times 10^{-2}$ ev. Neutral particles from an oven at 3000°K have an average translational energy of $\frac{3}{2}kT = 0.38$ ev.

3.2. Velocity and energy filters

In any charged or uncharged beam the particles never start from rest. Depending on the mode of production or the temperature of the source, their initial energies vary over a range that may be as large as 1 ev. For high speed particles with energies of several kev this spread in velocity introduces a negligible error, but for accurate measurements with low-speed particles the velocity distribution is an important factor. To eliminate the effect of velocity distribution, we pass the particles through a velocity filter.

For slow neutral particles a simple mechanical velocity filter is possible. Such filters involve rotating parts with apertures that are separated by some distance along the path of the particles and synchronized to present an unobstructed passage only to particles of a single velocity or a few selected velocities. A couple of possible arrangements are shown schematically in Fig. 3.1.

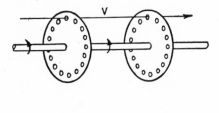

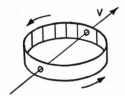

Fig. 3.1. Schematic diagram of two types of mechanical velocity filter.

For charged particles we can use combinations of electric and magnetic fields as velocity filters, The beam can pass through the fields consecutively or simultaneously. The simplest filter is that using superposed, crossed fields, as indicated in Fig. 3.2. In

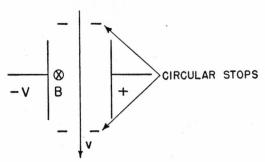

Fig. 3.2. Velocity filter.

this system the beam passes through two circular stops. Between the stops a uniform electric field E is introduced by plane electrodes parallel to the beam, and a uniform magnetic field B is created by coils or permanent magnets usually placed outside the evacuated region where the beam passes. The fields E and B are both perpendicular to the beam and to each other. The particles can pursue a straight path through the filter only if the magnetic and electric forces on them balance, when

$$qE = q'vB = q(v/c)B$$
$$v = cE/B \tag{3.1}$$

Here $c = 3 \times 10^{10}$ cm/sec is the velocity of light, and E and B are measured in absolute Gaussian (cgs) units. The conversions to practical mks, rationalized, etc., units are given in Appendix V. In the absolute Gaussian system the magnitude of a charge in emu is related to its magnitude in esu by q (esu) $= cq'$ (emu). Throughout the text we use q', e' to refer to charge in emu, and q, e for esu. The conversion factor c will be included where necessary, as in (3.1). In general, we shall write all final formulas in terms of e (esu) $= 4.80 \times 10^{-10}$.

Only particles with the velocity v given in (3.1) can pass through the filter undeflected; all others hit the exit stop. Note that v is independent of the charge q on the particle, as long as $q \neq 0$. When used with a stream containing different kinds of charged particles, the filter transmits all those which have the same velocity, regardless of how they differ in mass, charge, or energy. A beam with particles of constant velocity is sometimes called monochromatic.

We can also construct an energy filter, which selects particles of specific energies. In the velocity filter electric and magnetic forces balance each other: in the energy filter an electric field exerts a centripetal force, as shown in Fig. 3.3. The par-

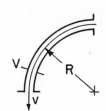

Fig. 3.3. Energy filter.

allel plates that produce the electric field are now concentric cylindrical sections of mean radius R. The uniform electric field E in the region between the plates is radially directed so that the force qE produces the centripetal acceleration necessary to keep the beam in a circular path:

$$qE = Mv^2/R$$
$$T = \tfrac{1}{2}Mv^2 = \tfrac{1}{2}qER \tag{3.2}$$

Here M is the mass of a particle and T its kinetic energy. For particles of fixed q this device acts as an energy filter, regardless of the mass or velocity. It is sometimes advantageous to pass a beam through an energy filter as well as a velocity filter.

3.3. Determination of specific charge, q/M

The deflection of a charged particle in steady, uniform electric and/or magnetic fields depends on the velocity v of the particle and on its specific charge, which is the ratio q/M of its charge q to its mass M. The velocity filter serves to determine v, and a separate measurement will fix q/M. It is impossible, by any combination of fields E and B to determine q and M individually. This is because all such methods measure only the kinematics of the particle—that is, the geometrical configuration of its path, velocity, or acceleration. No absolute measurement is ever made of the force on any particle. Thus all the information obtained is equivalent to the equation

$$a = \frac{d^2x}{dt^2} = \frac{F}{M} = \frac{q}{M}\left[E \quad \text{or} \quad \frac{v}{c}B\right] \tag{3.3}$$

or its time integrals. Equation (3.3) contains only q/M as a parameter and as long as we do not measure the force F directly, we cannot determine q and M separately. There are two general methods, with variations, for the measurement of q/M: magnetic deflection and parallel fields.

The method of magnetic deflection requires a monochromatic beam that has passed through a velocity filter. A strong, uniform magnetic induction B deflects the beam. Since the side thrust is always normal to the velocity of the particles, it acts as a centripetal force and bends the beam into a circular path of radius R, given by $Mv^2/R = qv/cB$, or

$$R = (M/q)(vc/B) \tag{3.4}$$

We keep the magnitude of B fixed and use a fixed value of v as supplied by the velocity filter. The particles describe a semicircle and are recorded on a photographic plate. With the plate adjusted normal to the incident beams the traces due to different particles have a separation of

$$s = 2R_1 - 2R_2 = (2vc/B)[(M/q)_1 - (M/q)_2] \tag{3.5}$$

Note that the traces record the (M/q) values of all particles in the incident beam on a linear scale.

Such a magnetic deflection apparatus is called a *mass spectrograph*. Strictly speaking, it records not the masses but the M/q values. We have, however, conclusive evidence that q is always a whole multiple z of the elementary charge. Particles of the same mass but different degrees of ionization z are readily distinguished. Thus the instrument can be calibrated directly in amu units.

The method of parallel fields uses a stream of particles with velocities that vary over a considerable range, such as "canal rays," i.e., positive ions. The beam passes through superposed fields E and B, which are perpendicular to the beam as in the velocity filter but act in the same direction, either parallel or antiparallel (unlike the velocity filter). To record the deflection of the beam, a phosphorescent screen or photographic plate is placed normal to the undeflected beam. In this arrangement the electric force qE is normal to the magnetic side thrust $q(v/c)B$. Define perpendicular coordinates x, y on this observation plate, and let x be the direction of the parallel fields. The particle suffers the accelerations $a_x = qE/M$, $a_y = q(v/c)B/M$. Since both components are constant, the deflection on the plate is $x = \frac{1}{2}a_x t^2$, $y = \frac{1}{2}a_y t^2$, where $t = d/v$ is the time required for a particle of velocity v to move the distance d from the entrance stop to the plate. Hence the deflections are $x = \frac{1}{2}(q/M)Ed^2/v^2$, $y = \frac{1}{2}(q/M)Bd^2/vc$, and elimination of v gives

$$x = (M/q)(2Ec^2/B^2d^2)y^2 = Cy^2 \tag{3.6}$$

For fixed values of E, B, and d, the value of C is constant for all particles with the same specific charge. Equation (3.6) states that these particles form on the plate a trace with the shape of a parabola. By reversing either E or B, or both, we can trace two complete symmetrical parabolas. Particles with different specific charge give different parabolas for given fields E, B. The intensity distribution along a parabolic trace depends on the velocity distribution of the particles. The velocities can be analyzed by noting that $v = c(E/B)(y/x)$.

The above derivation assumes that the deflections x and y are much smaller than the distance d between stop and plate. It is easy to satisfy this condition by a proper choice of experimental parameters.

The parallel field method yields a value of e/m for the electron, which is $e/m = 1.77 \times 10^8$ coulomb/g. In combination with the value $e = F/N_0 = 1.60 \times 10^{-19}$ coulomb, this gives $m = 9.1 \times 10^{-28}$ g for the electron mass. This is an extremely small mass, on the order of $1/1825$ amu. The positive ion masses, as determined by either of the methods above, always turn out to be on the order of A amu, where $A \geq 1$ is the molecular weight of the ion. It is natural to suppose that the electron is the only carrier of negative charge in the atom, since no other has ever been observed. It then appears that all but one part in several thousand of the mass of an atom is associated with its positive charge. The evidence from the moments of inertia of molecules, discussed in section 2.2 indicates that this preponderant mass is mainly concentrated at the center of the atom. Thus we are led to a model of the atom in which a very dense, heavy part at the center called the *nucleus* contains the positive charge and almost all the mass of the atom, while the negative electrons somehow manage to fill up most of the space in the atom, out to its radius of about 1 A. This is the celebrated nuclear model of the atom, due originally to Rutherford.

3.4. α particle scattering from the nuclear atom

The evidence presented thus far on the internal structure of the atom is rather indirect. It is desirable to have some direct test of the nuclear model in which the small, heavy, positively charged nucleus is surrounded by a cloud of the relatively light electrons. This test is provided by experiments on the scattering of α particles. Measurements of q/M reveal that α particles are just He^{++} ions, ejected from radioactive substances with speeds up to 10^9 cm/sec. These natural sources have the further advantage that the α particles emitted are monochromatic, having a single or at most a few distinct values of velocity v. When these high-speed α particles pass through an atom, they are scarcely affected by the electrons, which are about 7500 times lighter than an α particle. The α particle passes through the electron cloud like a bullet through a swarm of mosquitoes. The positively charged nucleus, however, is $A/4$ times as heavy as the α particles (of mass 4 amu), where A is the atomic weight of the substance used to scatter the particles. Since the nucleus is very small, there will be an intense coulomb field in its immediate neighborhood. We expect that this field can cause strong deflections of the doubly charged α particles. Such sharp deflections are indeed observed in cloud chamber experiments and lend qualitative support to the nuclear model of the atom.

The whole point of the science of physics, however, is that it deals in quantitative and not qualitative relationships. Therefore to verify the nuclear model, we require that the α particle scattering show quantitative agreement with the law predicted mathematically from the coulomb forces in the nuclear atom. This scattering law was first derived by Rutherford and bears his name.

Suppose that we have an incident particle of charge ze and mass M. Let the nucleus be of charge Ze and of effectively infinite mass, so that it suffers no recoil. The scattering effect of the electrons is neglected. The path of the particle is shown in Fig. 3.4. At a great distance from the nucleus the incident particle proceeds along a straight line with velocity

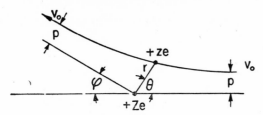

Fig. 3.4. Rutherford scattering by a fixed charge Ze.

v_0 . If we extend this incident path in an undeviated straight line, the distance of closest approach to the nucleus is p. This quantity is the impact parameter, related to the angular momentum L of the particle about the nucleus through the equation

$$L = Mv_0 p \qquad (3.7)$$

The polar coordinates of the incident particle relative to the nucleus are r, θ, as shown in Fig. 3.4. The electrostatic force between the particle and the nucleus acts only along the direction of the radius r, and it is a theorem of mechanics that radial forces conserve angular momentum. Therefore L is a constant throughout the scattering process, and we can write

$$L = Mr^2 \, d\theta/dt = Mv_0 p \qquad (3.8)$$

Together with the conservation of energy $\frac{1}{2}Mv_0^2$, Eq. (3.8) implies that the impact parameter of the scattered particle at large distances from the nucleus is also p.

The radial force of coulomb repulsion is $F = zZe^2/r^2$, which gives rise to a radial acceleration

$$a_r = d^2r/dt^2 - r(d\theta/dt)^2 = F/M = zZe^2/Mr^2 \qquad (3.9)$$

To solve (3.8) and (3.9), we transform coordinates by

$$r = 1/u \qquad (3.10a)$$

$$\frac{dr}{dt} = \frac{dr}{d\theta}\frac{d\theta}{dt} = -\frac{1}{u^2}\frac{du}{d\theta}\frac{Lu^2}{M} = -\frac{L}{M}\frac{du}{d\theta} \qquad (3.10b)$$

$$\begin{aligned}
\frac{d^2r}{dt^2} &= \frac{d\theta}{dt}\frac{d}{d\theta}\left[\frac{dr}{dt}\right] \\
&= \frac{Lu^2}{M}\left(-\frac{L}{M}\frac{d^2u}{d\theta^2}\right) \\
&= -\frac{L^2u^2}{M^2}\frac{d^2u}{d\theta^2}
\end{aligned} \qquad (3.10c)$$

In (3.10) we have used Eq. (3.8) to eliminate $d\theta/dt$. With (3.8) and (3.10) Eq. (3.9) becomes

$$\frac{d^2u}{d\theta^2} + u = -\frac{zZe^2M}{L^2} = -\frac{R}{2p^2} \tag{3.11}$$

Here $R = zZe^2/(\frac{1}{2}Mv_0^2)$ is the absolute minimum distance of approach of the particle to the nucleus. It is achieved only in a head-on collision and is the point at which the initial kinetic energy $\frac{1}{2}Mv_0^2$ is entirely converted into electrostatic potential energy zZe^2/R. For any given particle R and p are both constants and are convenient parameters to describe the Rutherford scattering.

The differential Eq. (3.11) is a standard form with the general solution

$$u = \frac{1}{r} = A \cos\theta + B \sin\theta - \frac{R}{2p^2} \tag{3.12}$$

There are two arbitrary coefficients A and B, as is necessary for a second-order differential equation. They are determined by requiring the mathematical solution (3.12) to correspond to the physical situation of Fig. 3.4. It is clear from the diagram that when $\theta \to 0$,

$$r \to \infty, \qquad u = 1/r \to 0 \tag{3.13a}$$

$$-\frac{L}{M}\frac{du}{d\theta} = \frac{dr}{dt} \to -v_0 \tag{3.13b}$$

Conditions (3.13a) and (3.13b) mean respectively that $A = R/2p^2$ and $B = Mv_0/L = 1/p$. The solution for scattering of a particle with impact parameter p becomes

$$u = \frac{1}{r} = \frac{1}{p}\sin\theta + \frac{R}{2p^2}(\cos\theta - 1) \tag{3.14}$$

This is the equation of a hyperbola in polar coordinates.

The asymptotes of the hyperbola are the straight lines in Fig. 3.4 passing through the nucleus. We find the angles θ that correspond to these asymptotes by putting $r \to \infty$, $u \to 0$ in (3.14). One solution is $\theta = 0$, which corresponds to the incident particle. The other solution, representing the scattered particle, is

$$\frac{2p}{R} = \frac{(1 - \cos\theta)}{\sin\theta} = \tan\frac{\theta}{2} = \cot\frac{\varphi}{2} \tag{3.15}$$

The angle φ represents the deviation of the particle from its original direction and is conventionally called the "scattering angle." Another significant geometrical feature of the particle path is the distance of closest approach to the nucleus, r_{min}. From the symmetry of the hyperbola, r_{min} clearly occurs at $\theta/2$ and is given by

$$r_{min} = \frac{R}{2}\left(1 + \csc\frac{1}{2}\varphi\right) \qquad (3.16)$$

If the scattering angle is small, $\csc\frac{1}{2}\varphi \approx 2/\varphi \gg 1$, so that

$$r_{min} \approx R/\varphi \approx p, \qquad \varphi \ll 1 \qquad (3.16a)$$

In an actual experiment there is not just one particle incident on a single atom, but a parallel beam of many particles impinging on a thin foil of material perpendicular to the beam. To inquire how many particles are scattered through an angle φ or greater is by (3.15) the same as asking how many particles have impact parameter with respect to some atom that is less than or equal to $p = (R/2) \cot \frac{1}{2}\varphi$. Suppose that around each atom we draw a little circular area πp^2 perpendicular to the beam. Also suppose the areas to be so small that the areas in the front of the foil do not appreciably shadow those in the rear. Then if n is the number of atoms per cm³ and t is the thickness of the foil in cm, the fraction of particles passing through the little areas is

$$F(\varphi) = nt\pi p^2 = \tfrac{1}{4}(nt)\pi R^2 \cot^2 \tfrac{1}{2}\varphi \qquad (3.17)$$

This is just the fraction of particles that is scattered through an angle φ or greater in passing through the foil.

Overlap of the areas πp^2 corresponds to multiple scattering of the incident particles. Such multiple scattering cannot be compared with the simple formula above and must be minimized. The mathematical condition for multiple scattering to be small is clearly

$$1 \gg nt\pi p^2 \qquad (3.18)$$

Of course for sufficiently small angles φ the condition (3.18) cannot be satisfied, and the comparison of theory with experiment must be restricted to larger angles. In order to satisfy (3.18) over the widest possible angular range, we must make the thickness t as small as possible. For this reason the scattering target is generally a thin metal foil.

The differential fraction of particles scattered into an angular range $d\varphi$ from φ to $\varphi + d\varphi$ is

$$f(\varphi)\,d\varphi = -dF(\varphi) = \frac{\pi}{4}\,ntR^2\,\frac{\cos\frac{1}{2}\varphi}{\sin^3\frac{1}{2}\varphi}\,d\varphi$$

$$f(\varphi)\,d\omega = \frac{ntR^2\,d\omega}{16\sin^4\frac{1}{2}\varphi} \qquad (3.19)$$

where the element of solid angle is

$$d\omega = 2\pi \sin \varphi \, d\varphi = 4\pi \sin \tfrac{1}{2}\varphi \cos \tfrac{1}{2}\varphi \, d\varphi$$

This final form (3.19) is Rutherford's law for scattering by a coulomb field.

Equation (3.19) has the peculiarity that the scattering becomes infinite as $\varphi \to 0$, which is of course physical nonsense; Eq. (3.19) simply does not apply for very small angles. For example, we might say that it does not apply for very large impact parameters because of multiple scattering effects. Substituting (3.16a) in (3.18), we have

$$\varphi^2 \gg nt\pi R^2 \tag{3.18a}$$

as a condition for validity of (3.19).

3.5. Experimental test; nuclear size and charge

Numerous experiments have verified the essential correctness of Rutherford's law (3.19) and hence of the atomic model on which it is based. Although Rutherford scattering appears daily in the measurements made with modern particle accelerators, the first and one of the most thorough verifications of (3.19) came from the classic experiments of Geiger and Marsden in 1913. They mounted a radon source of α particles behind a thin metal foil and observed the scintillations produced in a ZnS screen. The screen was under a microscope to make individual scintillations visible, and the angle of observation varied from $0°$ to $150°$. Counting the scintillations was a tedious process, since many counts were necessary, and the entire set of experiments represented a considerable feat.

To check the variation with φ, Geiger and Marsden determined the quantity $N = f(\varphi) \sin^4 \tfrac{1}{2}\varphi$ for angles from $\varphi = 5°$ to $\varphi = 150°$, on silver as well as gold foils. For each foil, N was constant to within about $\pm 17\%$ over the angular range. Since both f and $\sin^4 \tfrac{1}{2}\varphi$ vary by a factor of some 10^5 in this range, we must consider the relative constancy of N as verification of the $1/\sin^4 \tfrac{1}{2}\varphi$ feature of Rutherford's law. The linear increase of the scattering with the foil thickness t was verified for thin foils of gold, silver, copper, and aluminum. The linearity held only for such thicknesses and angles of observation (3.18a) that multiple scattering was negligible. The dependence of the scattering on v_0 was tested by using various α-particle sources with different particle velocities. The quantity fv_0^4 was constant to about $\pm 12\%$, although v_0 varied over a range of about ten.

After being established, Rutherford's law served in turn as a means of investigating internal atomic structure. Some experiments by Chadwick on α particle scattering had the specific purpose of determining the charge number Z of the nucleus. For copper, silver, and platinum he found $Z = 29.3$, 46.3, and 77.4, respectively, with estimated errors of 1 to 2 per cent. Since an atom is electrically neutral and contains an integral number of electrons, Z must also be an integer. The atomic numbers of these elements, giving their positions in the periodic table, are 29, 47, and 78. Within the experimental errors these measurements indicate that the positive charge on the nucleus in units of e equals the atomic number of the element.

The approximate size of the nucleus is also measurable in scattering experiments. Deviations from Rutherford scattering will appear whenever the distance of closest approach of the incident particle is smaller than the nuclear radius. For natural α particles this distance is generally a few units times 10^{-12} cm, and no deviations from Rutherford scattering are observed. This sets an upper limit on the size of the nucleus. With the fastest natural α particles against nuclei of low-Z elements like boron, or with artificially accelerated protons (H^+ nuclei) it is possible to observe deviations from Rutherford scattering. Such measurements show that the radii of all nuclei lie between 10^{-13} and 10^{-12} cm. Thus the atom finally appears to be mostly empty space! The atom itself has a radius of about 1 A, around 10^4 to 10^5 times the nuclear radius, and yet all but about 0.03 % of the atomic mass is concentrated in the nucleus. If the nucleus were the size of a large orange, the atom would be about a mile across. The space outside the nucleus is filled with Z electrons, where the atomic number Z runs from 1 to 92 or a little higher. The central problem of atomic physics is to determine the behavior of the electrons in these vast, empty reaches of the atom. One question that immediately arises is how the atom can behave like the impenetrable elastic sphere discussed in Chapter 2, if it is mostly empty space containing a few electrons. This apparent difficulty is related to more fundamental problems of atomic structure at the end of Chapter 6.

3.6. Isotopes

Another result of the specific charge measurements described in section 3.3 has been the discovery of isotopes. The mass spectrograph principle of circular deflection in a uniform magnetic field can be developed into an instrument of very high resolving power, to determine masses with an accuracy of 10^{-5} amu. Since it is difficult to produce ideally uniform magnetic fields over a large area, the instrument does not measure individual particles but rather the small differences between similar particles. If we take into account the fact that all ionic charges $q = ze$, where z is the valence of the ion, we can write (3.5) as

$$s = C[(M/z)_1 - (M/z)_2] \tag{3.20}$$

where C is a constant for any instrument, $C = (2vc/eB)$. It is entirely sufficient to measure only the differences s for various ions, because all the ionic masses are defined relative to $O = 16.000 \cdots$ as a standard. Thus by taking oxygen as one of the pair of ions in (3.20), we can determine the masses of a group of secondary standards; from these secondary standards we can proceed by difference measurements to a third set of ions, and so forth until we determine all ionic masses.

To be sure, the oxygen ions used for such an analysis do not have exactly the mass $16.000 \cdots$, because this value by definition refers to a neutral atom, and the oxygen ion of valence $+z$ is lighter than the atom by the removal of z electrons. This fact is, however, of no consequence for the determination of M/z from the difference s. To realize this, consider the case of two ions of valence z_1 and z_2 , and let the masses of the corresponding neutral atoms or molecules be M_1 and M_2 . The masses of the ions are then $M_1' = M_1 - z_1 m_0$ and $M_2' = M_2 - z_2 m_0$, where m_0 is the electron mass. The spectrograph records

$$s = C(M_1'/z_1 - M_2'/z_2) = C(M_1/z_1 - M_2/z_2) \qquad (3.21)$$

where the terms in m_0 have exactly canceled. This cancellation always occurs. Thus we see that we can interpret the mass spectrograph measurements as giving differences between neutral atomic or molecular masses, regardless of the fact that the measurements actually involve corresponding ions.

In contrast to chemical measurements of average molecular weights, the mass spectrograph shows that the mass of any individual atom or molecule is nearly a whole multiple of 1 amu. For atoms of the light elements the mass differs by less than 0.01 amu from an integer, and for heavy elements the difference is less than 0.1 amu. This fact has led to the introduction of the *mass number A* of an atom. This is the nearest integer to its actual mass in amu. The convention adopted is to write the number A as a right upper subscript to the chemical symbol of the element. To describe the element completely, the atomic number Z giving its order in the periodic system is added as a left lower subscript. Thus $_{10}Ne^{20}$ is the symbol for a neon atom. It is the tenth element and has a mass of 20.0004 amu. Order number and chemical symbol are synonymous and somewhat redundant, except that Z has the quantitative significance of being the positive charge on the nucleus, which must be equal to the number of electrons in a neutral atom.

The mass number is in general *not* identical with the usual chemical atomic weight, because the mass spectrograph has revealed the important fact that many elements possess atoms of different masses, though these atoms are chemically identical. Thus pure neon gas is found to contain atoms with the mass numbers 20 and 22: $_{10}Ne^{20}$ and $_{10}Ne^{22}$. Chemically identical atoms of different mass are called *isotopes* of the element. Some elements have many isotopes, such as tin $_{50}$Sn with the mass numbers 112, 114, 115, 116, 117, 118, 119, 120, 121, and 124. The existence of isotopes explains why the atomic weights are not integers and why samples of different origin, though chemically pure and identical, may show different atomic weight. The mass spectrograph serves not only to identify the isotopes of an element but also permits determination of their relative abundances. The independence of chemical properties of the nuclear mass is direct proof that these chemical properties depend only on the electron configuration outside the nucleus. This fact is already implicit in the equivalence of the number of electrons with Z, the order number in the chemical periodic table.

Molecules containing different isotopic atoms such as Cl_2, which can be Cl^{35}—Cl^{35}, Cl^{35}—Cl^{37} or Cl^{37}—Cl^{37}, possess different moments of inertia and therefore produce different infrared rotation spectra. The largest difference occurs in H_2, because H has an isotope $_1H^2$ called *deuterium* (also denoted by D), and these two atoms have the largest mass ratio of any isotopes, namely 1:2.

The existence of isotope mixtures among the elements necessitates a slight redefinition of the atomic mass scale. The "chemical" definition of the atomic mass unit was that one neutral oxygen atom should weigh precisely $16.0000 \cdots$ amu. Naturally occurring oxygen proves, however, to be a mixture of the isotopes $_8O^{16}$, $_8O^{17}$, and $_8O^{18}$ in the approximate ratio 1:0.0004:0.0020. The obvious "physical" definition of the atomic mass unit is that a neutral atom of the isotope $_8O^{16}$ weighs just $16.000 \cdots$ amu. The chemical amu is thus larger than the physical amu by a factor 1.00028. This factor is negligibly different from 1 for most applications; we shall refer to amu only on the "physical" scale.

Atoms of different elements but with the same mass number, like $_{50}Sn^{121}$ and $_{51}Sb^{121}$ are called *isobars*. If the masses of isobaric ions of the same valence were the same, their traces in the mass spectrograph would coincide. By using instruments of high resolving power it has been possible to show that their masses are not identical, and the differences can be measured with an accuracy of 10^{-5} amu. The same procedure can be applied to molecular ions with the same valence and mass number (sum of the atomic mass numbers) or to ions that have the same M/z values. Measurement of these small differences makes it possible to determine the masses of all atoms and their isotopes to five significant figures, by using suitable combinations as illustrated by the following example.

With a combination of methane and oxygen we have,[*] using the chemical symbol to indicate the mass

$$_6C^{12}(_1H^1)_4 - _8O^{16} = 364.15 \pm 0.08 \times 10^{-4} \text{ amu} \qquad (3.22)$$

[*] Values taken from K. Ogata and H. Matsuda, *Phys. Rev.*, **89,** 27 (1953).

Since O^{16} has by definition a mass of $16.000 \cdots$ amu, it follows that

$$_6C^{12} + 4\,_1H^1 = 16 + 364.15 \pm 0.08 \times 10^{-4}\,\text{amu} \qquad (3.23)$$

In a mixture containing monovalent D_3 and divalent $_6C^{12}$ ions, which have the same M/z values, we find the difference

$$D_3 - \tfrac{1}{2}\,_6C^{12} = 423.01 \pm 0.09 \times 10^{-4}\,\text{amu} \qquad (3.24)$$

In a similar fashion singly ionized H_2 molecules and D atoms give

$$(_1H^1)_2 - D = 15.492 \pm 0.008 \times 10^{-4}\,\text{amu} \qquad (3.25)$$

Equations (3.23 to 25) are three equations for the masses of $_1H^1$, $_1H^2$ and $_6C^{12}$, which yield

$$_1H^1 = 1 + 81.45 \pm 0.02 \times 10^{-4}\,\text{amu}$$

$$_1H^2 = D = 2 + 147.41 \pm 0.03 \times 10^{-4}\,\text{amu} \qquad (3.26)$$

$$_6C^{12} = 12 + 38.44 \pm 0.06 \times 10^{-4}\,\text{amu}$$

This procedure of comparing molecules with almost but not quite the same M/z ratio is sometimes called the *mass doublet* method. To see why it achieves such high accuracy, consider that the difference $C^{12}H_4^1 - O^{16} = 0.036$ needs to be measured only with an accuracy of 3 % to yield an accuracy of $3\% \times 0.036/16 \approx 0.01\%$ in the mass determination of $C^{12}H_4^1$ relative to the basic standard O^{16}.

Note that the deviations from integral values in (3.26) vary irregularly; they are not related to the atomic or mass number in a simple manner. They imply, for instance, that if C^{12} were made up of 12 $_1H^1$ units, some mass would have to be lost in packing the units together. The interpretation of these mass defects is of great importance in nuclear physics (see Chapter 13).

3.7. Deflection of neutral particles in inhomogeneous fields

Uniform electric or magnetic fields can deflect only beams of charged particles and have no effect on beams of neutral atoms or molecules. An inhomogeneous field, however, will deflect a beam of neutral particles provided that they possess a dipole moment μ. This deflection in the magnetic case was first studied by Stern and Gerlach. The theory is identical for both electric and magnetic fields but will be easier to discuss for the electric case. The resulting equations describe the magnetic case if we replace *E* by *B* and the electric by the magnetic dipole moment.

In the experiments an inhomogeneous field is established between a flat and a V-shaped electrode (or pole pieces of magnets), as indicated in Fig. 3.5, and the beam passes near the apex of the V in the symmetry

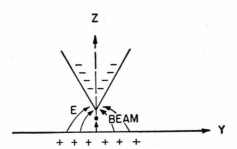

Fig. 3.5. Inhomogeneous electric field.

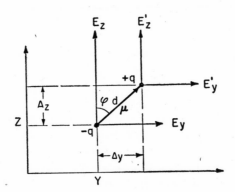

Fig. 3.6. Forces on electric dipole.

plane of the setup. If we denote the beam direction by x and the symmetry axis by z as shown, the field E at the position of the particles has the components $E_x = 0$, $E_y = 0$, while E_z will vary with z.

We consider first a more general case where $E_x = 0$, but where E_y and E_z are arbitrary functions of y and z. An electric dipole can be represented by two charges $+q$ and $-q$ a short distance d apart, as in Fig. 3.6. The position of $-q$ is denoted by y and z, that of $+q$ by $y + \Delta y$, $z + \Delta z$. If E_y, E_z denote the components of the field at $-q$, the field at $+q$ has the components

$$E_y' = E_y + \frac{\partial E_y}{\partial z} \Delta z + \frac{\partial E_y}{\partial y} \Delta y$$

$$E_z' = E_z + \frac{\partial E_z}{\partial z} \Delta z + \frac{\partial E_z}{\partial y} \Delta y$$

(3.27)

The dipole moment, considered as a vector of magnitude qd pointing from $-q$ to $+q$, has the components

$$\mu_y = q\,\Delta y, \qquad \mu_z = q\,\Delta z$$

(3.28)

Adding the products of charge and field components, we get for the components of the resulting force

$$F_y = \mu_y \frac{\partial E_y}{\partial y} + \mu_z \frac{\partial E_y}{\partial z}$$

$$F_z = \mu_y \frac{\partial E_z}{\partial y} + \mu_z \frac{\partial E_z}{\partial z}$$

(3.29)

The equations for the magnetic case are exactly the same, except that we substitute the magnetic induction B for the electric field E, and the dipole moment $\mathbf{\mu}$ refers to the magnetic dipole moment. The force components are

$$F_y = \mu_y \frac{\partial B_y}{\partial y} + \mu_z \frac{\partial B_y}{\partial z}$$

$$F_z = \mu_y \frac{\partial B_z}{\partial y} + \mu_z \frac{\partial B_z}{\partial z}$$

(3.30)

As we shall see in the next chapter, the magnetic dipole moment $\mathbf{\mu}$ of an atom is antiparallel to its angular momentum L. A magnetic induction B exerts a torque $T = \mathbf{\mu} \times B$ on the dipole. By elementary mechanics this torque produces a change in the angular momentum, $T = dL/dt$. In the present case dL/dt amounts to a precession of L and hence of $\mathbf{\mu}$ about the axis of B, as shown in Fig. 4.2. The precession frequency is on the order of megacycles even for a field of 1 gauss. Hence in passing through the Stern-Gerlach apparatus, the molecules will perform 10^4 or more precessional rotations. The only nonzero component of B at the beam position is B_z, so the precession occurs about the z-axis. The average forces on the molecules during their passage through the apparatus are

$$\bar{F}_y = \bar{\mu}_y \frac{\partial B_y}{\partial y} + \bar{\mu}_z \frac{\partial B_y}{\partial z}$$

$$\bar{F}_z = \bar{\mu}_y \frac{\partial B_z}{\partial y} + \bar{\mu}_z \frac{\partial B_z}{\partial z}$$

(3.30a)

where the bars indicate averages over the path through the magnet. Because of the precession

$$\bar{\mu}_y = 0, \qquad \bar{\mu}_z = \mu \cos \varphi \qquad (3.31)$$

where φ is the angle between the directions of $\mathbf{\mu}$ and B, and μ is the total magnitude of the magnetic moment. The net force on the molecules thus becomes

$$\bar{F}_y = \mu \cos \varphi \frac{\partial B_y}{\partial z}, \qquad \bar{F}_z = \mu \cos \varphi \frac{\partial B_z}{\partial z} \qquad (3.30b)$$

The symmetry of the field (Fig. 3.5) assures us that $B_y = 0$ along the z-axis, so of course $\partial B_y/\partial z = 0$ at the beam position. Thus the force on the molecules finally reduces to a single component,

$$\bar{F}_x = \bar{F}_y = 0, \qquad \bar{F}_z = \mu \cos \varphi \, \frac{\partial B_z}{\partial z} \qquad (3.30c)$$

Equation (3.30c) tells us several things about the force on the molecules: the force is entirely directed along the symmetry axis of the V-shaped pole piece and would be absent in a homogeneous field, for which $\partial B_z/\partial z = 0$. The magnitude of the force depends on the angle of orientation and is a maximum for $\cos \varphi = \pm 1$. Even the maximum force attainable with neutral atoms in an inhomogeneous magnetic field is rather small, so that the maximum deflections expected in a typical apparatus are on the order of a few millimeters.

Suppose that an incident particle has a velocity $v_x = v$ in the x-direction. This initial velocity component remains unchanged by the side thrust $\bar{F}$, which produces an acceleration $a_z = \bar{F}/M$. This acceleration occurs only for the time $t = l/v$ during which the particle is in the magnetic field, where l is the length of the edge of the V-shaped magnet. If we assume the acceleration a_z to be uniform, the particle emerges from the magnet with velocity and displacement in the z-direction equal to

$$v_z = a_z t = (\bar{F}/M)(l/v)$$
$$z = \tfrac{1}{2} a_z t^2 = \tfrac{1}{2}(\bar{F}/M)(l/v)^2 \qquad (3.32)$$

The path of the particle inside the magnet is a parabola, as in the case of a horizontally fired cannon ball under the constant vertical acceleration of gravity. After leaving the magnet, the particle follows a straight path. It strikes a detecting plate a distance s from the end of the capacitor. The deflection on this plate from the undeviated position with the field off is

$$\Delta z = z + \frac{v_z}{v} s = \bar{F} l \, \frac{(s + l/2)}{Mv^2} \qquad (3.33)$$

The deflection Δz is proportional to $1/v^2$, where v is the incident velocity. The source of the neutral particles is generally an oven with a small aperture through which the particles escape to form a beam with thermal velocities. The average value of v^2 given by the principle of equipartition of energy is $\tfrac{1}{2} M \bar{v^2} = \tfrac{3}{2} kT$, $\bar{v^2} = 3kT/M$. We can make a somewhat improved estimate of v^2 by taking into account the actual geometry of the source. The particles that emerge from the oven with a velocity v in a time interval Δt come from a cylinder behind the aperture of length $v\,\Delta t$. Thus the rate of particle emission through the aperture is v times the density of corresponding particles in the oven. The velocity distribution inside the oven is (2.23), and hence the velocity distribution of the emitted particles is

$$p'(v)\,dv \;=\; C'' e^{-Mv^2/3kT} v^3\,dv \tag{3.34}$$

where C'' is not the same as C' in (2.23). The mean square velocity of this distribution is

$$\overline{v^2} \;=\; \int_0^\infty \frac{v^2 p'(v)\,dv}{p'(v)\,dv} \;=\; \frac{4kT}{M} \tag{3.35}$$

This value for $\overline{v^2}$ is usually inserted in equation (3.33).

Since the force $\bar F$ varies with $\cos\varphi$, we should expect that a beam of neutral atoms with dipole moments in an inhomogeneous magnetic field would be smeared out in a continuous fashion along the z-axis. The striking result of the experiments, first performed by Stern and Gerlach, is that the beam does *not* smear continuously but splits into a finite number of uniformly spaced components. With neutral atoms of Ag and Na, for example, the beam splits into two well-distinguished parts, equally and oppositely placed from the undeflected position. This suggests that the dipoles can take only two possible orientations relative to the z-axis. This phenomenon is known as *space quantization*. The possible orientations are always restricted to a finite number, equally spaced in values of $\cos\varphi$; this number is not always two, as for Ag and Na, but it is usually small.

Space quantization appears to be a fundamental and unvarying law of nature. Like the deviations from Dulong and Petit's law, $C_v = 6R$ for solids, space quantization is inexplicable on the basis of classical mechanics. Both of these anomalies fit logically into the structure of quantum mechanics (wave mechanics), discussed in subsequent chapters.

SUMMARY

Studies with beams of charged and neutral particles are of great importance in revealing subatomic structure. Measurements on charged particle beams yield only the values of the specific charge q/M, and never q or M separately. Crossed electric and magnetic fields produce a velocity filter for monochromatizing charged beams; an electric field used to produce a centripetal force makes an energy filter. Two general principles for q/M measurements are circular deflection in a uniform magnetic induction and crossed electric and magnetic fields (parabola method).

The q/M measurements on electrons and positive ions show that the electron is many thousand times lighter than the average atom. This great mass is concentrated in the nucleus of the atom, which also contains the positive charge. Experiments on the scattering of α particles from naturally radioactive sources and of artificially accelerated protons give evidence that Rutherford's nuclear model of the atom is correct. These experiments show that the nuclear radius is between 10^{-13} and 10^{-12} cm, as compared with an atomic radius of order 10^{-8} cm. They also show that the atomic number Z of the element, giving its order in the chemical periodic table, equals the positive charge on the nucleus in units of e. Therefore Z also equals the number of extranuclear electrons in an electrically neutral atom.

The q/M measurements of positive ions reveal the existence of *isotopes*, which are chemically similar atoms with the same charge number Z but different atomic weights. It is found that all isotopic masses are close to integer values in amu, which permits the definition of an integral mass number A for each isotope. By means of a difference or "doublet" method we can measure the small deviations of M from A to order 10^{-5} amu. The nonintegral values observed for the atomic weights of some chemical elements arise from a mixture of different isotopes. In the case of oxygen there are three isotopes, $_8O^{16}$, $_8O^{17}$, $_8O^{18}$; the chemical amu, based on the natural mixture as $16.000 \cdots$ units, is therefore larger by 0.028% than the physical amu, based on $_8O^{16}$ as a standard.

Neutral atoms or molecules with permanent dipole moments will not respond to a uniform field but are deflected by an inhomogeneous field. In a simple geometry the force depends on the angle between the dipole vector and the symmetry axis of the field; we accordingly expect an incident beam to be smeared in a continuous fashion between certain limits. The magnetic experiments of Stern and Gerlach and others show, however, that the beam splits into a finite number of separate components, suggesting that the angle of orientation can assume only a few distinct values. This phenomenon of space quantization can be understood only in terms of quantum (wave) mechanics.

REFERENCES

W. Gerlach and O. Stern, *Z. Physik*, **9,** 349, 353 (1922).

J. Mattauch and S. Flügge, *Nuclear Physics Tables*, Interscience, New York (1946).

R. A. Millikan, *Electrons* (+ *and* −), *Protons, Photons, Neutrons, Mesotrons, and Cosmic Rays*, University of Chicago Press, Chicago (1947).

E. Rutherford, *Phil. Mag.*, **21**, 669 (1911).

Rutherford, Chadwick, and Ellis, *Radiations from Radioactive Substances*, Cambridge University Press, New York (1930).

J. J. Thomson, *Phil. Mag.*, **44**, 293 (1897).

ILLUSTRATIVE PROBLEMS

1. Design a mass spectrograph for which the doublet separation of $_1\text{H}^2$ and $_1\text{H}_2^1$ is 0.5 mm, using the following specifications. The singly charged ions pass through a velocity filter with a plate separation of 2 mm and a potential of 100 volts; the same magnetic induction B is used for the filter and for the circular deflection in the spectrograph. Compute the magnitude of B and sketch the instrument, indicating its dimensions and the directions of the electric and magnetic fields. The mass of H^2 is 2.014741 amu, of H^1 is 1.008145 amu.

Solution. According to (3.20),

$$s = \frac{2vc}{Be}\left[\frac{M_1}{z_1} - \frac{M_2}{z_2}\right]$$

Here $z_1 = z_2 = 1$, $M_1 = 2.01629$ amu, $M_2 = 2.01474$ amu, where 1 amu $= 1.66 \times 10^{-24}$ g. Also, by (3.1), $v = cE/B = (V/d)(c/B)$. Using $e = 4.8 \times 10^{-10}$ esu, $c = 3 \times 10^{10}$ cm/sec, and a conversion factor of $1/300$ from practical volts to statvolts (esu), we have

$$s = \frac{2c^2}{B^2}\frac{V}{de}(M_1 - M_2)$$

$$= \frac{2 \times 9 \times 10^{20} \times (100/300) \times 1.53 \times 10^{-3} \times 1.66 \times 10^{-24}}{B^2 \times 0.2 \times 4.8 \times 10^{-10}}$$

$$= 1.61 \frac{10^4}{B^2}$$

Thus, with $s = 5 \times 10^{-2}$ cm,

$$B = \sqrt{1.59 \times (10^4/5)} \times 10^2 = 5.6 \times 10^2 \text{ gausses}$$

The size of the instrument is determined by $R = (vc/Be)(M/z)$ for either ion. Comparing with the equation for s, we see that

$$2R = \frac{sM}{M_1 - M_2} = 5 \times 10^{-2} \times \frac{2}{1.53} \times 10^3 = 65 \text{ cm}$$

The magnetic induction must therefore be $2R = 65$ cm across. The apparatus is shown in Fig. 3.7.

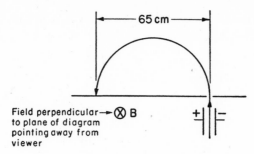

Fig. 3.7. Sketch of mass spectrograph.

2. Derive a relation for the number of alpha particles that will be deflected by an angle larger than 90°, assuming that Rutherford's law is valid up to 180°. Use the result to answer the following problem. In an experiment all forward scattered particles are collected and their charges recorded on an electrometer E_1. Similarly all backward scattered particles are collected to charge an electrometer E_2. The capacitance of E_1 is 1 μf, and that of E_2 is 10 $\mu\mu$f. The velocity of the alpha particles is 1.6×10^9 cm/sec. The scattering foil is of gold, $Z = 79$, $M = 197.2$, density 19.32 gm/cm³. Determine what thickness of the foil should be used so that the potential of the two electrometers increases at the same rate.

Solution. According to (3.19), the fraction of scatterings from 90 to 180° is

$$\int_{\pi/2}^{\pi} \left(\frac{\frac{1}{4}nt\pi R^2 \cos \frac{1}{2}\varphi}{\sin^3 \frac{1}{2}\varphi} \right) d\varphi = \frac{1}{4} nt\pi R^2 = f(90°)$$

The portion of scatterings between 90 and 0° is therefore $1 - f(90°)$. Note that the forward scattering cannot be computed directly from integration of (3.19), which would give an infinite result. This infinity is physically meaningless because it arises from integration over the region $\varphi \to 0$, for which Rutherford's formula does not hold because (3.18) is not satisfied. The expression for $f(90°)$, like the formula (3.19), is valid only for t small enough to avoid multiple scattering.

The charging rate of the electrometers is

$$\frac{q_2}{q_1} = \frac{f(90°)}{1 - f(90°)}$$

and the rate at which their potentials increase is

$$\frac{V_2}{V_1} = \frac{C_1}{C_2} \frac{q_2}{q_1} = 10^5 \frac{q_2}{q_1}$$

If $V_2/V_1 = 1$, then $q_2/q_1 = 10^{-5} \approx f(90°) = \frac{1}{4}nt\pi R^2$. For the present case

$$n = \frac{N_0\rho}{M} = \frac{6.03 \times 10^{23} \times 19.3}{197} = \frac{5.9 \times 10^{22}}{cm^3}$$

$$R = \frac{zZe^2}{\frac{1}{2}Mv_0^2}$$

$$= \frac{2 \times 79 \times (4.8 \times 10^{-10})^2}{\frac{1}{2} \times 4 \times (1.66 \times 10^{-24}) \times (1.6 \times 10^9)^2}$$

$$= 4.3 \times 10^{-12} \text{ cm}$$

Thus
$$t = \frac{10^{-5}}{\frac{1}{4}\pi nR^2} = 1.2 \times 10^{-5} \text{ cm}$$

3. The magnetic moment of neutral sodium atoms is 9.26×10^{-21} emu, and the boiling temperature of Na is 880°C. Assume that the induction in a Stern-Gerlach experiment has components (in emu)

$$B_x = 0$$

$$B_y = 10^4(-y - 2zy^2) \qquad (Note: \text{ div } B = 0)$$

$$B_z = 10^4(1 - z - 2z^2y)$$

and that the pole shoes are 10 cm long. Find how far from the end of the pole shoes the collecting plate must be placed to obtain a separation of 2 mm between the two beams of sodium atoms oriented parallel and antiparallel to the field. The incident beam passes along the x-axis, $y = z = 0$.

Solution. The force on an atom is

$$F = \mu \frac{\partial B_z}{\partial z} \cos \varphi = \mp 9.26 \times 10^{-17} \text{ dyne}$$

for $\cos \varphi = \pm 1$. The difference in deflections for $\cos \varphi = \pm 1$ is, by (3.33) and (3.35),

$$\Delta z = \frac{2Fl}{Mv^2}\left(s + \frac{l}{2}\right) = \frac{Fl}{2kT}\left(s + \frac{l}{2}\right)$$

Inserting $kT = 1.38 \times 10^{-16} \times 1153 = 1.59 \times 10^{-13}$ erg, and $l = 10$ cm, $\Delta z = 0.2$ cm, we have

$$s = \frac{0.4 \times 1.59 \times 10^{-13}}{9.26 \times 10^{-16}} - 5 = 64 \text{ cm}$$

PROBLEMS

1. To realize the tremendous value of the specific charge e/m of the electron, consider two charged particles, each of mass 1 g with the same specific charge as the electron.

(a) What force is required to hold these particles at a distance of 1 cm?

(b) If they start at this distance with zero velocity, what is their velocity when they are separated by a distance of 1 m? Note that both particles are released simultaneously and both move; neglect relativity.

(c) What is their energy at 1 m distance, in ergs, in electron volts, in calories?

(d) What is the magnetic force on the particles at 1 m distance if they are moving perpendicular to the earth's magnetic field of intensity 0.2 gauss?

2. In Fig. 3.8, C is a 90° section of a cylindrical capacitor with a plate separation d which is small compared with the average radius of curvature R of the two plates. A voltage V is applied across the plates and a uniform magnetic induction B is acting normal to the plane of the diagram. A beam of charged particles is to pass along a circle of radius R through the capacitor, in which electric and magnetic forces are acting on it. After leaving the capacitor, the particles remain in the same magnetic induction B and are found to fall on the collecting plate P at a distance x from the exit slit of the capacitor.

(a) Indicate the polarity of V and the direction of B required for positive rays to be focused at a distance $x < 2R$.

(b) Derive the equations for the velocity v and the q/m value of particles arriving at x, in terms of V, d, B, R, x.

(c) Can this arrangement be used as a velocity filter? Discuss its features and disadvantages relative to the crossed fields filter.

(d) Is the arrangement useful as a mass spectrograph? Can you see any advantages or disadvantages compared with the common type?

(e) With $V = 6$ volts, $R = 10$ cm, $d = 1$ mm, what magnetic field in gausses must be applied to have protons arrive at $x = R$?

(f) What is the velocity of these protons and what accelerating potential is required to provide them with this velocity?

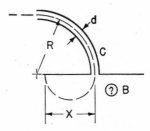

Fig. 3.8. Cylindrical condenser filter and spectrograph.

3. A mechanical velocity filter has two identical disks 4 cm apart, each with 12 equidistant holes on a circle of 2 cm radius, with the holes in the two disks lined up parallel to the rotation axis. The filter is to be used for a stream of He atoms entering the vacuum from a gas reservoir in which the temperature is 500°K and the pressure 1 atm.

(a) What must be the minimum angular velocity in rps if the filter has to transmit the atoms which have an energy corresponding to their average kinetic energy in the reservoir?

(b) At this angular velocity what is the energy of the other atoms capable of passing through the filter?

4. Monochromatic positive ions enter the analyzing chamber of a mass spectrograph through a narrow slit and are deflected by a uniform magnetic induction. If the initial velocities are spread over an angular range 2φ, what is the linear spread of the line on a photographic plate inclined at an angle ψ with respect to the direction of the incident beam? Show that to first order in φ the ions are focused on the plate when $\psi = 90°$. What is the second-order effect at this position?

5. (a) Using a discharge in pure water vapor as a source of positive ions, one may find in the mass spectrograph ions of $_1H^1$, $_1H^2$, $_8O^{16}$, $_8O^{17}$, $_8O^{18}$ and of the various OH compounds such as $(_1H_2^1 \, _8O^{16})$, etc. How many doublets or multiplets can be observed? Give their designations and compute their doublet separations in amu from the following table:

$$_1H^1 = 1.0081 \text{ amu}, \qquad _8O^{16} = 16.0000 \text{ amu},$$

$$_1H^2 = 2.0147 \text{ amu}, \qquad _8O^{17} = 17.0045 \text{ amu}$$

$$_8O^{18} = 18.0050 \text{ amu}$$

(b) A mass spectrum is produced with $COCl_2$ in the discharge tube, and lines are observed on the plate corresponding to the following mass numbers: 14, 16, 17.5, 18.5, 28, 32, 35, 37, 63, 65, 70, 72, 74. Identify the ion producing each of these lines, if C has isotopes $A = 12, 13$, O has isotopes $A = 16, 17, 18$, and Cl has isotopes $A = 35, 37$.

6. Assume that an alpha particle passing through a gas is deflected only when it strikes a nucleus of a gas atom. Compute the approximate fraction of alpha tracks in a cloud chamber that will end in a "fork" as the result of such an impact, if the chamber is filled with helium at normal pressure and temperature. The average velocity of the alpha particles is 10^7 m/sec, their normal range in the cloud chamber is 5 cm, and the radius of the He nucleus is 10^{-12} cm. What would be the range of the alpha particle if it could be stopped only by impact with a He nucleus? The much shorter actual range is due to impacts with many atomic electrons, which cause the alpha particle gradually to lose momentum.

7. The scattering of alpha particles with a velocity of 1.35×10^9 cm/sec from films of boron shows deviations from Rutherford's law above the scattering angle 150° in the center of gravity system. Assuming the proton to have the same radius as an alpha particle, compute the minimum velocity of protons which would show deviations from Rutherford's law in scattering experiments with thin boron films. What potential in volts is required to produce protons of this velocity? What value is indicated for the sum of the boron plus α particle radii? *Note:* in this case the scattering nucleus is not infinitely heavy relative to the scattered particle, and we must use the reduced mass of the particle appropriate to the center of mass system, $M' = MM_n/(M + M_n)$ where M_n is the mass of the nucleus.

8. Thorium emits α particles with an initial velocity of 1.41×10^9 cm per sec.

(a) What is their energy in mev?

(b) What is the radius of their path in a magnetic field of 10000 gausses?

(c) Using the same magnetic field, what electric field is required for a velocity filter to transmit these particles?

(d) Assuming the nuclei of all elements to have a radius of 10^{-12} cm, determine the largest order number of an element in a foil for which the scattering of these particles would deviate from Rutherford's law at large deflection angles.

9. The validity of Rutherford's law in any actual experiment rests on two conditions: (1) that practically none of the particles suffer more than one nuclear collision in passing through the target foil; (2) that the bombarding particle maintains a constant velocity throughout the foil, or hence must lose a negligible amount of kinetic energy by electron impacts. In practice, these conditions restrict experiments to very thin foils. Show this by a calculation along the following lines. Alpha particles of initial velocity 1.4×10^9 cm/sec bombard a gold foil ($_{79}Au^{197}$, density 19.3 g/cm^3, assume a random polycrystalline distribution); and it is required that neither the average energy loss per particle nor the fraction of particles suffering more than one collision exceeds 5%. All deflections are observed that amount to 2° or more.

(a) What is the maximum impact parameter for one of these alpha particles if it is to suffer a deflection of at least 2°?

(b) Neglecting the effect of electron impacts, use the result of part (a) to compute the mean free path of an alpha particle in gold for a deflection of at least 2°. This is the average distance traveled between two such collisions.

(c) Neglecting the effect of large deflections, compute the average loss in alpha-particle energy per unit distance of gold foil traversed, on the assumption that the loss by electron impact averages 100 ev for each Au atom traversed.

(d) Note that the calculation of part (b) neglects the effect of part (c) and vice versa. Why is this justified?

(e) From the results of (c) and (d) compute the maximum thickness of gold foil under the limitation that neither effect should exceed 5%.

(f) Compute roughly the percentage energy loss and fraction of multiple impacts for thicknesses one-half and two times as large as that of part (e). What can you say about the relative importance of these two effects for thin and thick foils?

10. Design a Stern-Gerlach experiment that will give a separation of 2 mm between the two beams of $_{11}Na^{23}$ atoms with a magnetic moment of 9.26×10^{-24} joule m^2/weber, when observed at a distance of 10 cm after leaving the magnet. Use the following data: the kinetic energy of the atoms is $2kT$, where $T = 1200°K$ is slightly above the boiling temperature of Na. The magnet is 10 cm long (neglect end effects) and made of iron with a flux density of 2 webers/m^2 at saturation. Consider the sharp edge of the V-shaped pole piece as a circle of radius r_0 and assume that the field around this edge decreases with the distance r from the center of the circle as D/r (analogy with a cylindrical capacitor). The beam enters the field at a distance $r = 2r_0$. Note that the transverse displacement of the atoms between the pole pieces must be very small, so that in first approximation the induction B acting on the particle when it is at a distance $r = 2r_0 + y$ can be written

$$B(y) = B(2r_0) + y \left(\frac{dB}{dr} \right)_{r=2r_0}$$

Compute the radius of curvature r_0 of the pole piece at the sharp edge.

Chapter 4

MAGNETIC, OPTICAL, AND ELECTRIC
PROPERTIES OF ATOMS

The nuclear model of the atom explains the moments of inertia of diatomic molecules and the large-angle scattering of α particles. The mathematical theory of this scattering turns out to be in excellent quantitative agreement with experiments performed to check it. On the other hand, it is difficult to reconcile this picture with the hard-sphere behavior of atoms toward each other. When such a dilemma arises, the next stage in the scientific procedure is to examine all the other physical implications of the nuclear model and apply quantitative tests to them also. If theory and experiment agree, we obtain further independent support for the model. If they disagree, it becomes necessary to modify and improve the model. Usually such changes do not mean scrapping the previously successful features of the model so much as refining the details. From these refinements in understanding of atomic structure has ultimately come wave mechanics, our most powerful modern tool for analyzing the microscopic physical world.

An application of the nuclear model, which will extend our understanding of its details, is to the magnetic, optical, and electric properties of atoms. Here we can score a number of qualitative successes, which lend strong general support to the model. Certain prominent difficulties arise, however, to be resolved only by additional hypotheses. The chief source of difficulty is the question of radiation by the electrons in the atom. Efforts to avoid the radiation difficulty on a purely classical basis lead to the introduction of a "static" as well as a "dynamic" atomic model. Neither of these versions is entirely correct, but each contains some elements of the truth. We should therefore examine both models to see how far they are adequate to explain the observed facts.

The natural dynamic model to assume is one where the electrons revolve in orbits about the nucleus, just as the planets around the sun. The attractive coulomb force in the atom can exactly replace the gravitational force in the solar system, since both follow inverse square laws. The electron revolving in its orbit experiences a centripetal acceleration, and according to classical electrodynamics should emit radiation. This radiation carries energy away from the electron, which should therefore spiral into the nucleus in a remarkably short time. We know atoms to be stable systems, however, and do not observe any such continuous radiation. Thus we have to entertain an alternative static model in which the electrons are supposed to occupy stationary equilibrium positions in the atom. An electron when disturbed from its equilibrium position experiences a harmonic restoring force to that position. This removes the difficulty with radiation but introduces another: it is not possible to achieve such stationary positions by electric forces alone, and no other forces are known to exist among electrons or between electrons and nuclei. By combining various features of each model, we can obtain some predictions in agreement with observation. This is hardly a satisfactory situation, however, and improved hypotheses are needed.

The solution of this dilemma—as well as those of the space quantization demonstrated by the Stern-Gerlach experiment and the deviation of specific heats from the constant values predicted by classical kinetic theory—requires the introduction of quantum mechanics into atomic problems. Since the quantum mechanical treatment is more complicated than the simple static and dynamic models, it is worth while for us first to consider in detail their successes and limitations.

4.1. Dynamic model and magnetic properties

The classical dynamic model is useful mainly for interpreting magnetic properties of atoms. We neglect for the time being the difficulty with radiation and assume the electron orbits to be stable. To simplify the discussion, consider the orbits to be circular and neglect any interaction between different electrons in an atom. If the radius of an orbit is r, the coulomb force of the nucleus on the electron is Ze^2/r^2, which produces the centripetal acceleration $r\omega^2$, where ω is the angular frequency of rotation. Thus the frequency of rotation is

$$\nu = \omega/2\pi = (e/2\pi r)(Z/mr)^{1/2} \tag{4.1}$$

The radius of the outermost electron orbit is of order $r \approx 10^{-8}$ cm, so that the corresponding $\nu \approx 10^{16}/\text{sec}$. This frequency corresponds to light of wavelength 10^{-5} to 10^{-6} cm, which is the ultraviolet and near-visible range. When atoms are forced to radiate in an electric discharge tube, they emit light of this wavelength range. It therefore seems reasonable to ascribe this optical radiation to the outermost or "optical" electrons of the atom. The infrared radiation of much longer wavelength ($\gtrsim 10^{-4}$ cm) is due to rotation and vibration of charged atoms in molecules.

An electron in its orbit represents an electric current $i = -e'\nu$ passing around a loop of area $A = \pi r^2$. Such a current loop produces a magnetic field equivalent to that of a magnetic dipole with magnetic moment

$$\mu = iA = \pi r^2 e'\nu = \pi r^2 e\nu/c \tag{4.2}$$

The magnetic moment is perpendicular to the plane of the orbit in the direction shown in Fig. 4.1. With the rough values above for r and ν the order of magnitude of the magnetic moment is $\mu \approx 10^{-9}$ esu $= 10^{-19}$ emu (gauss-cm). This moment is called the *orbital magnetic moment*.

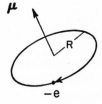

A rotating electron has a moment of inertia about the nucleus of $I = mr^2$ and an (orbital) angular momentum

$$L = I\omega = mr^2 2\pi\nu \qquad (4.3)$$

Fig. 4.1. Magnetic moment of rotating electron.

This angular momentum is a vector quantity and is also directed perpendicular to the plane of the orbit. For a negatively charged particle like the electron, the vectors μ and L are antiparallel; for a positive particle they are parallel. The ratio of the magnitudes of μ and L is

$$\mu/L = e/2mc = G \qquad (4.4)$$

The *gyromagnetic ratio* G has the remarkable property that it is independent of the size of the orbit, frequency of rotation, and magnitude Z of the nuclear charge. Although the constancy of this ratio is shown here only for circular orbits, its independence of all orbit parameters strongly suggests that it would be true for any shape of orbit. This can be shown to be the case.

The various electrons in an atom have their magnetic moments pointing in different directions. The magnetic moment of the atom is the vector sum of these moments. It turns out that this sum is zero for most atoms and molecules. They have no resulting moment and the substance composed of them is *diamagnetic*. Only in the relatively rare cases where the vector sum is nonvanishing does the atom possess a permanent magnetic moment and form a *paramagnetic* substance.

Suppose the atom to be placed in a uniform magnetic induction B, defined for convenience to be in the z-direction. This induction exerts on the orbital magnetic moment of each electron a torque of magnitude $T = \mu B \sin \gamma$, where γ is the angle between μ and B. We can represent this torque as a vector $T = \mu \times B$, normal to both μ and B. Since the torque is always normal to the angular momentum L of the electron, which has the same direction as μ, it cannot change the magnitude of L, but only its direction. Thus L executes a precession about the direction of B. To compute the precession frequency, we introduce a system of axes as shown in Fig. 4.2. With respect to these axes the angular momentum of magnitude L has the components

$$
\begin{aligned}
L_x &= L \sin \gamma \cos \varphi \\
L_y &= L \sin \gamma \sin \varphi \\
L_z &= L \cos \gamma
\end{aligned}
\qquad (4.5)
$$

and the torque has the components

$$T_x = -\mu B \sin \gamma \sin \varphi$$

$$T_y = \mu B \sin \gamma \cos \varphi \qquad (4.6)$$

$$T_z = 0$$

The equations of mechanics tell us that $T_x = dL_x/dt$, and similarly for the y- and z-components. Since the magnitude of L is constant, $T_z = 0$ implies that γ is also constant. The only quantity in (4.5) and (4.6) that can vary with time is φ, and if $\omega_L = d\varphi/dt$, we have

$$-\mu B \sin \gamma \sin \varphi = T_x = dL_x/dt = -\omega_L L \sin \gamma \sin \varphi$$
$$\mu B \sin \gamma \cos \varphi = T_y = dL_y/dt = \omega_L L \sin \gamma \cos \varphi \qquad (4.7)$$

From both Eq. (4.7) comes the condition

$$\omega_L = \mu B/L = BG \qquad (4.8)$$

Thus the application of a constant magnetic field causes each electron orbit to rotate so that its magnetic moment and angular momentum vectors precess about the field direction with an angular frequency ω_L. The corresponding linear frequency $\nu_L = \omega_L/2\pi$ is known as the *Larmor frequency*. Using the value of G from (4.4), we have

$$\nu_L = (e/4\pi mc)B = 1.41 \times 10^6 B \text{ (gausses)}$$
$$= 1.41 \times 10^{10} B \text{ (webers/m}^2) \qquad (4.9)$$

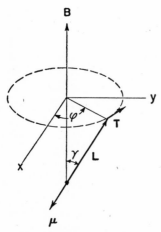

Fig. 4.2. Precession of magnetic moment in external field.

Note that the direction of the Larmor precession is independent of the direction in which the electron rotates. Reversal of the electron motion changes the sign of both L and T in Fig. 4.2 and leaves the precession unchanged. It is also independent of the size and shape of the orbit and the angle γ of its orientation relative to B. The precession would be reversed only if the charge of the electron were made $+e$ instead of $-e$, with a corresponding change of the sign of G in (4.8). Therefore all electrons in an atom undergo the same precessional motion. The effect of the magnetic field is to rotate the entire electronic system in a clockwise sense as seen from the direction of the field. This rotation serves to explain the three magnetic phenomena discussed in the following sections.

4.2. Gyromagnetic (Einstein-de Haas) effect

In the absence of a magnetic field many atoms have a total angular momentum equal to zero; they are called *diamagnetic*. The angular momentum vectors of the individual electrons are randomly oriented, and hence their vector sum is zero. When a magnetic field is applied, the Larmor precession of the electron gives to each atom an angular momentum L_B pointing in the field direction. We may estimate the order of magnitude of this momentum in the following way. Let $\overline{x_i^2}$ and $\overline{y_i^2}$ be the mean square values of these coordinates for the ith electron, which thus has a moment of inertia about the z-axis (direction of B) of $m(\overline{x_i^2} + \overline{y_i^2})$. The total moment of inertia of the atom about the z-axis is $I_B = \sum_i m(\overline{x_i^2} + \overline{y_i^2})$, where the sum is over all electrons in the atom. Under the Larmor precession, the entire electron configuration acquires an angular velocity ω_L about the z-axis. The angular momentum of the atom associated with this rotation is

$$L_B = \omega_L I_B = \frac{eB}{2mc} \sum_i m(\overline{x_i^2} + \overline{y_i^2}) \tag{4.10}$$

Since a spherical atom is symmetrical, we expect that

$$\sum_i \overline{x_i^2} = \sum_i \overline{y_i^2} = \sum_i \overline{z_i^2} = \tfrac{1}{3} \sum_i (\overline{x_i^2} + \overline{y_i^2} + \overline{z_i^2}) = \tfrac{1}{3} \sum_i \overline{r_i^2} \tag{4.11}$$

and hence

$$L_B = \frac{eB}{3c} \sum_i \overline{r_i^2} \tag{4.12}$$

A similar angular momentum in the same direction is given to each atom of the substance. With $\sqrt{\overline{r_i^2}} \approx 10^{-8}$ cm, a magnetic field of 10^4 gausses will induce an angular momentum on the order of 10^{-11} g cm^2/sec in every cm^3 of the sample.

Suppose now a macroscopic body to be suspended at rest on a fine wire and suddenly subjected to a magnetic induction B. There is no torque acting on the body from outside, so that if it was initially at rest with total angular momentum zero, the momentum must remain zero. The external field, however, has produced an angular momentum L_B in the electrons. To balance this and keep the angular momentum of the total system equal to zero, the body as a whole must rotate in the opposite direction to L_B. Thus the body should rotate counterclockwise when viewed in the direction of B. This extremely small rotational momentum, predicted by Einstein and de Haas, has been found in careful measurements by Barnes.

In the observations the body is suspended to form a torsion pendulum. First one measures the damping of the rotation without applied field. Then the field is switched on and periodically reversed when the pendulum passes through the zero position. The effect of the field is therefore to assist or oppose the oscillations, according as the gyromagnetic effect creates a torque in the direction of or opposite to the motion. What one observes is decrease or increase in the apparent rate of damping. The measurements verify the order of magnitude of the calculated angular momentum.

4.3. Diamagnetism and magnetic susceptibility

In addition to gaining angular momentum from the Larmor precession, an atom gains a magnetic moment. The effect of the Larmor precession is to rotate the ith electron about the z-axis in an orbit of area $\pi(\overline{x_i^2} + \overline{y_i^2})$ with frequency ν_L. Since the rotation is clockwise and the electron negatively charged, a net magnetic moment appears directed opposite to the field. This is in accordance with Lenz's law. The induced moment per cm^3 due to all the electrons is hence

$$M_d = -n_0 e' \nu_L \pi \sum_i (\overline{x_i^2} + \overline{y_i^2})$$

$$= -n_0 \left(\frac{e^2 H}{6mc^2} \right) \sum_i \overline{r_i^2} \tag{4.13}$$

where n_0 is the number of atoms per cm^3. In (4.13) we write H instead of B because the individual electrons are supposed to be moving in empty space devoid of any material medium.

The induced moment M_d is called *diamagnetic* because it opposes the action of the applied field. It arises from an intrinsic polarizability of each atom, and experimental verification would provide support for the dynamic model of the atom. Not all materials are suitable for measurement of this diamagnetic effect. Many materials show a *paramagnetism* (induced magnetic moment parallel to the applied field) that masks the diamagnetism (4.13). Paramagnetism occurs when the atoms or molecules of a substance have a permanent magnetic moment $\mathbf{\mu}$. The applied field tends to line up these moments, resulting in an induced moment M_p. We estimate M_p as follows: the magnetic moment per cm^3 has an average component along the direction of H equal to

$$M_p = n_0 \int \mu \cos \theta p(\theta) \, d\omega \tag{4.14}$$

Here $p(\theta) \, d\omega$ is the probability that a dipole $\mathbf{\mu}$ will be pointing in the solid angle $d\omega$ at an angle θ to the direction of $\mathbf{H}$. The component of $\mathbf{\mu}$ parallel to $\mathbf{H}$ is $\mu \cos \theta$, where μ is the magnitude of the permanent dipole moment per molecule; and n_0 is the number of molecules per cm^3. To determine $p(\theta)$, we note that the potential energy of a dipole $\mathbf{\mu}$ in a field $\mathbf{H}$ is $-\mu H \cos \theta$; and according to Boltzmann's principle (1.9) the probability $p(\theta) \, d\omega$ is

$$p(\theta) \, d\omega = \frac{d\omega}{4\pi} e^{(\mu H / kT) \cos \theta} \tag{4.15}$$

On substituting (4.15) into (4.14), we take $d\omega = d\varphi \sin \theta \, d\theta$,

$$\int_0^{2\pi} d\varphi = 2\pi, \quad \text{and} \quad e^{(\mu H / kT) \cos \theta} \approx 1 + \frac{\mu H}{kT} \cos \theta$$

The last is an approximation justified because $\mu H / kT \ll 1$ in experimentally realizable situations. Thus we obtain

$$
\begin{aligned}
M_p &= \frac{n_0}{2} \int_0^{\pi} \mu \sin \theta \cos \theta \left(1 + \frac{\mu H}{kT} \cos \theta \right) d\theta \\
&= \frac{n_0}{3} \frac{\mu^2 H}{kT}
\end{aligned}
\tag{4.16}
$$

The components of M_p perpendicular to H involve integrals of the form

$$\int_0^{2\pi} \sin \varphi \, d\varphi = 0, \quad \int_0^{2\pi} \cos \varphi \, d\varphi = 0$$

thus the induced moment is entirely parallel to H for a simple medium.

The total induced moment in the substance is

$$M = M_d + M_p \tag{4.17}$$

In order to describe the magnetic properties of a material in a way that does not depend on its density ρ, we define the *susceptibility* by

$$\chi = \frac{M}{\rho H} = \frac{n_0}{\rho} \left(\frac{-e^2}{6mc^2} \sum_i r_i^2 + \frac{\mu^2}{3kT} \right) \tag{4.18}$$

The negative and positive terms in (4.18) are, respectively, the dia- and paramagnetic susceptibilities. The diamagnetic term is always present, the paramagnetic term only when the atoms or molecules happen to possess permanent magnetic moments. In case the paramagnetic term is present, however, it is generally a couple of orders of magnitude (factors of 10) larger than the relatively small diamagnetic term. In cases where the paramagnetic term is absent, measurement of the negative susceptibility supports the dynamic model of the atom. The permanent magnetic moments are an *ad hoc* assumption here, so that measurement of paramagnetic susceptibilities does not provide any further insight into the dynamic model.

To estimate the magnitude of the diamagnetic effect, suppose that the Z electrons in an atom are uniformly distributed throughout a sphere of outside radius R. The number of electrons in a spherical shell of radius r and thickness dr is then $dn = 3Zr^2 \, dr/R^3$, and

$$\sum_i \overline{r_i^2} = \int_0^R r^2 \, dn = \tfrac{3}{5}ZR^2$$

Inserting this value in (4.18) and taking $n_0/\rho = N_0/A$, where N_0 is Avogadro's number and A is the atomic weight, we have for the diamagnetic susceptibility

$$\chi_d = -\frac{e^2}{10mc^2} N_0 \frac{Z}{A} R^2$$

$$\approx \frac{-e^2}{20mc^2} N_0 R^2 \approx -10^{10} R^2$$

(4.18a)

where we have taken $Z/A \approx \tfrac{1}{2}$ for all elements. The observed magnitude of the diamagnetic susceptibility is on the order of $\chi_d \approx -10^{-6}$ to -10^{-7}, so that by (4.18a) $R \approx 10^{-8}$ cm $= 1$ A. This is just the same order of magnitude for the atomic radius as obtained in our discussion of Chapter 2, considering the atoms as impenetrable spheres. The atomic model of electrons circulating in orbits does not seem much like a hard sphere, but it is given quantitative support by the fact that (4.18a) correctly predicts the sign and order of magnitude of the diamagnetic effect. About half the chemical elements and most organic compounds exhibit the negative χ characteristic of diamagnetism.

The discussion above assumes a single type of atom to be present; in a compound substance we must understand $(Z/A)R^2$ to be an average value for the atoms in the compound. This refinement is scarcely significant in view of the crudity of the model.

In case of a permanent magnetic dipole moment μ, paramagnetism is observed. Typical ions with $\mu \neq 0$ (from the 10- and 14-number groups of Fig. 1.1) have $\mu \approx 1\text{-}10\mu_0$, where $\mu_0 \approx 10^{-20}$ emu. Thus at room temperature the paramagnetic term is

$$\chi_p \approx \frac{1}{2} \times \frac{10^{-3}}{M} \left(\frac{\mu}{\mu_0}\right)^2 \approx 10^{-3} \text{ to } 10^{-6}$$

Neglecting χ_d in (4.18) as comparatively small, we can write

$$\chi \approx \chi_p = \frac{n_0}{\rho} \frac{\mu^2}{3kT} = \frac{C}{T}$$

(4.18b)

The form C/T exhibiting the inverse temperature dependence is called Curie's law, and C is Curie's constant for the material. Relation (4.18b) is by no means universal but has been verified for some substances over a wide temperature range (O_2 gas, copper- and iron-ammonium sulphates).

An improvement on Curie's law due to Weiss is to write

$$\chi = C/(T - T_c) \qquad (4.18c)$$

The addition of another adjustable parameter, the Curie temperature T_c, makes it possible to fit the experimental data on a wider range of substances. In particular, iron, cobalt, and nickel have large, positive Curie temperatures; for iron $T_c \approx 1000°K$. For temperatures $T > T_c$, these substances show paramagnetic behavior. As $T \to T_c$ from above, (4.18c) indicates that $\chi = M/H \to \infty$. Physically this means that for $T < T_c$, when (4.18c) does not hold, these substances can retain a finite magnetization M in the absence of an applied field ($H = 0$). Substances capable of making "permanent" magnets of this sort are *ferromagnetic*. The finite M in zero H arises from a spontaneous lining up of the permanent dipole moments μ.

4.4. The normal Zeeman effect

In the dynamic model we must neglect the normally expected radiation and say that an undisturbed atom will be stable and not lose energy by radiation. This assumption holds also under Larmor precession. Atoms can be forced to radiate, however, by passing an electric discharge through a gas-filled tube. Spectroscopic measurements show that atomic radiation contains a series of sharp frequencies called *spectrum lines*. On the basis of classical theory we know nothing else but to assume that the observed frequencies of radiation correspond to the frequencies of rotation of the electrons in their orbits. On this assumption we conclude that the frequency of the radiation would be altered when a magnetic field is applied. These frequency shifts of spectral lines in a magnetic field constitute the Zeeman effect. In some special cases the observations are in full agreement with the theory of the Larmor precession given here. Such lines are said to have a "normal" Zeeman effect. All other lines, by far the greatest majority, have anomalous Zeeman effects which we shall discuss later on. This situation again indicates that the simple dynamic model contains a considerable germ of truth but is deficient in some important details.

To understand the normal Zeeman effect in terms of the dynamic model, let the plane of an electron orbit make an angle γ with the xy-plane. In the absence of the field, choose the y-axis along the intersection of the orbit plane and the xy-plane. Then the coordinates of the electron as a function of time are

$$x = r \cos \gamma \cos \omega t$$

$$y = r \sin \omega t \qquad (4.19)$$

$$z = r \sin \gamma \cos \omega t$$

where r is the radius of the circular orbit. Now when the induction **B** acts in the z-direction, the x- and y-axes of the entire figure precess with an angular velocity ω_L. The coordinates x_0, y_0, z_0 of the electron relative to some fixed set of axes are then displaced by an angle $\varphi = \omega_L t$ in the xy-plane from the coordinates (4.19). Thus we have

$$x_0 = x \cos \varphi - y \sin \varphi$$

$$y_0 = x \sin \varphi + y \cos \varphi \qquad (4.20)$$

$$z_0 = z$$

By means of relations of the form

$$\sin A \cos B = \tfrac{1}{2}[\sin (A + B) + \sin (A - B)] \qquad (4.21)$$

and corresponding forms with $\sin A \sin B$ and $\cos A \cos B$, the electron coordinates relative to the fixed axes become

$$x_0 = r \left[\left(\frac{\cos \gamma + 1}{2} \right) \cos (\omega + \omega_L)t + \left(\frac{\cos \gamma - 1}{2} \right) \cos (\omega - \omega_L)t \right]$$

$$y_0 = r \left[\left(\frac{\cos \gamma + 1}{2} \right) \sin (\omega + \omega_L)t - \left(\frac{\cos \gamma - 1}{2} \right) \sin (\omega - \omega_L)t \right]$$

$$z_0 = r \sin \gamma \cos \omega t \qquad (4.22)$$

The first terms in the expressions (4.22) for x_0 and y_0 represent a rotation in the xy-plane with frequency $(\omega + \omega_L)$. Comparison with (4.20) shows that this rotation is in the same direction as the precession ω_L. The terms in (4.22) with frequency $(\omega - \omega_L)$ represent rotation in the opposite direction. The z_0-coordinate expresses a simple linear vibration with unaltered frequency ω.

According to classical electromagnetic theory the radiation emitted by a moving charge is determined by its equations of motion. The radiation from a rotating or oscillating electron therefore has the same frequency and general properties as the mechanical rotation or oscillation. For motion described by (4.22) an observer looking along the direction of **B** will see each spectral line of original frequency ω split into two components. The component with frequency $(\omega + \omega_L)$ is circularly polarized in a clockwise direction, which is the direction of the precession. The lower frequency component $(\omega - \omega_L)$ is circularly polarized in the opposite or left-hand direction. The vibration along the z-axis does not produce any observable light in this direction. Light is a transverse vibration and an observer can see radiation only from components of the electron motion that are perpendicular to his line of sight. If the radiation is observed at right angles to the field, the high- and low-frequency components appear to be plane polarized in the xy-plane perpendicular to B. The original frequency ω is also seen and is polarized along the z-axis, parallel to B, since it is radiated by that component of the electron motion. The longitudinal (in the field direction) and transverse Zeeman effects are shown schematically in Fig. 4.3.

Thus the normal Zeeman effect consists of a splitting of an original spectrum line of frequency ν into three equally spaced lines of frequencies ν, $\nu \pm \nu_L$. Only the two extreme lines can be seen in the field direction. They will be right or left circularly polarized as shown in Fig. 4.3, according as the direction of observation is along or opposite to B.

Note that these predictions of the circular polarization are independent of the direction of motion of the electron in its orbit. We have seen above that the direction of precession is independent of the electron motion. Changing the direction of rotation in (4.19) results only in the exchange of the factors $(\cos \gamma + 1)$ and $(\cos \gamma - 1)$ (4.22), which is without significance for associating polarizations with the frequencies $\omega \pm \omega_L$.

We may also understand the phenomenon in the language of radio circuits. The radiating electron corresponds to an antenna that is made to precess with an angular frequency ω_L. This produces a periodic amplitude variation at an observer. The light is amplitude modulated, and therefore the carrier of frequency ω acquires two side bands $\omega \pm \omega_L$.

For a line in the visible region of wavelength $\lambda = 6 \times 10^{-5}$ cm, the separation of the Zeeman lines in a field of 10^4 gausses is 0.17 A. It can be observed in a very good spectrograph, but for accurate measurement requires an interferometer or an exceptionally strong magnetic field like 10^5 gausses. The data on the lines with normal effect are in exact agree-

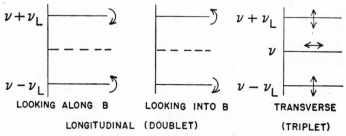

Fig. 4.3. Longitudinal and transverse normal Zeeman effects. Polarizations of the lines are indicated.

ment with the theory and furnish one of the most accurate determinations of e/m for the electron, while the polarization properties confirm the sign of the electronic charge.

4.5. The static model and dispersion

The dynamic model is useful chiefly for consideration of magnetic effects in atoms, which must arise from circulating currents of electrons. It has the difficulty that it should also predict spontaneous and continuous radiation from atoms, which would lead to their rapid collapse, in contradiction with their observed stability. Because of this difficulty with radiation, the static model generally replaces the dynamic model for a classical discussion of problems involving radiation or hence optical phenomena. In the static model we avoid the spontaneous radiation difficulty by assuming that every electron in the atom has a fixed rest position and is held in this position by an elastic restoring force. The nature of this force is not specified, since it is actually unknown. For the sake of the model, however, we associate a simple elastic spring constant f_i with each electron in the atom. Of course each atom of an element has the same set of f_i, but the f_i can vary among the different electrons in an atom.

Consider a light wave impinging on the atoms of a substance. The light wave consists of transverse E and H vectors that are periodic functions of the time at any fixed point in space. The force on the electron is $F = -e(E + v \times H/c)$ where v is the electron velocity and $-e$ is its charge. The electrons in atoms generally have velocities much less than c, the velocity of light. Therefore we can neglect the second term in the force equation, and the equation of motion of an electron becomes

$$md^2x_i/dt^2 = - f_ix_i - eE_0 \cos \omega t \qquad (4.23)$$

Here x_i is the vector coordinate of the ith electron in the direction of the electric vector $E = E_0 \cos \omega t$ of the incident light wave. The frequency of the light is $\nu = \omega/2\pi$. The first term on the right side of (4.23) represents the elastic force tending to restore the electron to its equilibrium position at $x_i = 0$. The second term is the force on the electron due to the light wave, where E_0 is the amplitude of the electric vector E. Equation (4.23) describes the forced vibration of a harmonic oscillator and has the solution

$$x_i = \frac{-eE_0/m}{(\omega_i^2 - \omega^2)} \cos \omega t \qquad (4.24)$$

$$\omega_i = \sqrt{f_i/m}$$

where ω_i is the natural frequency of the ith electron.

A displacement x_i of the ith electron produces an electric dipole moment $-ex_i$ in the atom, which has no moment in its equilibrium state. If there are Z electrons in the atom and n_0 atoms per cm³ of the substance, the total dipole moment per cm³ induced by the light is

$$P = \frac{n_0 e^2 E_0}{m} \cos \omega t \sum_{i=1}^{Z} \frac{1}{\omega_i^2 - \omega^2}$$
$$= \frac{n_0 e^2}{m} E \sum_{i=1}^{Z} \frac{1}{\omega_i^2 - \omega^2} \tag{4.25}$$

Note that P varies with time as $\cos \omega t$ and hence is just proportional to E at all times, as the second form of Eq. (4.25) shows. In a nonmagnetic medium the electric field E, displacement D, dielectric constant ϵ and refractive index n are related by (Eqs. 7a and 24, Appendix IV)

$$D = E + 4\pi P = \epsilon E = n^2 E \tag{4.26}$$

Substituting (4.25) for P, we obtain for the refractive index

$$n^2 - 1 = \frac{4\pi n_0 e^2}{m} \sum_{i=1}^{Z} \frac{1}{\omega_i^2 - \omega^2} \tag{4.27}$$

If $n \approx 1$, as is usually the case, we have the approximate relation

$$n - 1 = \frac{n^2 - 1}{n + 1} \approx \frac{n^2 - 1}{2} = \frac{2\pi n_0 e^2}{m} \sum_{i=1}^{Z} \frac{1}{\omega_i^2 - \omega^2} \tag{4.28}$$

This equation gives the *dispersion* of the refractive index, where the term "dispersion" refers to variation with frequency. In (4.28) the angular frequency $\omega = 2\pi\nu$ of the incident light is the variable. The fixed values ω_i are characteristic of the atom and are called the *resonance frequencies*.

Each term of the sum over i has a positive value when the frequency of the incident light is smaller than that of the ith resonance, $\omega < \omega_i$. When $\omega > \omega_i$ the corresponding term value is negative. As ω approaches ω_i, the term $1/(\omega_i^2 - \omega^2)$ becomes infinite. This is not a physical phenomenon but is due to our oversimplified derivation of the formula. Returning to (4.24), we see that this infinity at resonance corresponds to an infinite amplitude of oscillation for the electron. This is physically absurd, and we must suppose that there is a certain amount of natural damping of the electron's motion. We can supply this damping *ad hoc*, like the spring constants f_i, or we can obtain it from the radiation of a vibrating electron! Thus the radiation properties, which were a fundamental difficulty in the dynamic model, are actually a saving grace in the static model. This illustrates how the two imperfect models complement each other.

We show in section 4.7 that the inclusion of the damping factor replaces each factor $1/(\omega_i^2 - \omega^2)$ in (4.25) by

$$\frac{\omega_i^2 - \omega^2}{(\omega_i^2 - \omega^2)^2 + \gamma_i^2}$$

where γ_i is another parameter characteristic of each resonance. The term γ_i keeps $(n - 1)$ finite at the resonance, where the approximate form (4.28) is not applicable. The curve of refractive index versus frequency ν of the incident light therefore takes the form shown in Fig. 4.4.

Comparison of this curve with the experimental observations on simple gases like helium and sodium vapor shows that the theory is adequate in the following respects:

(1) At low frequencies the refractive index increases gradually with frequency. This increase is called "normal" dispersion because for most substances the first resonance point is in the ultraviolet region of the spectrum. They therefore show normal dispersion in the visible region.

(2) At the resonance frequencies the refractive index drops sharply with increasing frequency as shown (on an exaggerated scale) in the sketch. This phenomenon is called anomalous dispersion. Light of the resonance frequency is strongly absorbed and is re-emitted by the gas. The emitted light is called *resonance radiation.*

(3) After passing successive resonance points, the refractive index becomes smaller and finally for the high frequencies of X-rays becomes less than 1.

Thus in a qualitative way the formula is adequate. An essential feature of physics, however, is its insistence on exact, quantitative agreement. This has been one of the mainsprings of its progress, and quantitatively Eq. (4.28) is not satisfactory in the following respects:

(1) The number of resonance frequencies ν_i is not equal to the number Z of electrons in the atom but is usually much larger than Z.

(2) According to (4.28) each electron contributes a term of the same form to the summation. To fit the data with an equation of this type,

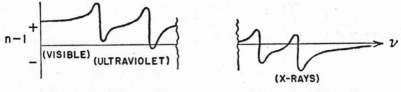

Fig. 4.4. Qualitative dispersion curve of refractive index. The approximate frequency ranges are indicated. As $\nu \to 0$, $n - 1 \to [n_0 e^2/2\pi m] \Sigma_i 1/\nu_i^2$; as $\nu \to \infty$, $n - 1 \to 0$ from the negative side. The last resonances are in the X-ray region.

however, we find that each oscillator must have a different "strength" z_i. The form of the equation is then

$$n - 1 = \frac{n_0 2\pi e^2}{m} \sum_{i=1}^{t} \frac{z_i}{\omega_i^2 - \omega^2} \tag{4.29}$$

where $t \gg Z$. On the basis of the static model, this might be interpreted to mean that the electronic charge in the atom is not split up into Z charges of $-e$ each, but t charges of different magnitudes $-z_i e$. To have the same amount of total charge in both cases, we expect that

$$\sum_{i=1}^{t} z_i = Z \tag{4.30}$$

This is indeed true and is known as a "sum rule," where it must be noted that t can be a very large or in fact infinite number. The oscillator strengths z_i are not generally integers and are usually smaller than 1, sometimes larger than 1.

Thus the static model of dispersion, if interpreted quantitatively, leads to the idea that the charge in the atom exists in all sorts of odd fractional units of $-e$. This is in contradiction to all the direct evidence of indivisible charge discussed in the preceding chapter. Therefore the static model must contain a serious error. On the other hand, it must contain some over-all truth, since it suggests the quantitatively correct sum rule (4.30).

4.6. The magneto-optical Faraday effect

From the above discussion it seems fair to say that the static and dynamic models frequently lead to qualitatively correct results but only occasionally to quantitative verification, as in the case of the normal Zeeman effect. We might also expect to obtain qualitatively correct results from a combination of the two. For example, the static model shows that the refractive index depends on the characteristic frequencies at which an atom absorbs and re-emits radiation. The dynamic model indicates that in a magnetic field each such characteristic frequency ν_i should break up into three components ν_i, $\nu_i \pm \nu_L$ with different polarization properties. Therefore we expect that the dispersion curve in a magnetic field will break up into two or three dispersion curves with slightly different resonance frequencies shifted by amounts $\pm\nu_L$. This is in fact observed and forms the basis of the Faraday effect.

Consider the simplest case, in which the light travels parallel to the magnetic field. Then there are two separate dispersion curves for right and left circularly polarized light. Far from resonance these curves will coincide, but in the neighborhood of a resonance they will differ as shown in Fig. 4.5. The L and R curves refer to observation along the direction of the field. The two curves have the same shape, but their resonance frequencies are separated by a shift $2\nu_L$. The region of visible light, in which the Faraday effect is observed, lies to the left of the resonances in Fig. 4.5.

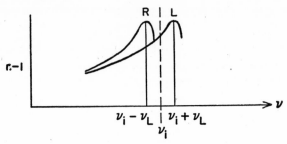

Fig. 4.5. Dispersion curves for right (R) and left (L) circularly polarized light.

Now suppose that the light transmitted in the field direction is plane-polarized. This can be represented as a linear superposition of right and left circularly polarized beams as illustrated in Fig. 4.6a. The electric vector E of the plane-polarized beam oscillates back and forth along the x-axis with amplitude E_0 and angular frequency $\omega = 2\pi\nu$. This can also be written as the vector sum of two vectors of constant magnitude $E_0/2$, which rotate in opposite directions with frequency ω. When the light beam travels a distance D along the magnetic field direction, the phases of the components are shifted by amounts $\varphi_{r,l} = \omega D / v_{r,l}$. Here $v = c/n$ is the velocity of the light wave in the material, and is different for the right- and left-hand components. The plane of polarization is accordingly rotated by an angle φ as shown in Fig. 4.6b. Then

$$\varphi = \frac{1}{2}(\varphi_r - \varphi_l) = \frac{\omega D}{2c}(n_r - n_l)$$

$$= \frac{\omega D}{2c}[n(\nu + \nu_L) - n(\nu - \nu_L)] \qquad (4.31)$$

$$\approx \frac{\omega D}{c}\nu_L \frac{dn}{d\nu} = \frac{2\pi\nu_L D}{c}\nu \frac{dn}{d\nu}$$

where the last approximation is valid because $\nu_L \ll \nu$, and we are in a region of the dispersion curve where n varies slowly with ν. It is more customary to express the variation of n in terms of λ, the wavelength of the light. Taking $\lambda\nu = c$ as good approximation for this purpose and substituting (4.9) for ν_L, one has

$$\nu\frac{dn}{d\nu} = -\lambda\frac{dn}{d\lambda}$$

$$\frac{\varphi}{D} = -\frac{1}{2}\frac{e}{m}\frac{\lambda}{c^2}\frac{dn}{d\lambda}B = CB \qquad (4.32)$$

Equation (4.32) gives the optical rotation of the plane of polarization per centimeter path length along a magnetic induction B. This phenomenon is the Faraday effect, Eq. (4.32) is Becquerel's equation, and the constant C is the Verdet constant of the material. Note that the plane of polarization is rotated in the same direction, regardless of whether the light beam travels along B or opposite to B. This means that a plane-polarized beam which travels along B and is reflected back again will be rotated through an angle 2φ.

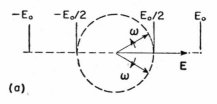

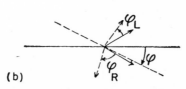

The qualitative features of the Faraday effect are all in agreement with the theory as expressed by equation (4.32). In the visible range where the dispersion is normal, $dn/d\lambda$ is nega-

Fig. 4.6. (a) Plane polarization as the sum of right and left circular polarizations. (b) Rotation of the plane of polarization in the Faraday effect.

tive and the rotation φ is clockwise as seen by an observer looking along the direction of B. The fact that the theory predicts this sign correctly is proof that negatively charged particles are responsible for the effect.

4.7. Radiation damping and the scattering of light

The static model is fundamentally designed to avoid the radiation difficulties that plague the dynamic model. Therefore it is no particular trouble to introduce radiation into the model. The instantaneous rate at which an accelerating charge e radiates energy is (Appendix IV)

$$\frac{dU}{dt} = \frac{2}{3} \frac{e^2 a^2}{c^3} \qquad (4.33)$$

where a is the acceleration. For an harmonic oscillation, $x = x_0 \cos \omega t$, the average rate of radiation per cycle is

$$\frac{dU}{dt} = \frac{2}{3} \frac{e^2 x_0^2 \omega^4 \overline{\cos^2 \omega t}}{c^3} = \frac{e^2 x_0^2 \omega^4}{3c^3} \qquad (4.34)$$

The effect of this radiation is to slow down the electron, acting in much the same way as a frictional force in ordinary mechanics. Such a frictional force is generally taken proportional to and opposing the velocity, $F = -sv$; and the rate of energy loss because of this friction is $dU/dt =$

$-Fv = sv^2$. In the harmonic oscillation above, the average energy loss per cycle would be

$$\frac{\overline{dU}}{dt} = \overline{sv^2} = sx_0^2\omega^2\ \overline{\sin^2 \omega t} = \frac{1}{2} sx_0^2\omega^2 \qquad (4.35)$$

We can therefore describe the radiation loss of the vibrating electron in terms of an equivalent frictional force by putting

$$s = \frac{2}{3}\frac{e^2\omega^2}{c^3} \qquad (4.36)$$

The equation of motion (4.23) for an electron in the electric field of a light wave now becomes

$$m\frac{d^2x_i}{dt^2} = -f_i x_i - s\frac{dx_i}{dt} - eE_0 \cos \omega t \qquad (4.37)$$

By inserting the trial solution $x_i = x_0 \cos (\omega t + \delta)$, we find that

$$x_i = \frac{(eE_0/m)\cos(\omega t + \delta)}{\sqrt{(\omega_i^2 - \omega^2)^2 + (\omega s/m)^2}}, \qquad \tan \delta = \left(\frac{\omega s/m}{\omega^2 - \omega_i^2}\right) \qquad (4.38)$$

The effects of the radiative damping are (1) to keep the amplitude of oscillation from becoming infinite at resonance ($\omega = \omega_i$) as is the case for an undamped electron, and (2) to shift the oscillation of the electron out of phase with the driving force by an amount δ. For obtaining the polarization P in (4.25), we use only the part of x_i that is in phase with the driving force,

$$\begin{aligned} x_i \text{ (in phase)} &= \frac{(eE_0/m)\cos \delta \cos \omega t}{\sqrt{(\omega_i^2 - \omega^2)^2 + (\omega s/m)^2}} \\ &= \frac{eE_0}{m}\frac{\omega_i^2 - \omega^2}{(\omega_i^2 - \omega^2)^2 + (\omega s/m)^2}\cos \omega t \end{aligned} \qquad (4.39)$$

The damping term $(\omega s/m)$ is important only for $\omega \approx \omega_i$, so that we can put approximately

$$\frac{\omega s}{m} = \frac{2}{3}\frac{e^2}{mc^3}\omega^3 \approx \frac{2}{3}\frac{e^2}{mc^3}\omega_i^3 = \gamma_i$$

Although the above derivation yields a specific expression for γ_i, we must remember that it is not possible to interpret the static model literally in all its details. It is more satisfactory to call γ_i a parameter associated with each resonance and allow its value to be determined from experiment, just as for the oscillator strengths in equation (4.29). If we include radiation damping in this way, the resonance factors in equations (4.25) to (4.29) become $\dfrac{\omega_i^2 - \omega^2}{(\omega_i^2 - \omega^2)^2 + \gamma_i^2}$; these improved resonance factors pass through zero instead of becoming infinite as $\omega \to \omega_i$, thus reproducing the observed dispersion curve.

We obtain the average radiation rate from the electron driven by the electric field of the light wave by inserting (4.38) in (4.34).

$$\frac{\overline{dU}}{dt} = \frac{1}{3} \frac{e^4 \omega^4}{m^2 c^3} \frac{E_0^2}{(\omega_i^2 - \omega^2)^2 + \gamma_i^2} \tag{4.40}$$

The intensity of the incident light beam is $I_0 = cE_0^2/8\pi$ for each direction of polarization (Appendix IV), so that

$$\frac{\overline{dU}}{dt} = \frac{8\pi}{3} \frac{r_0^2 I_0 \omega^4}{(\omega_i^2 - \omega^2)^2 + \gamma_i^2} \tag{4.41}$$

$$r_0 = \frac{e^2}{mc^2} = 2.8 \times 10^{-13} \text{ cm} \tag{4.42}$$

The quantity r_0 has the dimensions of a length and is known as the "classical radius" of the electron. This notation is more a convenient figure of speech than an exact physical dimension of the electron.

We sum (4.41) over all resonances in the atom to obtain the total radiation. By analogy with optical dispersion, we must expect to find many more resonances than electrons in the atom and must introduce the same fractional oscillator strengths as in (4.29). Thus the radiation rate becomes

$$\frac{\overline{dU}}{dt} = \frac{8\pi}{3} r_0^2 I_0 \omega^4 \sum_{i=1}^{t} \frac{z_i}{(\omega_i^2 - \omega^2)^2 + \gamma_i^2} \tag{4.43}$$

The energy radiated by the electron appears as light emerging in all directions except that parallel to the motion of the electron. This energy is supplied by the incident beam of light, so that the whole process corresponds to the physical phenomenon of light scattering by electrons bound in atoms.

It has become conventional in atomic and particularly in nuclear physics to specify any type of scattering phenomenon in terms of an equivalent *cross section*. In a scattering process we suppose the incident particles or light waves to form a beam, which approaches the scattering center (atom) along parallel, straight-line paths. The beam is everywhere of uniform density. The scattering cross section is a fictitious area located at the atom, perpendicular to the incident beam, and of such a size that the total scattering is correctly given by assuming that all of the beam passing through the area is scattered, and all of the beam passing outside is not affected. This is illustrated in Fig. 4.7. The scattering cross section is conventionally denoted by σ; it specifies the scattering quantitatively and is a simple and convenient concept to use. For example, the rate of energy scattering from a light beam of incident intensity I_0 is $\overline{dU}/dt = \sigma I_0$, where by comparison with (4.43) the cross section for scattering is

$$\sigma = \frac{8\pi}{3} r_0{}^2 \sum_{i=1}^{t} \frac{\omega^4 z_i}{(\omega_i{}^2 - \omega^2)^2 + \gamma_i{}^2} \tag{4.44}$$

The cross section always has the dimensions of an area. It is often convenient to specify a *differential* cross section for scattering of the beam into some particular element of solid angle. For example, we can describe the Rutherford scattering (3.19) in terms of a differential cross section.

$$d\sigma = \frac{R^2}{16 \sin^4 \varphi/2} d\omega \tag{4.45}$$

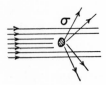

where $d\sigma$ is the cross section for scattering of an α particle through an angle φ into an element of solid angle $d\omega$.

Fig. 4.7. The scattering of a parallel beam through the cross section σ.

The failure of the static model is chiefly due to the circumstance that it makes too specific assumptions about the behavior of each individual electron. We cannot ascribe to each electron a particular force constant for harmonic binding and an associated resonance frequency. Hence it seems reasonable that the model will be quantitatively most accurate when its predictions are least dependent on these specific assumptions. This occurs both at low and at high frequencies ν of the incident light, when $\nu \ll \nu_i$ or $v \gg \nu_i$. At low frequencies (optical region), we have

$$\sigma = \frac{8\pi}{3} r_0{}^2 \omega^4 \sum_{i=1}^{t} \frac{z_i}{\omega_i{}^4} \tag{4.46}$$

Although we cannot in general evaluate the sum, it is at least a constant for low frequencies, so that σ is proportional to ω^4 or hence to $1/\lambda^4$, where $\lambda = 2\pi c/\omega$ is the wavelength of the light. This proportionality of the light scattering to $1/\lambda^4$ was deduced by Rayleigh and bears his name. It is found to be true for light in the optical region and is the reason for the apparent blue color of the sky. When sunlight passes through atoms of the upper atmosphere, more of the blue than the red component is scattered, according to the $1/\lambda^4$ law. The secondary scattering of this predominantly blue radiation to the eye of the observer on earth produces the effect of a blue sky. At the other extreme, when $\omega \gg \omega_i$, the scattering cross section per atom becomes

$$\sigma = \frac{8\pi}{3} r_0{}^2 \sum_{i=1}^{t} z_i = \frac{8\pi}{3} r_0{}^2 Z \tag{4.47}$$

This formula applies to X-rays of short wavelength and is the sum of the scattering cross sections of Z independent electrons in the atom each having a cross section of $(8\pi/3)r_0^2$. This scattering cross section would be appropriate to a free electron in classical electrodynamics and is sometimes called the *Thomson scattering*. Equation (4.47) will be discussed further in Chapter 5 on X-rays.

4.8. Electric polarizability and dipole moments

Since the forces holding electrons in atoms must in the last analysis be electric in nature, we do not expect that isolated atoms can display any permanent electric dipole moments. If any such moment should exist, the electrons would redistribute themselves to neutralize it. This is in distinction to the permanent magnetic dipole moment of an isolated atom, which requires for its existence only a steady current in the atom, as is provided in the dynamic model. Although isolated atoms cannot have permanent electric moments, they are readily polarized by an external electric field. In particular, this external field may be supplied by a neighboring atom in a molecule, with the result that some molecules have permanent electric dipole moments, although atoms do not.

We can estimate at least the order of magnitude of atomic polarizabilities by a combination of the static and dynamic models. Consider first the static model: when a uniform external field E is applied, the ith electron in the atom is displaced by an amount $x_i = -eE/f_i$. The corresponding dipole moment produced is

$$\mathbf{\mu}_i = -ex_i = e^2E/f_i = e^2E/m\omega_i^2 \tag{4.48}$$

which corresponds to (4.24) in the low-frequency limit as $\omega \to 0$. Now in the dynamic model we may picture the electron as rotating in a circular orbit about the nucleus. The Coulomb force of the nucleus on the electron is partly shielded by the other electrons present, so that the nucleus appears to have a positive charge Z_ie, where the "effective charge number" Z_i is smaller than the actual charge number Z of the nucleus. For the outermost electron in the atom, Z_i may not be much larger than 1. Replacing Z by Z_i in Eq. (4.1), we have

$$Z_ie^2/r_i^2 = m\omega_i^2r_i \tag{4.49}$$

where r_i is the orbit radius. Substituting (4.49) in (4.48) we obtain

$$\mathbf{\mu}_i = Er_i^3/Z_i = \alpha_iE \tag{4.50}$$

Here α_i is called the *polarizability* and applies to the ith electron; for the atom as a whole the polarizability is

$$\alpha = \sum_i \alpha_i \lesssim R^3 \tag{4.51}$$

where $R \approx 1$ A is the phenomenological radius of the atom, discussed in Chapter 2. The sum of the α_i is likely to be less than R^3 because for most of the electrons in an atom we expect that $r_i < R$, and $Z_i \gtrsim 1$.

The dipole moment of gaseous molecules is deduced from the dielectric constant ϵ of the gas by the relations (4.26), $P = E(\epsilon - 1)/4\pi$ where P is the polarization or dipole moment per unit volume of the gas produced by application of the field E. This polarization P arises partly from the intrinsic polarizability α of the molecule and partly from the orientation of its permanent electric moment μ. We calculate the orientation effect exactly as in the magnetic moment case (4.16), except that the electric field E replaces the magnetic field H, and by μ we understand the electric instead of the magnetic dipole moment.

The total dipole moment per unit volume, from both intrinsic polarizability and orientation effects is $P = n_0(\alpha + \mu^2/3kT)E$, where n_0 is the number of molecules per unit volume. Comparison with (4.26) shows that

$$\epsilon - 1 = 4\pi n_0(\alpha + \mu^2/3kT) \tag{4.52}$$

This experimental test of this equation consists in measuring the capacitance of a capacitor containing a fixed amount of gas as a function of the temperature T. Since n_0 is constant in this experiment, $\epsilon - 1$ should be a linear function of $1/T$. The plot of $\epsilon - 1$ against $1/T$ gives a straight line, of which the slope determines μ, the intercept determines α. In this way the dipole moment μ of the water molecule is found to be 1.87 Debye units (1 Debye unit $= 10^{-18}$ esu-cm). The molecules H_2, N_2, O_2, and CO_2 have no permanent dipole moments, and for some other molecules the moments in Debye units are $\mu(HCl) = 1.03$, $\mu(SO_2) = 1.76$, $\mu(CHCl_3) = 0.95$, $\mu(\text{nitrobenzene}) = 3.89$.

As a final application of the considerations of this chapter, we can derive Eq. (1.26) and (1.27), used to determine Avogadro's number N_0. From (4.48) and (4.50) we have $\alpha_i = e^2/m\omega_i^2$, so that for light of long wavelength ($\omega \ll \omega_i$), (4.29) becomes

$$n - 1 = n_0 2\pi \sum_{i=1}^{t} z_i \alpha_i \tag{4.53}$$

which is just the form of (1.26). Under the same conditions (4.46) yields for the scattering coefficient

$$S = \frac{3}{8\pi} n_0 \sigma = n_0 \left(\frac{\omega}{c}\right)^4 \sum_{i=1}^{t} z_i \alpha_i^2 = n_0 \left(\frac{2\pi}{\lambda}\right)^4 \sum_{i=1}^{t} z_i \alpha_i^2 \tag{4.54}$$

This is the form of (1.27); but note that $\sum z_i \alpha_i^2$ is only approximately equal to $(\sum z_i \alpha_i)^2$, so that we cannot expect great accuracy from this method for measuring N_0.

SUMMARY

The nuclear hypothesis of atomic structure suggests a dynamic model of the atom in which the electrons revolve in planetary orbits about the massive nucleus, the centrifugal force just balancing the electrostatic attraction of the positive charge on the nucleus. With each orbit is associated a magnetic dipole moment $\mathbf{\mu} = GL$, where L is the angular momentum of the electron and $G = -e/2mc$ is the *gyromagnetic ratio* of the electron. This relation is independent of the size and shape of the orbit.

This simple model is able to account for the Einstein-de Haas effect, in which application of a magnetic field imparts a small rotation to a suspended body. The observation of this phenomenon is the most direct evidence we have for the existence of circulating currents in the atom. Many atoms have total angular momentums and magnetic moments of zero, but show small induced moments on the application of a magnetic field. If the induced moment opposes the external field, the effect is called *diamagnetism*. The dynamic model predicts the observed order of magnitude for diamagnetism. It also correctly accounts for the normal Zeeman effect, in which a spectrum line of frequency ν splits in a magnetic induction B into three components of frequencies ν, $\nu \pm \nu_L$. Here $\nu_L = eB/4\pi mc$ is the Larmor frequency. The component of frequency ν is plane-polarized parallel to the direction of B, and the other components are circularly polarized about the direction of B.

The dynamic model fails to account for the fact that most atomic spectral lines show an anomalous Zeeman effect, which differs from the simpler "normal" effect. Therefore we must regard the dynamic model only as a first approximation that needs considerable improvement. One of the greatest difficulties of principle in the dynamic model is the neglect of radiation. On a classical basis the centripetal acceleration of an electron in an orbit should cause it to radiate its energy away very rapidly and spiral into the nucleus. Since we know this does not happen, the first major improvement in the dynamic model must be to correct this radiation difficulty. For this correction we must introduce the notion of the quantum.

As a simple alternative to the dynamic model, we may postulate a static model of the atom where the electrons are normally at rest and are bound by harmonic restoring forces to fixed positions in the atom. This model accounts qualitatively for the dispersion of the refractive index of an optical medium, with its many resonances between the visible and the X-ray wavelengths. A combination of the dispersion curve and the Zeeman effect accounts for the Faraday effect, in which the plane of polarization of a light beam is rotated on passage through a transparent medium in a magnetic field. The scattering of light by atoms can be computed with the static model and leads to results substantially independent of the model at very low (visible) and very short (X-ray) wavelengths. For visible light the scattering follows Rayleigh's $1/\lambda^4$ law, which explains the blue color of the sky; for X-rays the formula indicates independent scattering by each electron, regardless of the wavelength.

By a combination of the static and dynamic models we can estimate the electric polarizability of an atom to be $\alpha \lesssim R^3$, where $R \approx 1$ A is the phenomenological radius of the atom. Free atoms do not have permanent electric dipole moments $\mathbf{\mu}$, but some molecules do. Both $\mathbf{\mu}$ and α can be determined by dielectric measurements as a function of temperature. At long wavelengths we can relate α to the refractive index and to the scattering of light.

In all atomic scattering processes, such as that for light, it is convenient to introduce the concept of the cross section σ. This is a fictitious area normal to the incident beam, so as to give the correct quantitative scattering if we assume that all the incident beam passing through the cross section is scattered, all the beam passing outside the cross section is unscattered.

The static model does not have the radiation difficulties of the dynamic model, but has other equally serious defects. The number of resonances in the dispersion curve is far greater than the number of electrons in the atom, and we are forced to assign fractional oscillator strengths, even though the charge on the electron is indivisible. Worse than this, there are no known forces capable of holding the electrons in fixed positions in the atom. The difficulties of the static model, and indeed the distinction between static and dynamic models, are removed by the introduction of quantum mechanics.

REFERENCES

P. Debye, *Polar Molecules*, Dover Publications, New York (1945).

P. Drude, *Theory of Optics*, Longmans, Green, New York (1929).

C. Kittel, *Introduction to Solid State Physics*, Wiley, New York (1953).

Lord Rayleigh, *Phil. Mag.*, **61**, 107, 274 (1871). Correction to original formula given by Stiles, *Phil. Mag.*, **7**, 204 (1929).

E. C. Stoner, *Magnetism and Matter*, Methuen, London (1934).

R. W. Wood, *Physical Optics*, Macmillan, New York (1934).

P. Zeeman, *Researches in Magneto-optics*, Macmillan, London (1913).

ILLUSTRATIVE PROBLEMS

1. In the dynamic model of the atom, suppose an electron to be rotating in an orbit of radius 1 A with the force of the nuclear charge $(+Ze)$ producing the centripetal acceleration.

(a) What are the frequency ω of rotation and the wavelength of light having this frequency?

(b) What is the binding energy of the electron in this orbit?

(c) Assume that the electron starts from this orbit and radiates energy according to the classical law. How long will it be before the electron spirals into the nucleus, of radius 10^{-12} cm?

(d) How many revolutions will the electron make in this process?

(e) Compare the result of calculation (c) with experiment.

Solution. The condition for balancing of centrifugal and Coulomb forces is $m\omega^2 r = Ze^2/r^2$. The kinetic energy of the electron is $T = \frac{1}{2}m\omega^2 r^2$, the potential energy is $-Ze^2/r$, so the total energy is $U = T + V = -Ze^2/2r = -\frac{1}{2}m\omega^2 r^2$. This energy is negative because it is measured with reference to a zero point corresponding to an electron at rest an infinite distance from the nucleus.

(a) $\omega = (Ze^2/mr^3)^{1/2} = 1.6\sqrt{Z} \times 10^{16}/\text{sec}$

$\lambda = 2\pi c/\omega = 1.18 \times 10^3 \text{A}/\sqrt{Z}$

(b) The binding energy is the minimum necessary to liberate the electron; that is, $|U| = -U = Ze^2/2r = 7.2Z/r$ ev, where r is in Angstroms and 1 ev $= 1.6 \times 10^{-12}$ erg.

(c) The acceleration in the orbit is $a = r\omega^2/r = Ze^2/mr^2$, so that the rate of radiation of energy is

$$\frac{dU}{dt} = -\frac{2}{3}\frac{e^2 a^2}{c^3} = -\frac{2}{3}\frac{Z^2 e^6}{c^3 m^2}\frac{1}{r^4}$$

Substituting $U = -Ze^2/2r$, we have $dU/dt = (Ze^2/2r^2)\,(dr/dt)$, or hence

$$\frac{dr}{dt} = -\frac{4}{3}\frac{Ze^4}{m^2 c^3}\frac{1}{r^2}, \quad dt = -\frac{3}{4}\frac{m^2 c^3}{Ze^4} r^2\,dr.$$

Integrating from time $t = 0$ to $t = T$ and from corresponding radius $r = 1$ A to $r = R = 10^{-4}$ A, the nuclear radius, we have

$$T = \frac{1}{4}\frac{m^2 c^3}{Ze^4}(r^3 - R^3) \approx \frac{1}{4}\frac{m^2 c^3}{Ze^4} r^3$$

since $R \ll r$. Thus

$$T = \frac{1}{4}\frac{c}{r_0\omega^2}$$

where $r_0 = e^2/mc^2 = 2.8 \times 10^{-13}$ cm is the "classical" radius of the electron; or $T = 10^{-10}/Z$ sec.

(d) The number of revolutions is

$$N = \int_0^T \nu\,dt = \frac{1}{2\pi}\int_0^T \omega\,dt$$

The formula above for dt is of the form $dt = -Kd(r^3)$, where K is a constant. This is equivalent to $dt = -K'd(1/\omega^2) = 2K'd\omega/\omega^3$. In these terms $T = K'(1/\omega^2 - 1/\omega_T^2) \approx K'/\omega^2$, since the final frequency $\omega_T \gg \omega$, the initial frequency. Then

$$N = \frac{1}{2\pi} \int_0^T \omega \, dt = \frac{K'}{\pi} \int_\omega^{\omega_T} \frac{d\omega}{\omega^2} = \frac{K'}{\pi} \left(\frac{1}{\omega} - \frac{1}{\omega_T} \right) \approx \frac{K'}{\pi\omega} = \frac{\omega T}{\pi} = \frac{5.1 \times 10^5}{\sqrt{Z}}$$

(e) Atoms are observed to be stable, with constant $r \approx 1$ A. Therefore something is wrong with at least the radiation part of the model.

2. If a spherical particle of aluminum ($Z = 13$, $\rho = 2.70$, $M = 27$, $\chi = -1.8 \times 10^{-6}$) could be suspended to rotate without friction, what should its radius be to rotate at 1 rps in an induction of 1000 gausses?

Solution. The angular momentum of the sphere induced by the field is

$$L = \frac{Vn_0e'B}{3} \sum_i r_i^2 = -\frac{2Bm}{e'} \chi\rho V$$

where V is the volume of the sphere. This angular momentum equals $I\omega$, where $I = \frac{2}{5}\rho VR^2$ for a sphere. The radius R for a revolution frequency $\nu = \omega/2\pi = 1/\text{sec}$ is given by

$$R^2 = \frac{-5}{2\pi} \frac{Bm}{e'\nu} \chi = \frac{5}{2\pi} \frac{10^3 \times 9.1 \times 10^{-28} \times 1.8 \times 10^{-6}}{1.6 \times 10^{-20} \times 1}$$

$$= 7.8 \times 10^{-11} \text{ cm}^2$$

or $R = 0.9 \times 10^{-5}$ cm.

3. Light of wavelength 6000 A, traveling in the z-direction and plane-polarized with an electric vector of amplitude E_0 in the x-direction, passes through a gas of free electrons (e.g., the space charge of a radio tube). Neglecting the radiation emitted by the electrons, compute the intensity of the light in watts per cm^2 (1 watt = 10^7 erg/sec) for which the amplitude of the magnetic force on the electron amounts to 1 % of the amplitude of the electric force. What is the amplitude of vibration of the electron in this case? What general conclusion do you draw regarding usual values of v/c for electron motion in atoms?

Solution. The light wave has $H_0 = E_0$. If x_0 is the amplitude of the electron motion, the amplitude of its velocity is $v_0 = \omega x_0$. The amplitude of the electric force is eE_0, with e in esu units; the amplitude of the magnetic force is $(ev_0/c)H_0$, where e is again in esu. The ratio of these forces is $(ev_0/cH_0)/eE_0 = \omega x_0/c = f = 10^{-2}$. The amplitude of vibration is $x_0 = cf/\omega = (\lambda/2\pi)f = 9.6$ A for $f = 10^{-2}$, and light of $\lambda = 6000$ A. The vibration of a free electron is given by (4.24) with the elastic force constant $f_i \rightarrow 0$, or hence $\omega_i \rightarrow 0$. Then $x_0 = eE_0/m\omega^2$. The intensity of the incident beam is

$$I_0 = \frac{cE_0^2}{8\pi} = \frac{c}{8\pi}\left(\frac{mx_0\,\omega^2}{e}\right)^2 = \frac{c}{8\pi}\left(\frac{mc\,\omega f}{e}\right)^2 = \frac{mc\,\omega^2 f^2}{8\pi r_0}$$

where $r_0 = e^2/mc^2 = 2.8 \times 10^{-13}$ cm is the classical radius of the electron. Using $\omega = 2\pi c/\lambda = \pi \times 10^{15}/\text{sec}$, we have

$$I_0 = \frac{9 \times 10^{-28} \times 3 \times 10^{10} \times \pi^2 \times 10^{30} \times 10^{-4}}{8\pi \times 2.8 \times 10^{-13}}$$

$$= 3.8 \times 10^{21} \text{ erg/cm}^2 \text{ sec}$$

$$= 3.8 \times 10^{14} \text{ watt/cm}^2$$

The amplitude of vibration is ten times larger than an atom, instead of ten times smaller, as might be physically reasonable. The light beam required to produce this vibration carries an enormous energy unattainable by terrestrial means. Thus for this classical model, electrons in atoms are very unlikely to achieve speeds of $v/c = f = 10^{-2}$. This conclusion directly contradicts the actual facts and is another illustration of the failure of this model.

PROBLEMS

1. A free electron moves with a certain velocity perpendicular to a uniform magnetic field.

(a) Show that the orbit is a circle.

(b) Show that the frequency of rotation ω_0 is independent of the electron velocity and orbit size.

(c) Show that the "cyclotron" frequency ω_0 is twice the Larmor frequency ω_L.

2. In a chloroform ($CHCl_3$) molecule, the three Cl atoms form an equilateral triangle in the center of which are the C and H atoms; the C and H atoms are on an axis A perpendicular to the plane of the triangle. Since these latter are ions, the molecule has an *electric* dipole moment $\mu = 1.57$ Debye units (1 Debye unit $= 10^{-18}$ esu-cm.), and this moment points in the direction of the axis A. The moment of inertia of the molecule about this axis is 4×10^{-38} g cm^2. If such a molecule rotates in chloroform vapor about the axis A with thermal kinetic energy $\frac{1}{2}\omega_0^2 I = 1/2kT = 2 \times 10^{-14}$ erg, how will its motion be affected when an electric field E is applied in a direction making an angle γ with the rotation axis? Compute the precession frequency for a field E of 24 volts/cm.

3. Compute the root-mean-square atomic radii of the following elements:

Element	Z	Density	M	Magnetic Suscepti-bility (emu)
C	6	3.51	12.0	-0.49×10^{-6}
Sb	51	6.62	121.77	-0.87
Cu	29	8.94	63.57	-0.086
Au	79	19.32	197.2	-0.15
Pb	82	11.35	207.2	-0.12
Ag	47	10.50	107.88	-0.20

4. A hydrogen atom, assumed to consist of a proton with an electron rotating about the nucleus in a circular orbit of radius $r = 0.5$ A, is placed in a uniform electric field E of 1 statvolt per cm, directed normal to the plane of the orbit. Noting that the field cannot change the angular momentum of the orbital motion, compute the displacement δ of the plane of the orbit and calculate the electric polarizability α of the hydrogen atom. The displacement of the plane of the orbit can be considered small relative to its radius.

5. Compute the separation of the lines in the transverse Zeeman effect in a field of 10,000 gausses for spectral lines of 7000 A and 3000 A wavelength, giving the separation in A units.

6. A light source produces monochromatic light of wavelength 5800 $\pm$ 0.005 A; i.e., the spectrum line has a natural width of 0.01 A (due to Doppler effect arising from the thermal motion of the atoms in the source). The light is made right circularly polarized by a polarizer and a quarter-wave plate; it then enters a tube containing a gas with atoms having a resonance frequency equal to that of the light. Since the gas in the tube has a lower temperature than the source, the resonance radiation scattered by the gas atoms covers a smaller wavelength range, 5800 $\pm$ 0.002 A. A coil C with $n = 50$ turns per cm surrounds the tube and creates a magnetic induction $B = 0.4\pi nI$ gausses for a current of I amperes. What current must be passed through the coil to quench the resonance radiation entirely, if the resonance line has a normal Zeeman effect? Quenching occurs when the incident and scattered frequencies do not overlap.

7. Compute the amplitude of vibration of an elastically bound electron under the influence of a linearly polarized beam of green light ($\lambda = 6000$ A) with a luminous flux of 1 lumen per $cm^2 = 1.6 \times 10^{-3}$ watts/cm^2, if the resonance frequency of the electron is 4 times larger than the frequency of the light. What intensity would be required to create an amplitude of 1 A?

8. Measurements of the dispersion of sodium vapor (monatomic) at a temperature of 644°C furnish the following values for the refractive index n.

$\lambda =$ 5460 A	$n =$ 0.999829	$\lambda =$ 5916 A	$n =$ 1.00297
5827	0.9988	5960	1.00116
5875	0.9954	6013	1.00029

Assuming one effective electron per sodium atom, calculate the pressure of the sodium vapor. Use a single resonance of the dispersion formula.

9. The refractive properties of glasses are commonly described by stating the refractive index for the Na line 5390 A (the so-called Fraunhofer D line). The dispersion is given by $n_F - n_C$, where F refers to the Fraunhofer F line of $\lambda = 4861$ A, and the C line has the wavelength 6562 A. The values of n_D and $(n_F - n_C)$ range over the values

$$n_D = 1.516; \quad n_F - n_C = 0.00737 \quad \text{for light crown glass}$$
$$n_D = 1.9626; \quad n_F - n_C = 0.04882 \quad \text{for heaviest flint}$$

Assuming a linear change of n with λ, compute the extreme values for the Verdet constant of glasses. Give these values in angle of rotation (degrees) per gauss per cm light path, for the D line. With an induction of 1000 gausses, what is the minimum length of a glass block to attain a Faraday rotation of 45°?

10. A parallel-plate capacitor is between the poles of a magnet which can produce a field of 50,000 oersteds. The capacitor has plates of 2 cm^2 area and is filled with liquid NO ($M = 30$) at a temperature $T = 120°$K where it has a density of 1.2 g/cm^3 and a magnetic susceptibility of 1.6×10^{-4} emu. The capacitor is connected to an electrometer; the lumped capacitance of the capacitor, leads, and electrometer is 33.3 $\mu\mu$f, and the electrometer has a sensitivity of 1 scale division per millivolt. Assume that the electric dipole moment of the NO molecule is 10^{-18} statcoulomb-cm. Compute the scale deflection of the electrometer when the magnetic field is applied, using the hypothesis that the electric and magnetic dipole of the molecule are always parallel, so that when one is oriented the other is also oriented. Failure in actual experiments to observe anything approaching the enormous deflection calculated here demonstrates that the hypothesis is incorrect.

Proceed as follows: find the magnetic moment of NO and compute the magnetization M in the field H. The resulting electric polarization is $P = M \times$ (electric moment of NO/magnetic moment of NO). Polarization P creates a charge $Q = PA = CV$ on the capacitor.

Chapter 5

X-RAYS

The dynamic model of the atom gives us a rough correlation between the frequency of atomic radiation and the radius of the corresponding atomic orbits. This correlation suggests that the optical radiations in the wavelength range $\lambda \gtrsim 1000$ A are associated with orbits of radius on the order of one to a few A. Since this is the apparent radius of an atom, we conclude that visible light and ordinary optical phenomena have to do only with the electrons on the outer edge of the atom. The same observation holds for the magnetostatic and electrostatic phenomena discussed in the preceding chapter, for a static field is in general equivalent to a light wave of zero frequency or infinitely long wavelength.

Now the radius of the nucleus is no more than 10^{-12} cm, and the "classical radius" of an electron is only 2.8×10^{-13} cm. Therefore an electron should find a great deal of empty space inside an atom of radius 10^{-8} cm. We may ask whether the electrons are all on the outer surface of the atom or whether, as seems more likely, they are distributed more uniformly throughout the atomic volume. Formula (4.1) indicates that the innermost electrons are associated with the atomic radiations of shortest wavelength. These radiations are called X-rays and cover a loosely defined region from about $\lambda = 10$ A to $\lambda = 0.1$ A. The electron orbit radius that corresponds to these wavelengths is about 10^{-10} cm. Thus the atom is populated with electrons in to about 1 % of its outer radius.

We expect, then, that the study of X-rays will reveal some characteristics of the interior electronic structure of atoms. There is no reason to suppose that this structure is any different in principle from the electronic structure near the outer edge, but the X-ray data provide further information that must be accommodated in any final, quantitative model of the atom.

The study of X-rays shows some features in accordance with the simple static model of the atom and also provides valuable quantitative information on the structure of matter—the location of atoms in a crystalline solid, for example. X-rays help to determine precise values for fundamental constants of atomic physics like e and N_0. They even furnish some information on the internal distribution of electrons in an atom. Finally, X-ray phenomena raise a number of questions that cannot be answered at all by classical physics, and are fundamental to the further development of atomic understanding.

5.1. Production and detection of X-rays

In 1895 Roentgen discovered a new type of radiation, which he called X-rays because of their unknown nature. He found that a high-vacuum (and therefore necessarily high-voltage) gas discharge tube produced radiation that would penetrate a cardboard and cause fluorescence in outside materials. The X-rays also affected photographic plates. Their penetrating power was greatest through light materials and least through dense substances. This property received immediate application to medical examination of bones in living tissue.

A modern tube for producing X-rays contains as high a vacuum as feasible and two high-voltage electrodes. The cathode consists of a heated filament that forms a thermionic source of electrons, as in a radio tube. The high voltage, some tens or hundreds of kilovolts (1 kilovolt = 1000 volts), accelerates these electrons to the anode. The anode or "target" is generally a piece of fairly heavy metal with a high melting point, like tungsten or molybdenum. X-rays are produced when the high-energy electrons strike the anode. Considerable heating occurs in the anode, since all the electrons stop in the anode and give up most of their energy as heat. A large X-ray tube has a water-cooled anode.

A standard detector for X-rays is a photographic plate, since X-rays will expose photographic emulsion. Another useful instrument for X-ray detection is the ionization chamber. This is an airtight chamber containing gas, usually argon, and two electrodes, which are frequently the outside metal tank of the chamber and a central wire inside. The X-rays enter through a thin window provided in the chamber, and in passing through the gas liberate a number of electrons from the atoms of the gas. The atoms that lose electrons become positive ions. A collecting potential of a few hundred volts is placed across the electrodes of the chamber, drawing the + and − charges to opposite electrodes. Thus a small current on the order of 10^{-13} amperes is made to flow through the chamber. If the collecting voltage is small, many of the ions will recombine with electrons before being collected. The current flow is then correspondingly small and will increase with increasing voltage until "saturation" is reached. At this point essentially all the ions and electrons produced are collected without recombination, and the current does not increase appreciably with moderate increases in voltage. The chamber therefore is usually operated at saturation, where the rate of current flow is a direct measure of the instantaneous X-ray intensity. Since extreme amplification is necessary for the small saturation current, the chamber and amplifier circuit must be constructed with care.

The problem of how X-rays manage to produce gaseous ions is a practically insurmountable difficulty for classical physics, and will be discussed in Chapter 6. This phenomenon led Bragg to suggest before 1910 that the X-rays were corpuscles of some sort. The bulk of the evidence, however, is that X-rays are electromagnetic radiation like visible light, only of much shorter wavelength. There are several pieces of evidence in favor of this interpretation: (1) classical electromagnetic theory predicts that the stopping of electrons in a target will be accompanied by electromagnetic radiation; (2) no combination of electric and magnetic fields can deflect X-rays; (3) a double scattering experiment shows that X-rays are transversely polarized; (4) X-rays exhibit diffraction phenomena characteristic of light with a wavelength of a few A.

An accelerated charge e in classical electrodynamics radiates energy (Appendix IV, Eq. 25). When the high-speed electrons stop in the anode, they are subject to a strong deceleration and should therefore radiate. Classical theory indicates that this radiated light should extend over a continuous range of wavelengths, including the X-ray region around a few A.

Ordinary light is the principal type of "ray" in our previous experience that remains undeviated in any electric or magnetic field, so it is natural to suppose that X-rays are similar in nature. The only other type of undeviating "ray" among those that we have encountered would be a beam of neutral atoms or molecules with no permanent electric or magnetic dipole movements. It is easy to show experimentally that X-rays do not consist of such a beam; for instance, a beam of neutral atoms or molecules would have little penetrating power, in contrast to the observed high penetrating power of X-rays.

The transverse nature of X-rays was first shown by Barkla (1906) in a double scattering experiment. As indicated in Fig. 5.1, scattering of a transverse wave through 90° results in a plane-polarized wave. When this polarized wave scatters a second time through 90°, the resulting intensity ranges from a maximum in the plane of the first scattering to zero in a direction perpendicular to the first plane. X-rays are found experimentally to behave in this fashion. Therefore, if we are to consider X-rays as wave motion, they must be transverse.

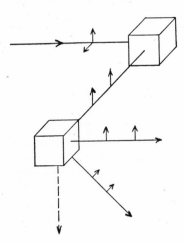

Fig. 5.1. Double scattering experiment to show transverse nature of X-rays.

The diffraction of X-rays is the subject of section 5.4.

5.2. *Absorption and scattering of X-rays*

Experiment shows that when a beam of X-rays passes through matter, its intensity diminishes with distance in a roughly exponential fashion. The intensity I (erg/cm^2 sec) of a beam after passing through a thickness t of material is

$$I = I_0 e^{-\mu t} \tag{5.1}$$

where I_0 is the incident intensity and μ is the attenuation coefficient. Expressed in differential form, the decrease of intensity in proceeding a distance dt through the material is

$$dI = -\mu I \, dt \tag{5.2}$$

We find that for any given substance μ is proportional to the density ρ. A parameter independent of the density is the *mass attenuation coefficient*, μ/ρ, which is characteristic of the material and not of its physical condition.

There are two effective contributions to the attenuation coefficient measured in a simple exponential beam experiment. The true absorption coefficient is denoted by μ_a. In addition, the beam loses intensity because of scattering by the atomic electrons, as mentioned at the end of the preceding chapter. In this scattering the electrons do not actually absorb much energy from the beam, but reradiate it in all directions. Since this reradiated energy is mostly lost to the forward direction of the beam, it appears to a straightforward transmission measurement as an additional attenuation effect. If the coefficient for this scattering is μ_s, then

$$\mu = \mu_a + \mu_s \tag{5.3}$$

We may relate these coefficients to corresponding atomic cross sections. When an X-ray beam passes through a slab of infinitesimal thickness dt, the fraction of the area that appears to be covered by atomic cross sections is $n_0 \sigma \, dt$, where n_0 is the number of atoms per cm^3 and σ is the atomic cross section. Thus the fractional loss in intensity of the beam as it passes through the slab is

$$dI/I = -n_0 \sigma \, dt \tag{5.4}$$

Comparison with (5.2) shows that

$$\mu = n_0 \sigma \tag{5.5}$$

We can divide the atomic cross section into two independent parts,

σ_s and σ_a, the first describing scattering of the beam, the second true absorption. Then

$$\mu_s = n_0 \sigma_s, \qquad \mu_a = n_0 \sigma_a \qquad (5.5a)$$

$$\sigma = \sigma_s + \sigma_a \qquad (5.5b)$$

The true absorption coefficient is incapable of explanation on a simple classical basis (see Chapter 6), but we can interpret the scattering in terms of the static model of the atom. The cross section per atom for scattering of high frequency light is given by (4.47). For an element of density ρ and atomic weight A, $n_0 = N_0 \rho / A$, where N_0 is Avogadro's number. Hence

$$\frac{\mu_s}{\rho} = \frac{8\pi}{3} r_0^2 N_0 \frac{Z}{A} \qquad (5.6)$$

For all elements but hydrogen, $Z/A \approx \frac{1}{2}$, as indicated by the α particle scattering experiments. We may therefore expect the corresponding value of

$$\frac{\mu_s}{\rho} = \frac{8\pi}{3} (2.8 \times 10^{-13})^2 \times 6.0 \times 10^{23} \times \tfrac{1}{2} \approx 0.2$$

to hold for all elements and to be independent of wavelength (frequency) of the X-rays. A major exception is hydrogen, for which the measured μ_s/ρ is 0.4, indicating that $Z/A = 1$. The prediction $\mu_s/\rho \approx 0.2$ agrees with experiment only for elements with $A \lesssim 30$ and X-rays of wavelength λ around $0.2 - 1.0$ A. For heavier elements μ_s/ρ increases with Z and tends to vary as Z^2/A instead of as Z/A. Moreover, it does not remain entirely independent of λ, but increases with increasing λ.

We can make some qualitative arguments to bring these deviations into accord with the static model. Suppose that the wavelength λ of the incident X-rays is small compared with the radius of the atom. Then $\omega \gg \omega_i$, and each electron vibrates like a free electron. Moreover, because $\lambda \ll R$, each vibrating electron has a random phase relation with all other electrons. Thus the atom scatters X-rays as if it contained Z free, independent electrons. This independent, random-phase scattering is called *incoherent*, and is the situation to which (4.47) applies. Now suppose that the wavelength λ is somewhat longer, being about the size of the atom. It is still generally true that $\omega > \omega_i$, so that we can again neglect resonance effects and consider the vibrating electrons as essentially free. They no longer have random phase relations, however, because they are all located in a region with dimensions on the order of a wavelength. The electrons therefore tend to vibrate more or less in phase: that is, as if they were a single particle of charge $-Ze$ and mass Zm. Such a particle would have a scattering cross section of

$$\sigma_{\text{coh}} = \frac{8\pi}{3} Z^2 r_0^2 \tag{5.7}$$

The subscript stands for *coherent* scattering, the usual term for such in-phase phenomena. Thus the scattering coefficient μ_s/ρ will vary as Z for perfect incoherence, as Z^2 for perfect coherence.

Of course, for X-ray wavelengths comparable with the atomic radius, neither of these ideal conditions will obtain, and the coefficient will be intermediate between Z and Z^2. The detailed variation of the scattering coefficient with wavelength therefore gives some information about the distribution of electrons in the atom. In this way X-rays provide a direct means of "seeing into" the interior of atoms. An example of this type of application of X-rays is given at the end of section 5.5. Scattering of α particles shows the location of the massive positive charge in atoms, while scattering of X-rays indicates the average positions of the light, negatively charged electrons.

Studies of the variation in scattering with wavelength show that for increasingly heavy elements there is an increasing concentration of electrons near the nucleus. Heavy elements have most of their electrons within a relatively small radius, although the outside radius of the atom is roughly constant at 1 A. Thus for X-rays of fixed wavelength on the order of 1 A there is an increasing tendency toward pure coherent scattering for heavy elements. This qualitatively explains observed deviations from (5.6); namely, that the Z^2/A (coherent) scattering becomes predominant for heavy elements and large λ.

5.3. Total reflection of X-rays

Another implication of the static atomic model that X-ray experiments can check is total reflection at a material surface. Consider relation (4.28) for the refractive index of an element: for X-rays of wave length $\lambda = c/\nu$ this becomes

$$\delta = 1 - n = \frac{n_0 Z e^2}{2\pi \nu^2 m} = \frac{n_0 Z}{2\pi} r_0 \lambda^2 \tag{5.8}$$

where n_0 is the number of atoms per unit volume, Z is the number of electrons per atom. For ordinary X-rays on silver, $\delta \approx 10^{-4}$ to 10^{-5}. The important fact that $n < 1$ implies* that total reflection must be

---

* It also implies that the velocity of the X-rays in the crystal is $v = c/n > c$. This seems to contradict one form of the relativity postulate (Chap. 8), namely, that no energy can be transmitted with a velocity greater than that of light in free space. The dilemma is resolved by realizing that the velocity c/n is the *phase* velocity of the X-rays (see Chap. 9), and that energy transmission is associated with the *group* velocity, which is $<c$ in this case. See Chap. 9, problem 1.

observable at a plane boundary between a solid sample and a vacuum (or air). An X-ray beam incident on the solid from the air is totally reflected if it makes a glancing angle Δ with the surface smaller than the *critical angle* Δ_c . The critical glancing angle is given by

$$n = \cos \Delta_c \approx 1 - \Delta_c^2/2 \qquad (5.9)$$

where the last expression is an approximation valid for $\Delta_c \ll 1$, as is always the case with X-rays. Comparing (5.9) and (5.8), we see that

$$\Delta_c = \lambda (n_0 r_0 Z/\pi)^{1/2} \qquad (5.10)$$

Equation (5.10) in principle provides a means of determining the number of electrons Z per atom if the wavelength λ of the X-rays is known.

An experiment to verify this law consists of rocking a polished metal plate about the point where a narrow beam of X-rays is incident. The distribution of the reflected intensity is observed on a photographic film as shown in Fig. 5.2. The region of the film corresponding to total reflection is markedly darker than the rest. This region comes to an abrupt end at the position corresponding to $\Delta = \Delta_c$. From Eq. (5.10) it follows that for X-rays of about 1 A wavelength, $\Delta_c \approx 10^{-2}$ radian or about 1°. With a distance of 50 cm between metal plate and film we can measure this angle to an accuracy of 1%. The data substantiate equation (5.10) to within experimental accuracy. It is found that Δ_c is proportional to λ and to $(n_0 Z)^{1/2}$ by using a series of different metals. Since n_0 is known, such experiments serve to determine the number of electrons per atom. This turns out to be approximately equal to the order number Z of the element in the periodic table, within experimental accuracy. The precision of such measurements is limited by experimental difficulties in obtaining sufficiently flat and uniform metal plates.

Here again X-ray scattering provides information complementary to α particle scattering. With α particles the charge number Z of the nucleus is found to be approximately equal to the atomic number, while X-rays establish a similar rule for the number of electrons. Of course,

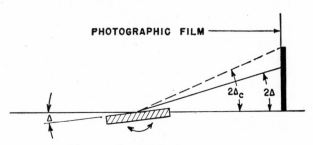

Fig. 5.2. Total reflection of X-rays.

nuclear charge number and external electron number must be the same in a neutral atom.

5.4. Diffraction of X-rays

In the foregoing sections we assumed for the sake of exposition that X-rays were light of short wavelength. The experiments discussed do not, however, absolutely require this assumption. All phenomena such as scattering, absorption, and even total reflection can be equally well explained on a corpuscular hypothesis. It therefore seems desirable to find some experimental means for establishing without doubt the wave-like character of X-rays. The one property peculiar to waves, which cannot be duplicated by a suitably chosen set of particles, is interference between two parts of what was initially the same wave. The basic phenomenon of interference is responsible for all so-called diffraction patterns. The medium for producing a diffraction pattern with X-rays is any crystalline substance like NaCl or a metal, where the atoms are in a regular geometrical array of constant spacing. Diffraction results from interference of X-rays scattered by different atoms in the crystal. The experimental observation of X-ray diffraction in crystals, dating from the pioneer work of Laue, Friedrich, and Knipping in 1912, is conclusive evidence of the wave nature of X-rays.

Crystal diffraction of X-rays has a twofold importance. It allows a detailed study of the lattice structure of crystals and has been of great usefulness in understanding the solid state of matter. On the other hand, the crystals are natural optical gratings for measuring the wavelengths and spectral distributions of the X-rays themselves. The second application is of interest to us here, since the X-ray spectra yield information about the atomic processes in which they originate.

An elementary picture of X-ray diffraction is due to Bragg. The atoms in a crystal are regularly arranged, and we shall consider only the simplest example of a cubic lattice. The atoms are centered at the corners of a perfect cube, which pattern is repeated throughout the crystal. Sodium chloride is a crystal of this type (Fig. 1.2). Through the lattice points (atomic centers) of such an array it is possible to draw an infinite variety of parallel planes separated by constant spacings d. We may now assume that an incident X-ray is partially reflected at each of the planes. In general these reflected waves will cancel each other by destructive interference. Constructive interference occurs only when the path difference for two successive reflections is an integral multiple of the wavelength λ of the X-rays. This is the case in Fig. 5.3 when

$$AB + BC = j\lambda, \quad j = 1, 2, 3, \cdots \quad (5.11)$$

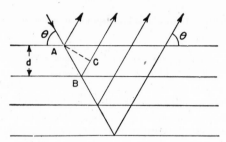

Fig. 5.3. Reflection from Bragg planes.

In discussions of X-rays it is customary to specify the direction of the incident beam by the glancing angle with the lattice plane. This angle is the complement of the angle of incidence used in ordinary optics. If the spacing of the Bragg planes is d, then $AB = d/\sin \theta$, and $BC = AB \cos (180° - 2\theta) = -AB \cos 2\theta$. Thus (5.11) becomes

$$j\lambda = \frac{d}{\sin \theta} (1 - \cos 2\theta) = 2d \sin \theta \qquad (5.12)$$

which is known as Bragg's law.

If the incident beam has a continuous distribution of wavelengths, the reflected beam at any angle θ contains only a selected number of wavelengths, $\lambda_1 = 2d \sin \theta$, $\lambda_2 = \frac{1}{2}\lambda_1$, $\lambda_3 = \frac{1}{3}\lambda_1$, $\cdots$. The integer j is called the *order* of the reflection. If the incident beam is monochromatic, there will usually be no reflection. To obtain a reflection, the crystal must be turned until θ reaches one of the angles given by Bragg's law. Thus by observing the reflections of a monochromatic beam from a "rocking" crystal, we can find the orientation and spacing of its lattice planes. Instead of rocking the crystal, it can be ground into a powder, with the grains in the powder possessing all possible orientations for Bragg reflections. This powder method makes it possible to study the crystal structure of substances for which no large single crystal is available. These investigations have shown that all solids except glasses possess a lattice structure.

In order to have a systematic designation for the many possible Bragg planes, the *Miller indices* are convenient. Suppose that a plane makes intercepts X, Y, and Z on the corresponding axes of a coordinate system. The Miller indices h, k, l of the plane are the smallest whole numbers proportional to $1/X$, $1/Y$, $1/Z$. The coordinate system is attached to the crystal lattice in the simplest and most symmetric fashion. In a simple cubic lattice the x-, y-, and z-axes are along the cube edges. Note that it is only the ratio of the indices that matters, so that the (4 2 2) planes are the same as the (2 1 1) planes. Thus a given set of Miller indices specifies an infinite set of parallel planes in the (infinite) crystal.

A Miller index zero means that the planes are parallel to the corresponding axis. Thus the principal planes are (0 0 1), (1 0 0) and (0 1 0). Negative as well as positive indices are of course possible and are designated
by bars over the indices. Thus the $(2\,\bar{1}\,0)$ and $(2\,1\,0)$ planes are independent sets, although of course $(\bar{2}\,\bar{1}\,0) = (2\,1\,0)$ and $(\bar{2}\,1\,0) = (2\,\bar{1}\,0)$,
since the indices of one set differ by a constant factor -1 from those
of the other. The reader can convince himself with a little coordinate
geometry that if the principal spacing of a cubic lattice is d_0, the spacing
of the $(h\,k\,l)$ planes is

$$d_{hkl} = \frac{d_0}{\sqrt{h^2 + k^2 + l^2}} \tag{5.13}$$

The relative intensities of reflection from different Bragg planes are
indicated by the following considerations. The X-ray reflected from a
given lattice plane has an electric vector proportional to n_{hkl}, the number of atoms per unit area of an hkl plane. The jth order diffraction corresponds to perfect constructive interference between reflections from
every jth plane, so that the total electric vector scattered from one such
set of planes is $E_1 \sim (J/j)n_{hkl}$ with corresponding scattered intensity
$I_1 \sim E_1^2 \sim n_{hkl}^2/j^2$. Here $J \gg 1$ is the total number of planes. There
are j equivalent sets of these planes with perfect scattering incoherence
among them,* giving a total scattered intensity of $I = jI_1 \sim n_{hkl}^2/j$.
Now if n_0 is the number of atoms per unit volume of the crystal, then

$$n_{hkl} = n_0\, d_{hkl} = \frac{n_0\, d_0}{\sqrt{h^2 + k^2 + l^2}}$$

by (5.13) for a simple cubic lattice, if we neglect the difference in scattering power among different types of atoms. With these simplifications
we have for the diffracted intensity

$$I_j(hkl) \sim \frac{1}{j(h^2 + k^2 + l^2)} \tag{5.13a}$$

Equation (5.13a) shows the general trend of I with order number and
the Miller indices. More careful studies of intensity variations yields
detailed information about electron distribution in atoms in crystals
(cf. section 5.5).

Because of (5.13a) any actual experiment reveals only a finite number
of Bragg reflections. Some of these are suggested by the planes in Fig.
5.4, but there are many more planes in three dimensions. A schematic
experimental arrangement is indicated in Fig. 5.5. X-rays scattered
from a single crystal produce a regular two-dimensional pattern in the

---

* That is, the total scattered intensity is simply the sum of the separate intensities from each set of planes.

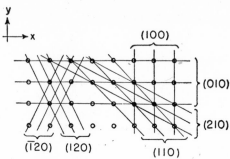

Fig. 5.4. Miller indices of some simple planes parallel to the z-axis.

plane of the photographic plate. This so-called *Laue diagram* is symmetric about the axis of the incident beam. A powder sample would effectively rotate the pattern about this axis to form a series of concentric rings. From the symmetry of the Laue diagram the symmetry of the crystal lattice structure can be inferred.

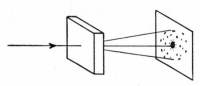

Fig. 5.5. Production of Laue diagram.

The discovery of Bragg's law (5.12) did not immediately solve the problem of X-ray measurement, for it related two quantities, λ and d, which were both unknown at the outset. From analysis of the intensities and angles of the spots in a Laue diagram, however, it is possible to show unambiguously that NaCl, for example, has a simple cubic lattice. We can then obtain the lattice constant from the molecular weight M,

$$d_0 = (M/N_0\rho)^{1/3} \tag{5.14}$$

where ρ is the density of the material. For NaCl, $d_0 = 2.814$ A. With this information we can use the crystal as a sort of optical grating for measuring the X-ray wavelength. The accuracy of this procedure depends on the precision with which we know Avogadro's number N_0.

A precision method for measuring X-ray wavelengths without depending on N_0 involves ruled gratings of the same sort as used for visible and ultraviolet light. There would seem at first sight to be some difficulty with this method. Light of wavelength λ incident normal to a grating with a distance b between ruled lines produces diffraction maxima at angles φ to the normal, where

$$\sin \varphi = j\lambda/b, \quad j = 1, 2, 3, \cdots \tag{5.15}$$

Gratings are available in the spectroscopic laboratory with ten thousand lines per cm or $b = 10^{-4}$ cm. Thus for X-rays of wavelength 1 A the

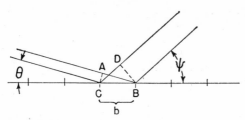

Fig. 5.6. Grazing angle reflection from a ruled grating.

successive diffraction maxima would be spaced apart by about 10^{-4} radians $\approx \frac{1}{2}$ minute of arc. These lines could be resolved if registered on a photographic plate some 10 meters away from the grating. With ordinary light such an arrangement is possible, but only with the help of lenses and mirrors. As lenses and mirrors do not exist for X-rays, this direct approach is not feasible.

The solution to this problem takes advantage of the total reflection of X-rays at grazing angles. At grazing angles the effective grating spacing presented normal to the beam is greatly reduced. From Fig. 5.6 it is apparent that the condition for interference maxima is

$$j\lambda = (AB - CD) = b(\cos \theta - \cos \psi) \tag{5.16}$$

Using the small angle approximation $\cos x = 1 - \frac{1}{2}x^2 + \cdots$, we have

$$\psi^2 - \theta^2 = 2j(\lambda/b) \tag{5.17}$$

For an incident angle $\theta \approx 1°$ and a grating spacing of 10^{-4} cm, the angles ψ for successive maxima have a separation also on the order of $1°$. Thus the angles to be measured are some 10^2 times larger than in the case of normal incidence. This method has been refined to the point where X-ray wavelengths are accurate to 5 significant figures. They are sometimes expressed in X-ray units, $1 A = 10^3$ X.U. With this high accuracy in λ we can use (5.12) and (5.14) together for a precise determination of Avagadro's number N_0. This method is mentioned in section 1.4c(h). We first use (5.17) to determine the exact wavelength of monochromatic (single wavelength) X-ray. Then from Bragg's law diffraction of this X-ray in a simple cubic crystal, we find d_0 for that crystal. Then finally (5.14) yields $N_0 = M/\rho d_0^3$. Such X-ray determinations of N_0 are the most accurate now available.

5.5. Derivation of Bragg's law

In this section we shall give a somewhat more rigorous derivation of Bragg's law. The assumption of lattice planes as partial mirrors for X-rays has no obvious foundation in the physical situation. There are in fact no mirrors for X-rays, and the lattice planes are a geometrical invention to describe the crystal structure. At best the lattice planes contain the atomic nuclei, but it is the electrons rather than nuclei that scatter X-rays. Our knowledge of lattice distances and atomic radii clearly indicates that the entire space between lattice planes must contain electrons.

A rigorous demonstration of Bragg's law must take into account scattering by all the electrons in the crystal. As an example we shall consider only the simplest ideal case, where the lattice is of simple cubic form with the nuclei of identical atoms at the lattice points. The electrons are distributed in some way in the intervening space. This distribution is presumably most concentrated in the neighborhood of the nuclei because of the Coulomb attraction between electron and nucleus. Only one other feature of the electron distribution is certain, but it is of importance for the derivation; namely, the distribution is periodic in the three perpendicular lattice directions with period d_0, the lattice constant.

To describe these facts mathematically, introduce an electron density function $D(x, y, z)$ such that the number of electrons in a volume element dV at position x, y, z is $D(x, y, z)\,dV$. An arbitrary nucleus is chosen as origin of the coordinate system, and the x-, y-, z-axes point along the cube edges. The variation of D with x must be periodic with equal maxima at $x = 0, d_0, 2d_0, \cdots$. Fourier's theorem states that this variation can be described by a series containing only cosine terms:

$$D(x) = \sum_{j=0}^{\infty} A_j \cos \frac{2\pi}{d_0} jx$$

The depencence of D on y and z must be of the same form, because of the perfect symmetry of the cubic lattice. This implies that $D(x,y,z)$ can be represented by a three-dimensional Fourier series

$$D(x,y,z) = \sum_{j} A_j \cos\left(\frac{2\pi}{d_0} jx\right) \sum_{j'} A_{j'} \cos\left(\frac{2\pi}{d_0} j'y\right) \times$$

$$\times \left[\sum_{j''} A_{j''} \cos\right]\left(\frac{2\pi}{d_0} j''z\right) \quad (5.19)$$

where j, j', and j'' run from 0 to ∞, and the A_j are unspecified constants. The general term of this series is of the form

$$A_j\, A_{j'}\, A_{j''} \cos\left(\frac{2\pi}{d_0} jx\right) \cos\left(\frac{2\pi}{d_0} j'x\right) \cos\left(\frac{2\pi}{d_0} j''x\right)$$

By means of simple trigonometric identities any such product can be represented as a sum of terms of the form

$$\cos\left(\frac{2\pi}{d_0} (\pm jx \pm j'y \pm j''z)\right)$$

Therefore (5.19) can also be written

$$D(x,y,z) = \sum_{h=-\infty}^{\infty} \sum_{k=-\infty}^{\infty} \sum_{l=-\infty}^{\infty} B_{hkl} \cos\left(\frac{2\pi}{d_0}(hx + ky + lz)\right) \quad (5.20)$$

In this this summation the indices (h, k, l) assume all integral values from $-\infty$ through 0 to ∞, and all possible combinations of (h, k, l) must be taken into account.

The first terms of this series, which will be the largest ones, are

$$D(x,y,z) = B_{000} + 2B_{100}\left(\cos\frac{2\pi}{d_0}x + \cos\frac{2\pi}{d_0}y + \cos\frac{2\pi}{d_0}z\right)$$

$$+ 2B_{110}\left[\begin{array}{c}\cos\dfrac{2\pi}{d_0}(x+y) + \cos\dfrac{2\pi}{d_0}(y+z) + \cos\dfrac{2\pi}{d_0}(z+x) \\[2mm] + \cos\dfrac{2\pi}{d_0}(x-y) + \cos\dfrac{2\pi}{d_0}(y-z) + \cos\dfrac{2\pi}{d_0}(z-x)\end{array}\right]$$

$$2B_{111}\left[\begin{array}{c}\cos\dfrac{2\pi}{d_0}(x+y+z) + \cos\dfrac{2\pi}{d_0}(x+y-z) \\[2mm] + \cos\dfrac{2\pi}{d_0}(x-y-z) + \cdots\end{array}\right] \quad (5.21)$$

In writing out (5.21), we have made use of the fact that

$$B_{100} = B_{-100} = B_{010} = B_{0-10} = B_{001} = B_{00-1} \quad (5.22)$$

and similar relations for the B_{110}, B_{111}, etc. This follows algebraically from the fact that the A_j were identical for the distributions in the x-, y-, and z-directions; or what is the same thing, relations of type (5.22) can be inferred directly from the complete symmetry of the cubic lattice. Any single one of the cosine terms in (5.20) or (5.21) represents a sine wave with crests at the positions

$$(hx + ky + lz) = \frac{j}{d_0} \quad (5.23)$$

where j is an integer. But this is the equation of a plane with x-, y-, z-intercepts equal to

$$\frac{j\,d_0}{h}, \quad \frac{j\,d_0}{k}, \quad \frac{j\,d_0}{l}$$

Therefore the indices (h, k, l) that appear naturally in the Fourier expansion (5.20) of the crystal electron density are just equivalent to the Miller indices of the Bragg planes. To prove the Bragg equation, it is now only necessary to show that the diffraction effect produced by a single cosine term in (5.20) or (5.21) is equivalent to a Bragg "reflection."

To this purpose consider the diffraction effects produced when the electron density is represented by a single cosine function, taken as

$$D(x) = B \cos \frac{2\pi x}{d} \tag{5.24}$$

No special restrictions are imposed by this choice, because any one of the cosine terms can be written in this form if the coordinate axes are properly rotated. Here d is the distance between successive lattice (Bragg) planes and is not necessarily equal to d_0. Consider now a plane wave of X-rays incident in an arbitrary direction specified by a unit vector i. The scattering by crystal electrons is observed at a very great distance away from the crystal, so that all the scattered waves have essentially the same direction. This direction is specified by the unit vector o.

Let the amplitude of the incident light vector be E_0; then the observed amplitude of the light scattered from a volume dV is

$$dE = (\text{const}) \; E_0 D(x) \; dV \cos (\omega t + \varphi) \tag{5.25}$$

Polarization relations are of no concern and are accounted for by the (const) factor in (5.25). The time variation is given explicitly, and distance factors are contained in the phase angle φ. The total scattered amplitude E is the integral of (5.25) over the volume of the crystal. Thus only the relatiue values of φ are of importance, and one may arbitrarily set $\varphi = 0$ for the scattered ray that passes through the origin O of coordinates in the crystal. The phase angle φ for scattering from any other point P in the crystal is

$$\varphi = \frac{2\pi}{\lambda} (AP - OB) \tag{5.26}$$

as illustrated in Fig. 5.7.

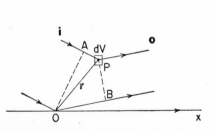

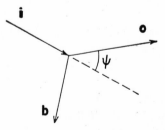

Fig. 5.7. Diagram for scattering by a   Fig. 5.8. Definition of $b = i - o$.
volume element at P.

It is convenient to introduce the vector $r = OP$. Since i and o are unit vectors, $AP = r \cdot i$, $OB = r \cdot o$. Then if the vector b is defined by $b = i - o$ as in Fig. 5.8,

$$\varphi = \frac{2\pi}{\lambda}\,(r \cdot b) \tag{5.27}$$

The vector b bisects the angle $(180 - \psi)$ between i and o and is of length $b = 2 \sin \psi/2$. Introducing (5.27) and (5.24) into (5.25), one has

$$dE = (\text{const})\, E_0 B \cos \frac{2\pi x}{d} \cos \left[\omega t + \frac{2\pi}{\lambda}\,(xb_x + yb_y + zb_z) \right] \times$$

$$\times\, dx\, dy\, dz \tag{5.28}$$

The total scattering amplitude observed is the integral of (5.28) over all the volume of the crystal. Consider the integral over z: unless $b_z = 0$, the integrand oscillates like a simple cosine function of z, and the integral is zero. Likewise for the integration over y, so that the scattered intensity is zero unless

$$b_y = b_z = 0 \tag{5.29}$$

Thus b must point entirely in the x-direction, normal to the set of lattice planes we have been considering according to (5.24). The vectors i and o specifying the directions of the incident and scattered beams therefore satisfy the relations of specular reflection from the lattice planes (Fig. 5.9).

The idea of reflection at the lattice planes, used in the elementary derivation of Bragg's law, is thus seen to be valid. Bragg's law itself follows from the product of the two cosine terms in x, which can be expressed as the sum of terms in $\cos [\omega t + 2\pi x(1/d + b/\lambda)]$ and $\cos [\omega t + 2\pi x(1/d - b/\lambda)]$. By the same argument as above, the integrals of these terms over x vanish unless

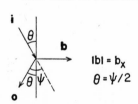

Fig. 5.9. Scattering equivalent to reflection from lattice plane.

$$\lambda = \pm bd \tag{5.30}$$

Since λ, b, and d are intrinsically positive quantities, only the positive sign can hold, and (5.30) becomes

$$\lambda = 2\, d \sin \psi/2 = 2\, d \sin \theta \tag{5.31}$$

This is just Bragg's law for a first order reflection. The higher order reflections come from other Fourier components in (5.20) that lead to variations (5.24) of the form

$$\cos \frac{2\pi}{d}(2x), \quad \cdots, \quad \cos \frac{2\pi}{d}(jx), \quad \cdots$$

All such variations correspond to planes with Miller indices that are simple multiples of each other and hence the same. Thus a complete verification is possible of the Bragg law in all its details. Note that the constant term B_{000} in (5.21) makes no contribution to the diffraction of X-rays.

The intensity of Bragg reflection is proportional to $\left| \int dE \right|^2$ or hence to $|B|^2$, the absolute square of the Fourier component. Intensity measurements of reflection from various lattice planes furnish in principle a complete set of amplitudes for the Fourier series (5.20). Therefore the electron distribution in a lattice can be determined from an analysis of X-ray data. The use of X-rays to "see" into the internal structure of the atom has been mentioned in section 5.2 above.

The type of information obtainable from intensity measurements may be illustrated by the following example. Consider reflection on the (1 1 1) planes of an NaCl or KCl crystal. These planes are normal to the body diagonal of the cubic lattice. Call the direction of this diagonal x, so that the Fourier components representing these planes to all orders are

$$D(x) = B_1 \cos\left(\frac{2\pi}{d}x\right) + B_2 \cos\left(\frac{2\pi}{d}2x\right) + \cdots \qquad (5.32)$$

The successive planes contain atoms all of one kind, either Na (K) or Cl. In NaCl there will be more electrons near the Cl planes than the Na planes, because $Z = 11$ for Na, while $Z = 17$ for Cl. For KCl, however, the distributions will be more nearly equal, because $Z = 19$ for K. The two situations are illustrated schematically in Fig. 5.10. For KCl the curves are nearly symmetrical for K and Cl planes, which implies that they vary much more like $\cos (2\pi/d)(2x)$ than $\cos (2\pi/d)x$, or that $|B_2| \gg |B_1|$. In fact, experiment shows that the first-order reflection in KCl does not occur at all, which means complete symmetry between the K and Cl planes. This is direct proof that in the crystal K and Cl exist as positive and negative ions with 18 electrons apiece. In NaCl the intensity ratio of first and second order reflections again

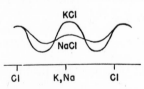

Fig. 5.10. Relative electron distributions in KCl and NaCl.

proves that the crystal is ionic in character, with 10 electrons forming Na^+ and 18 forming Cl^-.

Thus we see how crystal diffraction of X-rays confirms the nuclear model of the atom. In particular, this technique provides information relevant to the static model. It serves to count the number of electrons surrounding a nucleus and reveals their average distribution within the atom. The maxima of $D(x,y,z)$ at periodic intervals imply that the electron density is highest in the neighborhood of the nuclei.

SUMMARY

X-rays are penetrating electromagnetic radiation produced by electrons of many kev energy impinging upon a target. They are, in fact, identical in nature to ordinary, visible light, except that their wavelength is on the order 0.001 that of visible light. X-ray wavelengths are accordingly sometimes measured in X units, where 1 X.U. $= 10^{-3}$ A $= 10^{-11}$ cm. The basic form for attenuation of an X-ray beam on passage through matter is an experimental law $e^{-\mu t}$. The attenuation coefficient is $\mu = n_0(\sigma_s + \sigma_a)$, where n_0 is the number of atoms per unit volume, σ_s is the X-ray scattering cross section per atom, and σ_a is the absorption cross section per atom. Because of the factor n_0, μ is proportional to the density ρ of the material; it is frequently replaced by the mass attenuation coefficient μ/ρ, which is characteristic of the substance and independent of its condition.

The scattering cross section is incoherent for X-ray wavelengths around $0.2 - 1$ A and $A \lesssim 30$, $\sigma = (8\pi/3)r_0^2 Z$. For longer wavelengths and heavier atoms, where the electrons are more crowded together, the electrons tend to vibrate in phase with each other instead of randomly. This coherent motion gives rise to a scattering cross section that approaches $(8\pi/3)r_0^2 Z^2$ for pure coherence.

The total reflection of X-rays at a material surface measures the number of electrons per atom. Within experimental error this equals the order number Z of the atom in the periodic table. This phenomenon also makes it possible to measure absolute X-ray wavelengths by ruling a diffraction grating on a polished metal surface and observing interference patterns in the reflection at grazing angles. At these small angles the effective grating spacing is greatly reduced, making it possible to deal with wavelengths as short as those of X-rays.

The diffraction from crystals provides definite proof that X-rays have wavelike character. The Bragg law $j\lambda = 2d \sin \theta$ describes crystal diffraction as ordinary reflection from the symmetry planes of the crystal. The symmetry planes of a crystal are conveniently designated by the

Miller indices h, k, l; in a cubic crystal the spacing of the symmetry planes is $d = d_0/\sqrt{h^2 + k^2 + l^2}$, where d_0 is the separation of atomic centers. From diffraction measurements it is possible to determine crystal spacings very accurately, and from these to obtain a precise value of Avogadro's number N_0. The Bragg law of crystal diffraction can be derived from the mere assumption that the electron density in the crystal varies periodically. X-ray measurements furnish information about this distribution and thereby provide a means of "seeing into" the atom.

REFERENCES

C. G. Barkla, *Proc. Roy. Soc.*, **A77**, 247 (1906).

W. H. and W. L. Bragg, *X-rays and Crystal Structure*, Bell, London (1924).

A. H. Compton and S. K. Allison, *X-Rays in Theory and Experiment*, Van Nostrand, New York (1935).

M. v. Laue, *Die Interferenz der Röntgenstrahlen*, Akademische Verlagsgesellschaft M.b.H., Leipzig (1923).

H. G. J. Moseley, *Phil. Mag.*, **26**, 1024 (1913); **27**, 703 (1914).

M. Siegbahn, *The Spectroscopy of X-rays*, Oxford, London (1925).

ILLUSTRATIVE PROBLEMS

1. Observations of the total reflection of X-rays at the surface of a calcite crystal (CaCO$_3$) show that $(n - 1)/\lambda^2$ has the constant value -3.67×10^{10} cm^{-2}.

(a) What is the angle of total reflection for X-rays of wavelength 2.5 A?

(b) Compare the experimental value with the theoretical: the density of calcite is 2.8 and the atomic numbers are Ca = 20, C = 6, O = 8. The molecular weight of CaCO$_3$ is 100.

Solution. (a) By (5.9),

$$\Delta_c = [2(1 - n)]^{1/2} = \left[\frac{2(1 - n)}{\lambda^2}\right]^{1/2} \lambda$$

Here for $\lambda = 2.5 \times 10^{-8}$ cm,

$$\Delta_c = (2 \times 3.67 \times 10^{10})^{1/2} \times 2.5 \times 10^{-8} = 6.8 \times 10^{-3} \text{ radian} = 3.88°$$

(b) By (5.8), $n - 1/\lambda^2 = (-n_0 Z/2\pi)r_0$. In this case we take $n_0 = N_0\rho/A = 6.02 \times 10^{23} \times 2.8/100 = 1.69 \times 10^{22}$ as the number of molecules per unit volume, and $Z = \sum n_i Z_i$ as the total number of electrons per molecule. The Z_i are the order numbers of the atoms (equal to the number of electrons per neutral atom), and the n_i the number of atoms of the ith type per molecule. Then in $CaCO_3$, $n_1 = n_2 = 1$, $n_3 = 3$, and corresponding $Z_1 = 6$, $Z_2 = 20$, $Z_3 = 8$; hence $Z = 6 + 20 + 3 \times 8 = 50$. Thus the theoretical value is

$$\frac{n-1}{\lambda^2} = \frac{-1.69 \times 10^{22} \times 50}{2\pi} \times 2.8 \times 10^{-13} = -3.77 \times 10^{10} \text{ cm}^{-2}$$

The discrepancy between observed and theoretical values is less than 3%.

2. A cube of an NaCl crystal is irradiated with a beam of X-rays covering a continuous spectrum from 1 to 5 A. The beam is incident normal to a cube face. The lattice constant of NaCl is 2.814 A.

(a) What is the wavelength and what is the polarization of the X-rays diffracted at right angles to the incident beam?

(b) If the crystal is subjected to pressure in a direction parallel to the incident X-rays, determine how much pressure P in kg/cm^2 must be applied to alter the Bragg reflection in part (a) by an angle of 1°. Young's modulus for NaCl is $Y = 45.4 \times 10^{10}$ dynes/cm^2, and Poisson's ratio is 0.126.

Solution. (a) The incident beam is unpolarized and can be considered as consisting of two plane-polarized beams, one polarized parallel to the reflected beam at 90°, the other polarized perpendicular to the plane of the incident and reflected beams. The reflected beam can contain only these polarizations and must in addition be a transverse vibration. It is therefore plane polarized perpendicular to the plane of the incident and reflected beams.

We can write Bragg's law in the form

$$j\sqrt{h^2 + k^2 + l^2} = \left(\frac{2\,d_0}{\lambda}\right)\sin\theta,$$

where j is the order of the reflection, h, k, l are the Miller indices, $d_0 = 2.814$ A is the lattice constant, and θ is the glancing angle made by the beam with the planes specified by h, k, l. For a 90° reflection, $\theta = 45°$. Under the restriction $1 \text{ A} \leq \lambda \leq 5 \text{ A}$ the only planes that make an angle of 45° with a beam incident along the z-axis, for example, are the (1 0 1), (0 1 1) (1 0 $\bar{1}$) and (0 1 $\bar{1}$) planes. For these planes $\lambda = 2\,d_0 \sin\theta/j\sqrt{2} = d_0/j = 2.814$ A, 1.407 A for $j = 1$, 2. These are the only two wavelengths within the specified range that are reflected at 90°.

(b) The pressure shortens the crystal along the z-axis and enlarges it along the directions perpendicular to z. The relative enlargement is 0.126 times the contraction effect; thus if the relative contraction in the z-direction is $\Delta z/z$, the corresponding change in θ is $\Delta(\tan\theta)/\tan\theta =$

1.126 $\Delta z/z$ = 1.126 P/Y = 2 $\Delta\theta/\sin 2\theta$. The angle of reflection is φ = 180° − 2θ, so that $\Delta\varphi$ = −2 $\Delta\theta$ = 1° = 0.017 radius. Thus for sin 2θ = 1 the pressure in kg/cm^2 (1 kg = 9.8 × 10^5 dynes) is

$$P = \frac{(2\,\Delta\theta)Y}{1.126 \sin 2\theta \times 9.8 \times 10^5} = \frac{45.4 \times 10^{10} \times 0.017}{1.126 \times 9.8 \times 10^5} = 7.0 \times 10^3\,\text{kg/cm}^2$$

3. A monochromatic beam of X-rays of wavelength λ is incident normal to an edge of a cubic crystal of lattice constant d. The crystal is rotated about this cube edge as axis.

(a) Derive a relation for the angles φ formed with the incident beam by all diffracted beams that are in the plane normal to this rotation axis.

(b) For NaCl with d = 2.814 A, what is the maximum wavelength that the beam can have in order to obtain at least 7 reflected beams on each side?

Solution. (a) the angle φ = 2θ, where sin θ = $j\lambda/2\,d$. The Miller indices involved have $l \equiv 0$ because the reflection plane is parallel to a cube axis;

$$d = \frac{d_0}{\sqrt{h^2 + k^2}} \quad \text{and} \quad \varphi = 2 \sin^{-1}\left(\frac{j\sqrt{h^2 + k^2}}{2}\frac{\lambda}{d_0}\right)$$

Here j, h, k are positive integers, restricted to values such that the argument of $\sin^{-1}$ does not exceed 1; either h or k but not both can be zero.

(b) The seven lowest values of $j\sqrt{h^2 + k^2}$ are 1, $\sqrt{2}$, 2, $\sqrt{5}$, 2$\sqrt{2}$, 3, $\sqrt{10}$. The condition on the argument of $\sin^{-1}$ requires that

$$\frac{\sqrt{10}}{2}\frac{\lambda}{d_0} \leq 1, \quad \text{or} \quad \lambda \leq \frac{\sqrt{10}}{5}\,d_0 = 1.500\,\text{A}$$

PROBLEMS

1. After what distance is the intensity of a parallel beam of X-rays (0.2 A wavelength) reduced to 5% of its initial value (a) in oxygen at STP; (b) in gold. Assume that the attenuation coefficient for O$_2$ equals the theoretical value for incoherent scattering, while the attenuation coefficient in Au is $\frac{1}{4}$ the theoretical value for completely coherent scattering.

2. To obtain strong reflections in diffraction experiments of X-rays on a grating, the glancing angle of the incident beam should be smaller than the glancing angle for total reflection. For X-rays of λ = 1.537 A, the glancing angle for total reflection on gold is 31′ 24″. With a grating ruled on gold of 10,000 lines per cm, at what glancing angle will the first-order diffraction maximum occur when the incident light has the above wavelength and is incident at the critical angle for total reflection?

3. Obtain the simplest approximation for the polarization and intensity distribution of scattered X-rays. Use the approach of section 4.7, in which the incident light causes electron vibration parallel to its electric vector E. The vibrating electrons reradiate in all directions. The radiation reaching any point P from an oscillating electron has its electric vector proportional in magnitude to the amplitude of the electron oscillation as seen from P, and polarized in the same direction as the electron motion.

(a) Let the points of observation P all lie a constant distance from the scattering atom. Show that the scattered intensity from an initially unpolarized beam varies as $(1 + \cos^2 \theta)$, θ, where θ is the angle between the incident and scattered beam directions. Note that an unpolarized beam is mathematically equivalent to the sum of two plane-polarized beams with mutually perpendicular planes of polarization.

(b) Using the result of (a), find the differential atomic cross section $d\sigma\,(\theta)/d\omega$ that corresponds to (4.47). This differential cross section represents scattering into the solid angle $d\omega$ located at the angle θ. The requirement that it must satisfy is

$$\int_0^{2\pi} d\varphi \int_0^{\pi} \sin \theta \; d\theta \; (d\sigma/d\omega) \; = \; \sigma$$

the total scattering cross section (4.47).

(c) In a double scattering experiment unpolarized X-rays are incident upon a block of material A, from which they scatter at an angle θ to block B. The radiation scattered from B makes an angle φ with the plane of the angle θ. Find the dependence of the scattered intensity on θ, φ, and show that it vanishes only for $\theta = \varphi = 90°$.

4. A parallel beam of X-rays with a continuous spectrum extending from $\lambda = 0.5$ to 3 A is incident in the direction indicated on a crystal in which the atoms form hexagonal rings.

(a) What is the wavelength of the X-rays scattered in the plane of the diagram at an angle of 120° to the incident beam?

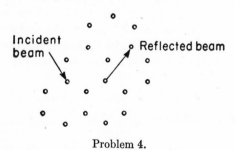

Problem 4.

(b) How many diffraction orders can be obtained in this direction and how will their intensities compare?

5. The intensities of the Bragg reflections from various lattice planes vary in inverse proportion to the sum of the squares of the Miller indices; thus the (0 0 1) reflection is the most intense.

(a) If the strongest line in a diffraction pattern made with monochromatic X-rays and a powder of NaCl appears in the direction at 60° to the incident beam, where will the three next most intense lines occur, and what is the wavelength of the incident beam? Illustrate the diffraction pattern in a diagram and compute the diffraction angles.

(b) Answer the same question as in part (a) for the case of a pattern made with a single crystal that is rocked about an axis normal to the incident beam, the axis being parallel to a cube axis of the lattice.

6. Consider a crystal with an orthorhomboid unit cell (rectangular box) of dimensions $d_1 = 3$ A along x, $d_2 = 2$ A along y, and $d_3 = 1.5$ A along z. The cell contains only one atom which may be assumed to be located at the corners of the cell. Consider a lattice plane passing through the first atom on the x-axis, the third atom on the y-axis, and the second atom on the z-axis.

(a) What are the Miller indices for this plane and those parallel to it?

(b) What is the lattice distance d between these planes?

(c) Find the wavelength of the X-rays, incident in the z direction, which produce Bragg reflection on these planes.

(d) What is the angle between the incident and the diffracted beams of part (c)?

7. An X-ray beam is incident parallel to a cube axis of a cubic crystal with a lattice constant of 2 A. The Laue pattern is to be recorded on a photographic plate, normal to the beam at a distance of 4 cm from the crystal. Construct a diagram showing the position of the most intense diffraction spots and the wavelengths of the X-rays at these spots. Assume the plate is 10 cm square. The most intense spots correspond to low indices h, k, l; do not use indices larger than 3 and note that it is sufficient to locate the spots in half a quadrant of the plate.

8. Derive an expression for the Bragg law, taking into account the index of refraction n of the crystal. Assume the surface of the crystal to be parallel to the planes from which Bragg reflection occurs. What is the change $\Delta\theta$ upon inclusion of a refractive index $n = 1 - 5 \times 10^{-5}$ when $\theta = 45°$?

9. The density and refractive index fluctuation produced by sound waves in liquids or solids have the same effects on visible light as the electron density variations in crystals have on X-rays. Compute the frequency of a sound wave (supersonic) that produces "Bragg reflection" at 90° to the incident beam for green light of 6000 A wavelength in a liquid with a sound velocity of 1500 meter/sec. For a standing sound wave the Bragg reflection is periodically interrupted with the frequency ν_s of the sound wave; hence the reflected beam is modulated and its frequency is that of the two "side bands" $\nu \pm \nu_s$, where ν is of the frequency of the incident light. Compute the difference of the wavelengths in Angstroms of the two side bands. By varying the direction of the sound wave, determine at which direction of observation the separation of the sidebands is a maximum. Note: in applying Bragg's law, note that it refers to the wavelength of the light in the medium. Assume a refractive index of 1.5.

10. The blackening of a photographic film containing AgCl reaches a sharp maximum when the wavelength of the X-rays coincides with one of the "absorption limits" (Chap. 6) of silver. The K-limit is at 0.48 A, and one of the L limits is at 3.464 A. In studying the continuous radiation from an X-ray tube with a rotating crystal spectrometer, the effect of the above L limit is observed on the film when the reflected beam strikes the film at an angle $\Delta = 60°$ from the position of the incident beam. At what angle is the corresponding effect of the K limit observed?

Chapter 6

PHOTONS AND X-RAY SPECTRA

In the last chapter we saw that X-rays behave in many ways like transverse electromagnetic vibrations—that is, light of very short wavelength around a few A. The wavelike character of X-rays is conclusively established by diffraction in crystals. On the other hand, certain prominent features of X-rays require for their explanation something more than the mere assumption that X-rays are light waves obeying Maxwell's equations. These "nonclassical" features are the short wavelength limit of the continuous emission spectrum, the critical absorption wavelengths, and the line emission spectrum with its K-, L-, M- . . . groups corresponding to the critical absorption. Even the ionizing properties of X-rays, so useful in their detection, are not adequately explained by classical electrodynamics.

It turns out that a single new idea is sufficient to interpret all these difficulties; namely, the concept of the photon or light quantum. In this chapter we shall introduce the photon concept and illustrate its fruitfulness by application to X-ray phenomena. In the next chapter the same principles will be applied to optical spectra.

6.1. The photon

Max Planck first introduced the quantum in 1900 in a study of black body radiation. He considered an enclosure of finite volume containing light waves in thermal equilibrium with the container walls at a temperature T. If a small aperture is made in the container, the light waves are emitted as if from a perfect black body radiator. In obtaining the first successful formula to fit the observations on black body radiation, Planck was forced to a rather peculiar assumption. Let the light of frequency ν have a total energy in the enclosure of $W(\nu)$; then Planck's hypothesis is that $W(\nu)$ cannot take any arbitrary value but is restricted to the values*

$$W(\nu) = (n + \tfrac{1}{2})h\nu, \qquad\qquad n = 0, 1, 2, \cdots \qquad (6.1)$$

Here Planck's constant h is a fundamental constant of nature like the electronic charge e. Measurements of black body radiation indicate a

---

* Planck's original hypothesis was that $W(\nu) = nh\nu$. The additional $\tfrac{1}{2}h\nu$ arises from a more modern mathematical treatment of the problem. Its introduction here is merely a formality, since it plays no observable role in any physical process.

value on the order of $h = 10^{-26}$ erg-sec. The energy in the enclosure, because it could assume only the discrete values (6.1), was said to be *quantized*.

Planck's hypothesis represents a radical departure from "classical" ideas, according to which $W(\nu)$ should be able to range continuously over all values. Quantization was at first so uncomfortable a notion that even Planck made serious efforts to find a way of dispensing with it. It remains, however, the only means for a satisfactory interpretation of the black body radiation spectrum. Today so much independent evidence has accumulated in support of the quantum hypothesis that we cannot doubt its correctness.

Einstein generalized the relation (6.1) by discarding the artificial restriction of the enclosure and regarding the monochromatic radiation itself as consisting of indivisible quanta or photons, each of energy $h\nu$. Thus the integer n in (6.1) simply represents the number of quanta in the box. The extra $\frac{1}{2}h\nu$ is known as a "zero-point energy": it must always be present, even in a complete vacuum. We can never in any way observe it directly, however, and can therefore neglect it in all physical processes.

The light quantum or photon recalls Newton's old corpuscular theory of light. The essential improvement over the corpuscular theory is that the photon is quantitatively related to the wave picture for the same light through

$$W = h\nu \tag{6.2}$$

Here W is the energy of each photon and ν is the frequency of the same light, considered as transverse electromagnetic waves. Since the photon is indivisible, the emission or absorption of light by any system must occur in units of whole photons. A system as small as an atom usually absorbs or emits only one photon at a time. This fact, used in connection with (6.2) is of great importance in the interpretation of X-ray and optical spectra.

In the following sections we see that only the photon concept is adequate to explain the "nonclassical" features of X-rays, such as the short wavelength limit of the continuous spectrum, absorption edges, and emission lines. On the other hand, the phenomenon of crystal diffraction clearly shows that we must think of X-rays as wave trains. That is, somehow or other light manages to have simultaneously the properties of two concepts that have previously seemed to be mutually exclusive—waves and particles. For there is no doubt that the photon behaves in every way like a particle: it has momentum, can suffer elastic or inelastic collision, etc. These properties will be further elaborated in Chapter 9. The fact that light simultaneously possesses wave and particle aspects is already implicit in (6.2), which is the connecting link between the two concepts.

So far no way has been found of resolving this wave-particle dilemma, and we must therefore just learn to live with it. We can put this truism in the form of a "principle of complementarity," which states that the wave and particle pictures are both valid aspects of the same reality and must be viewed as complementing rather than contradicting each other. In practice this means that both the wave and particle pictures must be borne in mind, and the more appropriate one applied to any given situation. With practice this becomes relatively easy and occasions no confusion. There are many situations in which either picture will lead to equivalent results. For instance, two independent states of polarization can be ascribed to the photons as well as to transverse waves. Instead of plane polarization, it is particularly convenient to use circular polarization for photons. In the wave picture we can represent circularly polarized light by means of E and H vectors that rotate continuously about the direction of the light beam as an axis. Clockwise and counterclockwise rotation are the two independent types of circular polarization. On the photon picture we can think of the particle as continuously spinning about its own axis. This axis is parallel to the direction of motion, and the two independent polarizations are represented by spins in clockwise and counterclockwise senses (see Chap. 9).

We can extend the energy relation (6.2) to determine the amplitude of an electromagnetic wave associated with one photon. Suppose that one photon of frequency $\nu = \omega/2\pi$ and a single state of (plane) polarization is contained in a volume V. In the wave picture the electric vector of the light is of amplitude

$$E = E_0 \cos \omega t = \tfrac{1}{2}E_0 e^{i\omega t} + \tfrac{1}{2}E_0 e^{-i\omega t},$$

and the energy in the whole volume is

$$W = VE_0^2/8\pi = h\nu \tag{6.3}$$

We have used (6.2) because there is just one photon in the volume. A detailed consideration of the problem, beyond the scope of this section, shows that in the photon picture we must distinguish between photons of positive and negative frequencies, $\pm \omega = \pm 2\pi\nu$. The amplitude associated with a single frequency is

$$E_\nu = \tfrac{1}{2}E_0 = \sqrt{\frac{2\pi h\nu}{V}} \tag{6.4}$$

In a similar fashion $H_\nu = \sqrt{2\pi h\nu/V} = E_\nu$. Equation (6.4) completes the quantitative relationship between wave and particle pictures of light; it gives the amplitude of the electric vector E_ν in the wave picture that corresponds to the presence of one photon of frequency ν (or $-\nu$) in a volume V. As numerical example consider a green light beam ($\lambda = 6000$ A) of one lumen ($1/700$ watt/cm^2) intensity. For this intensity we have from (6.3) $I = (n/V)cW = (n/V)hc^2/\lambda$, where n/V is the number of photons per cm^3 in the beam. In this case

$$\frac{n}{V} = \frac{\lambda I}{hc^2}$$

$$= \frac{6 \times 10^{-5} \times \frac{1}{700} \times 10^7}{6.6 \times 10^{-27} \times 9 \times 10^{20}}$$

$$= \frac{1.3 \times 10^5}{\text{cm}^3}$$

This photon density is infinitesimally small in comparison with typical atomic densities of $10^{22}/\text{cm}^3$; even a good vacuum produced in the laboratory contains on the order of 10^9 molecules/cm^3.

6.2. The short wavelength limit

Measurements with a crystal spectrometer allow a study of the *spectrum* of any X-ray beam. The spectrum is the distribution of intensity as a function of wavelength (or frequency). The spectrum directly produced by an X-ray tube consists of two parts: the *continuous* spectrum and superposed on this the *line* or *discrete* spectrum. The continuous spectrum has the remarkable property that it cuts off sharply at a minimum wavelength $\lambda_{\min}$. It has no definite long wavelength limit. The short wavelength cutoff is independent of the anode material in the tube and varies inversely as the applied voltage. It is given by

$$\lambda_{\min} = 12.4\text{A}/V \text{ (kilovolts)} \tag{6.5}$$

The line spectrum, on the other hand, is characteristic of the anode material that serves as target for the bombarding electrons. It is independent of the applied voltage, except that at any voltage only those lines appear which have $\lambda > \lambda_{\min}$. If the discrete spectrum contains additional lines of shorter wavelength, these will first appear at higher accelerating voltages. This situation is illustrated schematically in Fig. 6.1.

In this section we consider the continuous spectrum and particularly its short wavelength limit. On a classical picture we certainly expect radiation to be emitted when electrons stop in the target. An electron accelerated by a voltage V has an energy eV when it strikes the tar-

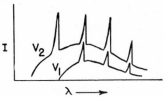

Fig. 6.1. Spectrum from an X-ray tube at two voltages, $V_2 > V_1$.

get. It quickly loses all this energy by making collisions with the electrons and nuclei in the atoms of the target. The struck electrons in turn collide with other electrons and nuclei; the energy eV of an incident electron is rapidly converted into heat by this process. The collisions involve brief but extremely large accelerations. According to classical theory we should expect strong radiation during these collisions, with a spectrum extending over all frequencies. Although classical theory can account for the radiation of X-rays, it cannot explain the short wavelength limit.

The quantum theory also predicts that the electrons will emit radiation at these collisions, but as individual photons instead of the continuous radiation of the classical formula. In such a radiative process during collision an electron may radiate any part ΔW of its initial energy. Since single-photon emission (or absorption) is about 100 times more likely than two-photon emission, we expect the wavelength of the corresponding photon to be

$$\lambda = c/\nu = hc/\Delta W \qquad (6.6)$$

For an electron beam of incident energy eV we have $\Delta W \leq eV$, so that

$$\lambda = hc/\Delta W \geq hc/eV = \lambda_{min} \qquad (6.7)$$

Relation (6.7) follows from the photon hypothesis and is in complete agreement with experiment. Reversing the argument, we see that the observation of a short wavelength cutoff for X-ray spectra is evidence for the existence of the photon.

Comparing the experimentally observed constant in (6.5) with (6.7), we have

$$hc/e = 12.398 \text{ A kilovolt} \qquad (6.8)$$

We can quote the constant from (6.5) to such accuracy because of the high precision possible with X-ray measurements. Since precise values of e and c are also available, we have a means of determining Planck's constant with great accuracy:

$$h = 6.625 \times 10^{-27} \text{ erg-sec} \qquad (6.9)$$

For many applications it is useful to express hc and its reciprocal in terms of the energy unit electron-volts (ev):

$$hc = 12.398 \text{ A kev} = 1.2398 \times 10^{-4} \text{ cm ev}$$

$$1/hc = 8066 \text{ cm}^{-1} \text{ ev}^{-1} \qquad (6.8a)$$

Of course the complex collision processes in the X-ray target produce many photons of lower energy than the maximum value eV. These photons have $\lambda > \lambda_{min}$ and form the total continuous spectrum. The shape of this spectrum as calculated from a quantum mechanical formula is in reasonable agreement with observation. The radiation of photons in the deceleration of charged particles goes by the general name given it in such quantum mechanical calculations, *Bremsstrahlung* or "brake radiation."

It is important to realize the differences between the classical and quantum-mechanical description of radiation. Classically, we determine the trajectory of a charged particle and compute the radiation from its acceleration along that trajectory. (In a refined calculation the radiative energy loss must be taken into account in determining the trajectory.) From this trajectory the radiation intensity and frequency distribution are completely determined. Classically the motion of the charged particle is the primary phenomenon, and the radiation is a secondary effect derivable from the motion. Quantum mechanics in a sense reverses this procedure: the radiation is a primary effect, described directly by $\Delta W = h\nu$; the deceleration of the charged particle is derived from the fact that it has lost the energy ΔW. Quantum mechanics provides no detailed description of the particle motion; we simply say that the particle "jumps." The success of the quantum mechanical description extends beyond the prediction of the short wavelength limit. Since it does not describe the motion of the particle at all but only specifies the radiated energy, it can accomodate charged particle motions in which $\Delta W = 0$ but the acceleration is not zero. This feature in principle provides a way of freeing the dynamic model of the atom from its classical radiation difficulties. We shall see in succeeding chapters that quantum mechanics does avoid the radiation difficulties in just this way, but at the expense of being unable to ascribe specific trajectories to atomic electrons. Strangely enough, the loss of this specific descriptive power proves no hindrance to our present understanding of the atom.

6.3. Ionization

The photon concept is equally useful in explaining processes of absorption as well as emission of light (X-rays). Applied to absorption, it accounts for the ionizing properties of X-rays. It also accounts for the K-, L-, M-, $\cdots$ absorption edges, if we make the further important assumption that the electrons occupy fixed, invariable orbits in the atom.

The remarks of section 6.2 suggest that it may be possible to neglect the classically predicted radiation in the dynamic model of the atom. Such neglect would make the orbits stable. If the ith electron is in a stable circular orbit of radius r_i, its kinetic energy is $\frac{1}{2}mv_i^2$ and its potential energy is $-Z_i e^2/r_i$. Here $Z_i < Z$, the charge number on the

nucleus, because of shielding of the nucleus by electrons interior to the
ith. The total energy of the electron is, using Eq. (4.1),

$$U_i = \tfrac{1}{2}mv_i^2 - Z_ie^2/r_i = -\tfrac{1}{2}mv_i^2 = -\tfrac{1}{2}Z_ie^2/r_i \qquad (6.10)$$

The total energy U_i is negative, which means that energy from an external source must be supplied to the electron to separate it from the
atom. We call an electron in this situation *bound* to the atom. The
energy necessary to liberate it is $W = |\,U_i\,| = -U_i = B_i$. The nega-
tive of the total energy is a positive quantity, the *binding energy B_i*.
Any energy W that equals or exceeds B_i is sufficient to liberate the
electron; an energy W less than B_i can only move the electron out to a
radius r_i' such that $U_i' - U_i = W$. The radius r_i' will remain finite,
however, so that the electron is still bound to the atom.

Still neglecting radiation by the electrons, we may suppose them to
be distributed in various stationary orbits throughout the atom. To
each orbit corresponds a fixed, definite binding energy B_i. If we irradiate the atom with X-rays of wavelength λ, one of the electrons may
absorb energy from the incident radiation. According to the quantum
hypothesis, this absorption must involve at least one quantum or photon
of energy $W = h\nu = hc/\lambda$. It is in fact most likely to involve just one
quantum. If the photon energy W exceeds the binding energy B_i, this
absorption will liberate the electron from the atom. Any excess energy
$W - B_i$ will appear as kinetic energy of the liberated electron. Of course
this electron liberation converts the neutral atom into a positive ion.
Thus the photon hypothesis provides a possible mechanism for the
observed strong ionizing properties of X-rays.

To check whether this mechanism is really a satisfactory explanation,
we should determine whether the average $h\nu$ of X-ray photons exceeds
the binding energy of atomic electrons. For the outermost electron in
an atom, $Z_i \approx 1$, because the nucleus is shielded by all the other electrons. The radius $r_i \approx 10^{-8}$ cm, so that by (6.10) $B_i = -U_i = e^2/2r_i \approx$
$2.3 \times 10^{-19}/(2 \times 10^{-8}) = 1.2 \times 10^{-11}$ erg $= 7.5$ ev. An X-ray photon
of wavelength 1 A has an energy $W = h\nu = hc/\lambda = 1.2 \times 10^4$ ev.
Thus X-ray photons certainly satisfy $W > B_i$ for the outermost atomic
electrons; they also satisfy this condition for many of the inner electrons.
Consider an interior orbit in a heavy atom, with $Z_i \approx 50$, $r_i \approx 10^{-10}$
cm, $B_i \approx 3.7 \times 10^4$ ev. An electron in this orbit can escape from atom
by absorbing a photon of wavelength shorter than $\lambda = hc/W \approx 0.3$ A;
an X-ray of longer wavelength cannot liberate this electron.

From these examples it is clear that by going to the shortest X-rays
around 0.1 A we can liberate any electron in even the heaviest atoms.
This process is called *photoionization* or is sometimes included under the
more general heading of the photoelectric effect. Thus the concept of

the photon provides a ready explanation of the ionizing properties of X-rays. We should also demonstrate, however, that only the photon concept is in accord with the observed facts of photoionization. We postpone this discussion to the optical photoelectric effect considered in the next chapter.

In section 5.2 we split the attenuation coefficient for X-rays into a scattering term μ_s and a true absorption coefficient μ_a. The term μ_s varies only slowly with λ of the incident X-rays, but the total μ or hence the absorption μ_a shows marked variation for certain wavelengths, which reflects a corresponding variation in the absorption cross section σ_a. This variation is shown schematically in Fig. 6.2. For X-ray wavelengths on the order of 1 A, the mass absorption coefficient increases rapidly with wavelength until a critical wavelength is reached at which the absorption drops sharply. The absorption "edge" at shortest wavelength is designated by the letter K. Next comes a group of three relatively close L absorption limits, and at still longer wavelengths five M limits are observed. For heavy substances there are beyond

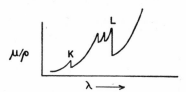

Fig. 6.2. Critical absorption edges for X-rays.

these N, O, $\cdots$ groups with 7, 9, $\cdots$ edges, but their observation becomes increasingly difficult. The critical absorption wavelengths at which the sharp breaks occur are characteristic of each element, and become shorter in regular fashion with increasing atomic number of the absorbing element. We can in fact represent the absorption edge frequencies by the formula

$$\nu = (Z - \sigma)^2 Rc/n^2 \tag{6.11}$$

where $n = 1, 2, 3, \cdots$ for the K, L, M, $\cdots$ edges. Here c is the velocity of light and $R = 1.097 \times 10^5$ cm^{-1} is a universal constant known as the Rydberg constant; Z is the order number of the element, and $\sigma = 1$ for the K edges. For the L, M, $\cdots$ edges, σ becomes progressively larger— for example, it is on the order of 10 for the L edges, and 30 for the M edges. Furthermore, except for the K edges, σ shows a pronounced tendency to increase with Z.

Our previous discussion of photoionization makes it natural to assume that the high absorption peaks correspond to ionization of a few particular electrons in the atom. The "edge" occurs at a wavelength corresponding to $h\nu = B_i$; for longer wavelengths $h\nu < B_i$, and ionization cannot occur. With this interpretation of the absorption edges, we can put

$$B_i = h\nu = (Z - \sigma)^2 hcR/n^2 \tag{6.12}$$

for the electron binding energies in the orbits. Comparison with Eq. (6.10) $(U_i = -B_i)$ permits us to draw the following inferences:

(1) $Z_i = Z - \sigma$, so that σ represents the extent to which the charge on the nucleus is shielded or "screened" by the other electrons; σ is therefore called the screening constant.

(2) The number of different groups of absorption edges, K-, L-, M-, etc. is much smaller than the total number Z of electrons in the atom, although a sufficiently high frequency X-ray can eject any atomic electron. We must therefore assume that the electrons are arranged in "shells" in the atom. All electrons in a given shell have practically the same binding energies. We call these the K-, L-, M-, etc. shells to correspond to each group of absorption edges. The separate absorption edges in each group correspond to relatively minor differences in the electron binding energies in a single shell.

(3) There are more electrons in a shell than there are edges in the corresponding absorption edge group. The number of distinct edges in a group is $(2n + 1)$, or 1, 3, 5, $\cdots$ for K, L, M, $\cdots$. The screening constant σ indicates that there are 2 electrons even in the K shell, and considerably more than 3 or 5 in the L or M shells, respectively.

(4) The radii of the K, L, $M \cdots$ shells in an atom vary in the ratio $1^2 : 2^2 : 3^2 : \cdots = 1 : 4 : 9 : \cdots$. For different elements the radius of a given shell varies as $1/(Z - \sigma)$. This explains qualitatively why the atoms of heavy elements are not much larger than those of light elements. The heavy elements have more shells, but the radii of corresponding shells are smaller in the heavy elements.

We must regard these conclusions as of a semiquantitative nature only. Nevertheless, they show that the photon concept is again successful in relating the frequencies of the absorption edges to the properties of the electron orbits in the atom. We see here how consistent application of the photon hypothesis to X-ray data begins to tell us something definite—e.g, shell structure—about the internal arrangement of the atom.

6.4. Energy levels and term values

The absorption edges make clear one fact that the phenomenon of ionization alone does not show, namely, that the electrons in atoms occupy fixed orbits with definite, unvarying binding energies B_i. The sharpness of the absorption edges indicates that there is no variation in the frequency $\nu_i = B_i/h$ at which the photon energy just equals the binding energy. On a classical picture this constancy is surprising: even if we neglect radiation, the electrons should exchange energy because of the Coulomb forces between them. Thus on a classical picture an electron in any atom should have a continuously variable binding energy. This conclusion is contradicted by the photon interpretation of the absorption edges.

Another way of phrasing the problem posed by the discrete absorption edges is to ask why the atom contains just those corresponding orbits and no others. Classically, the radius r of an electron orbit in an atom can have any value whatever, and the corresponding B also varies in a continuous fashion. The observations tell us, however, that in any atom the electrons lie in a fixed set of orbits with prescribed radii, r_1, r_2, $\cdots$, r_n. Why should we never find an electron in this atom with an orbit radius r lying between r_j and r_k? This problem is made more acute by the fact noted in section 6.3 that most occupied orbits in an atom contain more than one electron each.

These questions will be settled in Chapters 9 and 10 by a further application of quantum principles. For the moment let us be content to note the experimental fact that atomic electrons cannot have arbitrary binding energies but only certain particular values B_i. In terms of the total electron energy $U_i = -B_i$ we say that an electron in an orbit of radius r_i is in an *energy level* U_i. We will frequently talk about the energy levels of an electron without specifying the corresponding orbits explicitly. It is also often convenient in discussion to plot these energy levels in a vertical diagram, as shown in Fig. 6.3a. The horizontal axis is the line of zero energy: all levels below this line correspond to bound

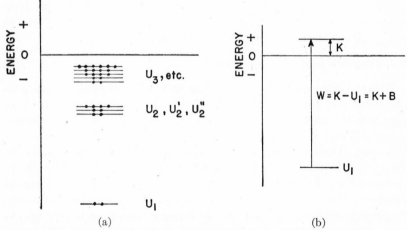

(a)   (b)

Fig. 6.3 (a.) Energy levels in a hypothetical atom; the levels U_n correspond to orbits in the nth shell. The dots represent electrons occupying the levels (orbits); they are usually omitted. All the levels below the line of zero energy represent bound states. (b.) Energy level diagram of photoionization of a K electron by a photon of energy W, leaving the electron with a positive kinetic energy of $K = W + U_1 = W - B$.

electrons. This is in the spirit of section 6.2, where we noted that quantum mechanics specifies energies or energy changes but does not say anything definite about electron trajectories.

To illustrate the application of an energy level diagram, Fig. 6.3b shows photoionization by an X-ray photon of energy $h\nu$. The vertical arrow indicates absorption of a photon, and the electron after absorption has a positive kinetic energy K. This energy is given by $K = h\nu - B_1 = h\nu + U_1$. In general, the energy of the photon required to lift an electron from energy level U to U' is

$$h\nu = U' - U \tag{6.13}$$

It is frequently more convenient to deal with the frequency or wavelength of the photon than its energy $h\nu$. In spectroscopy, in particular optical spectroscopy, the custom has arisen of specifying radiation by its *wave number* $k = 1/\lambda = \nu/c$ generally measured in units of cm^{-1}. Then the energy of a photon is $h\nu = hck$, and (6.13) reads

$$k = U'/hc - U/hc = T - T' \tag{6.14}$$

$$T = -U/hc = B/hc, \qquad T' = -U'/hc = B'/hc \tag{6.14a}$$

The quantity T is called the *term* corresponding to the energy level U. It is a positive quantity for bound levels and has units of cm^{-1} for convenience in spectroscopic applications such as (6.14). It is of course possible to plot Fig. 6.3 as a term diagram instead of an energy level diagram simply by changing scale from energy units (usually ev) to cm^{-1} units. The conversion is given in (6.8a).

6.5. Discrete emission spectra

The radiation emitted by an X-ray tube consists of the continuous spectrum and the superimposed discrete or line spectrum. We have seen how the photon concept satisfactorily accounts for the continuous spectrum, and it will prove equally useful in understanding the line spectrum. These lines are characteristic of the element that forms the target for the electron beam in an X-ray tube. They fall into groups designated K-, L-, M-, $\cdots$. The K emission lines all have wavelengths similar to that of the K absorption edge of the target substance. The important difference is that the K emission wavelengths are always somewhat longer than the K absorption edge wavelength. The same relation holds for the L-, M-, $\cdots$ absorption edges and corresponding emission lines. There are many more emission lines than absorption edges in any particular group. For instance, there is one K absorption edge and two to six regularly observed emission lines. No emission lines of a group appear at all, however, unless the energy of the electrons hitting the target in the X-ray tube exceeds the energy $h\nu$ of the absorption edge corresponding to this group. This is true even when the electron energy is in the narrow energy range that exceeds the $h\nu$ of the emission lines but is less than the $h\nu$ of the absorption edge.

Studies of the X-ray emission lines, pioneered by Moseley in 1913–1914, show that the frequency of a particular K line, designated by K_{α_1}, K_{α_2}, K_{β_1}, K_{β_2}, etc., increases regularly as we go to higher atomic number Z. The frequency of any such line can be well represented by the formula

$$\sqrt{\nu} = C_K(Z - 1) \tag{6.12a}$$

This is of the same form as Eq. 6.12 for B_i; in this case it actually represents a difference $B_i' - B_i$ of two energy levels of type (6.12). Equations similar to (6.12a) hold for the L-, M-, $\cdots$ emission lines: the corresponding constants C become progressively smaller, and the term -1 in (6.12a) is replaced by progressively larger screening constants $-\sigma$. Figure 6.4 is a graph of (6.12a) for K emission lines. Such "Moseley diagrams" are of considerable practical usefulness in the analysis of unknown samples. For L-, M-, $\cdots$ lines the Moseley diagrams show more curvature than Fig. 6.4, suggesting that C and/or σ do not remain quite constant throughout the periodic table. These experimental curves are still useful for analytic purposes, however.

The discussion of the preceding sections, particularly of the absorption

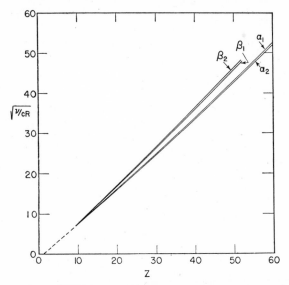

Fig. 6.4. Moseley diagram for K emission lines. Here $c = 3 \times 10^{10}$ cm/sec, $R = 1.097 \times 10^5$ cm^{-1}.

edges, has led us to conclude that in atoms the electrons exist in states of definite, fixed energy. When an external agent such as a photon ionizes the atom by removing one electron, a vacancy is left in one of the normally filled energy levels U_i of the atom. If this vacancy corresponds to an orbit in one of the inner electron shells of the atom, there will still be many electrons in the atom in higher energy levels, $U_i' > U_i$. Any one of these higher energy electrons could jump into the vacancy if there were some means of conserving energy in the process. The photon provides this possibility: the electron in jumping from the level U_i' to U_i radiates a photon of wave number $k = T_i - T_i'$. The energy carried off by this photon is just $W = h\nu = hck = U_i' - U_i$, so that energy is conserved.

Consider the K emission lines, which we may represent as diagonal lines on the term diagram 6.5. This is the same as the energy level diagram 6.3, except that we plot term values $T = -U/hc$ instead of energies directly, and we have separated horizontally the L-, M-, N-, $\cdots$ term groups for pictorial clarity. An atom in the X-ray target is ionized by collision of a high-energy incident electron. The incident electron knocks out one of the K shell electrons of the atom, which is represented on Fig. 6.5 by raising the electron from its normal position in the level at T_K to a free state above the $T = 0$ line, where the electron has positive energy and can escape from the atom. A hole now remains in the K shell, and it is rapidly filled by an electron from the L-, M-, N-,$\cdots$ shell. In jumping from its original shell to the K shell, this electron emits a photon of wave number $k = T_K - T_{L,M,N,...}$ as indicated by the

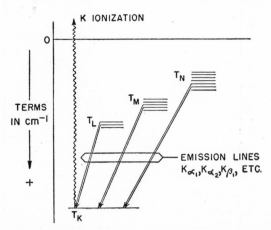

Fig. 6.5. The K lines in X-ray emission following ionization of an electron in the K shell. The wave number of the emitted photon is obtained directly from the difference of the term values as plotted: $k = T_K - T_{L,M,N}$.

diagonal lines in Fig. 6.5. In any individual atom only one of these several possible jumps will occur, after which the K shell will be filled again and no more electrons will fall into the K shell. Figure 6.5 simply shows all the various possibilities at once.

We can understand the observed features of discrete X-ray emission spectra in terms of Fig. 6.5. The K absorption edge corresponds to a photon of wave number $k = 1/\lambda = T_K$. The K emission lines, however, correspond to photons of wave numbers $k' = 1/\lambda' = (T_K - T_{L,M,N}) < T_K$. Thus $\lambda' > \lambda$, or the emission line wavelengths are always longer than that of the corresponding absorption edge, as observed. There is a multiplicity of emission lines corresponding to each absorption edge, because a vacancy in any shell or subshell can be filled by electrons from several other subshells. Each such transition produces a photon of slightly different wave number. Of course no K emission lines appear at all unless the energy of the external agent (photon or bombarding electron) exceeds $h\nu_K = hcT_K$, even though this energy exceeds that of any of the K emission photons, $h\nu'$.

The L-, M-, $\cdots$ emission lines have a similar interpretation: first ionization occurs by loss of an electron from an L-, M-, $\cdots$ subshell. An electron from a higher subshell then jumps into the resulting vacancy, emitting a photon of appropriate wave number in the process. The emission spectra of the higher shells become progressively more complicated because of the increasing number of subshells. Of course the K-, L-, M-, $\cdots$ emission spectra can follow each other progressively. The K_α emission lines result when an electron jumps from an L subshell into the K shell. This fills the vacancy in the K shell but leaves one in the L subshell, which can now be filled by an electron from an M subshell with emission of an L line. The resulting vacancy in the M subshell leads in turn to an M emission line, etc. These secondary emission lines that result from previous emissions are called "fluorescence radiation." In an X-ray tube at any energy of the bombarding electrons, the first (shortest wave length) set of emission lines follows directly from ionization, and the higher sets are partly direct radiation and partly fluorescence radiation.

Sometimes an atom converts the emission X-ray from an inner shell into a photoelectric effect on one of the outer electrons. The photon accompanying an L-K transition has sufficient energy to produce ionization by ejecting another L-, M-, N-, $\cdots$ electron. When ionization occurs in the same atom as the original X-ray emission, it is called the *Auger effect,* or occasionally by the more general term of *internal conversion.* Mathematical analysis of this process shows that we should not really consider the photon as actually emitted and then reabsorbed; rather the direct forces between the electron charges and currents themselves cause a rearrangement in which an electron drops from an L subshell into the K shell, and energy conservation is maintained by the ionization of another electron. Of course the L- and higher emission lines can show the Auger effect, as well as the K lines.

6.6. The combination principle and selection rules

It is important to emphasize the general principle from which we obtain the wave numbers or frequencies of all spectral lines. It is the *combination principle*, which states that all wave numbers of discrete spectra are representable as a difference of two terms:

$$k = T - T' \tag{6.15}$$

The complete set of different terms T is characteristic of the atom. For X-rays the terms have the form (6.11).

$$T = R(Z - \sigma)^2/n^2 \tag{6.16}$$

Physically the combination principle simply reflects the following facts, which we have discussed above: (1) the electrons in atoms exist in definite energy states; (2) when they change these states, energy conservation is accomplished by emission of a single photon; (3) the wave number and energy of the photon are related by $W = hck$. Historically, however, the combination principle was enunciated as an algebraic relationship by Ritz long before the photon concept was fully developed. The combination principle is very useful in the empirical analysis of spectra, because it reduces the large number of observed lines into fewer and simpler components, the terms T. A group of n spectral lines is reducible to as few as approximately $\sqrt{2n}$ separate terms. Term analysis by means of the combination principle is especially useful for optical spectra (Chapter 7) which are more complex than X-ray spectra.

On considering the X-ray emission lines in somewhat greater detail, we are led to postulate certain *selection rules*. These rules state that electron transitions do not occur between every possible pair of energy levels, but only between certain selected pairs.

If we now survey the X-ray emission lines, we find lines with wave numbers $k = T_{KI} - T_{LII}$, $k = T_{KI} - T_{LIII}$, but no line corresponding to $T_{KI} - T_{LI}$.

In order to state the selection rules for X-rays precisely, we must introduce the notion of *subshells*. Figure 6.5 indicates that the K-, L-, M-, $\cdots$ level groups actually contain 1, 3, 5, $\cdots$ levels of relatively narrow spacing. This structure is inferred by counting the number of distinct absorption edges in a single group. If we relate these energy levels to radii by means of (6.10), we may say that the L-, M-, $\cdots$ shells are subdivided into subshells (the K-shell has no subdivisions).

These subshells are numbered in order of increasing radius (decreasing term value) by subscripts I, II, III, $\cdots$. Thus the L-subshells are L_I, L_II, L_III ; the M-subshells are M_I, M_II, M_III, M_IV, M_V . In Fig. 6.5 the diagonal lines connect the K-level to the L_II, L_III, M_II, M_III, N_II, N_III levels. It turns out that the single K-level should be designated as K_I to be consistent with this scheme. The number of subshells in any given shell is not so large as the number of electrons in that shell. Some of the subshells, at least, must contain more than one electron. There are also K emission lines corresponding to $T_{K\mathrm{I}} - T_{M\mathrm{II}}$, $T_{K\mathrm{I}} - T_{M\mathrm{III}}$, $T_{K\mathrm{I}} - T_{N\mathrm{II}}$, $T_{K\mathrm{I}} - T_{N\mathrm{III}}$, but none representing combinations between K_I and any of the other I, IV, V, $\cdots$ levels. Extending these observations to the L series of emission lines, we find $k = T_{L\mathrm{I}} - T_{M\mathrm{II}}$, $T_{L\mathrm{I}} - T_{M\mathrm{III}}$, $T_{L\mathrm{I}} - T_{N\mathrm{II}}$, $T_{L\mathrm{I}} - T_{N\mathrm{III}}$, but no combinations of $T_{L\mathrm{I}}$ with any other term. We can generalize these facts to the rule that the X-ray terms with subscript I combine only with those of subscripts II and III to give observed X-ray emission lines. This selection rule is independent of whether the terms involved are K-, L-, M-, N-, $\cdots$.

In a similar fashion we can find selection rules for combinations involving other terms. The collected selection rules for X-ray spectra read as follows:

(1) Terms I combine only with terms II and III.

(2) Terms II combine only with I and IV.

(3) Terms III combine only with I, IV and V.   (6.17)

(4) Terms IV combine only with II, III and VI.

(5) Terms V combine only with III, VI and VII; etc.

(6) All of the foregoing rules are independent of whether the terms involved are K-, L-, M-, N-, $\cdots$.

The existence of selection rules (6.17) is an experimental fact, which any complete and satisfactory picture of the atom must explain. Again we must postpone this explanation until after a discussion of quantum mechanics.

From the empirical point of view we may say that the combination principle (6.15) needs to be supplemented by certain selection rules (6.17) that prescribe which of the many theoretically possible combinations will actually occur in practice. We will encounter a similar need for selection rules in the study of optical spectra in the next chapter.

6.7. Further questions

The preceding discussion has shown how the photon concept is instrumental in explaining all the nonclassical features of X-rays. Working out these explanations requires the introduction of some new ideas, which lead in turn to further questions. The principal innovation that we had to introduce was the notion that electrons in atoms exist in fixed, definite energy states U_i. By Eq. (6.10) these definite energy levels correspond to discrete orbits of radii r_i. This forces us to conclude that, contrary to all classical expectations, only a few definite orbits are available to the electrons in an atom; the vast majority of possible orbits are for some reason forbidden. We describe this situation by saying that the orbits are *quantized*. From (6.10) and (6.12), the radii of the quantized orbits are

$$r_i = -\tfrac{1}{2}Z_ie^2/U_i = \tfrac{1}{2}Z_ie^2/B_i = \tfrac{1}{2}n_i^2e^2/Z_ihcR \qquad (6.18)$$

Although the quantized orbits are themselves a problem, they do provide an answer for one of our previous perplexing questions, that of the stability of the dynamic model against radiation. Classically, the electrons should radiate energy continuously and spiral rapidly into the nucleus, causing complete collapse of the atom. This process requires, however, that the orbit radius be continuously variable and able to assume any arbitrary value. If the orbits are quantized, an electron cannot spiral continuously in but can only jump from one permitted orbit to the next, emitting light quanta in the process. The cascade emission of M, L, K X-rays by an electron as it jumps to the successively smaller M-, L-, and K-orbits is the quantized analogue of the classical spiraling in with continuous radiation. Under quantization, this process stops abruptly when the electron reaches the smallest of the quantized orbits. The stability of atoms against radiative collapse thus derives from the fact that the quantized orbits have a lower limit, below which there are no permitted orbits. The question of why this minimum orbit exists is just a specially important case of the general problem posed by the quantized orbits.

Another immediately apparent feature of these quantized orbits is their strictly limited capacity to hold electrons. Classically it is possible for any number of electrons to occupy orbits of the same radius. If the same were true of the quantized orbits, a normal atom would have all its electrons in the smallest orbit, namely, the K shell. The interpretation of X-ray spectra requires, however, that only about two of the atomic electrons be located in the smallest or K orbits, and that the rest be distributed among the successively larger L-, M-, N-, $\cdots$ orbits. Since even the heaviest atoms contain electrons only out to the P or Q shells, the L-, M-, $\cdots$ orbits must have capacities which, though still finite, are larger than the capacity of two for the K shell.

A shell completely filled with electrons is called "closed." Evidence that the lowest shells in an atom are normally closed comes from the X-ray absorption edges. The K absorption edge, for example, corresponds to complete ionization of the K electron ($k = T_K$); there is no absorption edge that corresponds to lifting the K electron into the L shell ($k = T_K - T_L$), the inverse process to emission of a K_α line. The absence of such an absorption edge must mean that in a normal atom the L shell is filled or closed and will not admit an additional electron. These missing absorption edges are among the most direct experimental evidence that there is a maximum capacity of electrons for each energy level. Of course there are K absorption edges where the K electron is lifted to an open shell, say N-, O-, $\cdots$, with $k = T_K - T_N$, $T_K - T_O$, $\cdots$. The terms T_N, T_O, $\cdots$ are so small relative to T_K, however, that these additional absorption edges appear merely as fine structure on the main ionization edge. Observations have been made of such fine structure, indicating that there is no hindrance of the transition if the shell to which the electron jumps is not filled.

We may characterize this limited orbit capacity by saying that the electrons obey some kind of *exclusion principle*. After a certain number of electrons assemble in an orbit, this principle acts to exclude all further electrons from entering that orbit. The net effect of the exclusion principle is to keep the electrons from associating too closely with each other. The exclusion principle provides a ready answer to a question that arose in Chapter 3 where we first considered the nuclear model of the atom. If the atom is really mostly empty space, how can the simple classical considerations of Chapters 1 and 2 be so successful, when we consider atoms to be hard spheres with fixed radii of about 1 A? According to our present discussion, atoms normally have their innermost shells filled. Only the outermost shells have any vacancies for further electrons, and the radii r_i of these outermost shells are always on the order of 1 A. Thus when two atoms approach each other, the exclusion principle prevents the electrons of the first atom from entering orbits any closer than about 1 A from the second nucleus, and vice versa. Thus the atoms do behave like hard spheres with radii about equal to r_i, the radius of the outermost, unfilled shell.

The problem of the hard-sphere behavior of "mostly empty" atoms is therefore equivalent to the more fundamental problems of why only certain quantized orbits exist in atoms, and why they fill up according to an exclusion principle.

We will need to develop many more of the details of orbit quantization before we can state the exclusion principle in precise form. We can already see, however, a connection between the periodic table of elements and the exclusion principle. The lowest values of the atomic number Z for which X-ray evidence shows the existence of the various shells are the following: $Z \approx 10, 20, 40, 50, 90$, for L-, M-, N-, O-, P-shells, respectively. This regular progression strongly suggests that the periodic table is determined by the filling up of successive atomic shells in accordance with the exclusion principle. We consider this point in more detail in Chapter 12.

SUMMARY

The concept of the photon or light quantum is necessary for the interpretation of "nonclassical" X-ray phenomena. Here "classical" phenomena are those we can explain by regarding X-rays as transverse light waves, described by Maxwell's equations. The nonclassical phenomena are the short wavelength limit of the continuous emission spectrum, the ionizing properties of X-rays, the absorption edges, and the discrete emission spectra.

The photon first appeared in Planck's successful derivation of a black body radiation formula: it behaves like an indivisible particle. Its relation to the corresponding wave picture is

$$k = 1/\lambda = \nu/c = W/hc = 8066 \text{ cm}^{-1} \text{ ev}^{-1} W$$

where k is the *wave number* of the light in the wave picture and W is the energy of the corresponding photon. Here $h = 6.625 \times 10^{-27}$ erg-sec is a universal constant of nature called Planck's constant. All radiative processes of atoms involve emission and absorption of single photons.

The necessity of postulating the photon does not mean that the wave picture of X-rays is incorrect. Both wave and particle pictures are valid aspects of the same entity and must be used to complement rather than contradict each other. Many phenomena can be interpreted on either basis, but some phenomena specifically require one or the other.

The short wavelength limit of the continuous X-ray spectrum is explained by noting that an electron of energy eV striking the target in an X-ray tube can radiate a photon of maximum wave number $k = eV/hc$.

The ionization of atoms by X-rays is effected when an electron absorbs a single photon of energy $W = h\nu$, where W exceeds the *binding energy* B_i of the electron in the atom. The photon is indivisible in such an absorption process, so that light of frequency ν can give energy to the atomic electrons only in units of $W = h\nu$. For X-rays this energy is on the order of 10^4 ev, which is sufficient to ionize even the inner electrons of many atoms.

The X-rays absorption edges correspond to this ionization process. Their sharp values indicate that electrons exist in atoms at definite, fixed energy levels, $U_i = -B_i$. The corresponding radii of the electron orbits are $r_i = \frac{1}{2}Z_i e^2/B_i$. Using the observed Moseley law for the frequencies ν_i of the absorption edges, one finds $r_i = \frac{1}{2}(e^2/hcR)n_i^2/Z_i$, where $R = 1.097 \times 10^5$ cm^{-1} is the Rydberg constant. Here $n_i = 1, 2,$

3, $\cdots$ for the K-, L-, M-, $\cdots$ *shells*, with no orbits in the relatively wide intervening spaces. We say that the orbits are *quantized*.

The discrete emission spectra are the photons radiated when an electron jumps from one shell to another lower shell, such as an L-K transition. These transitions occur only after some external agent like a photon or bombarding electron beam has knocked an electron out of the lower shell (K shell for an L-K emission line), leaving a vacancy in the shell.

According to the *combination principle*, the wave numbers of all emission lines are representable as the combination of two *term values*, $k = T - T'$. Here $T = B/hc = -U/hc$, $T' = B'/hc = -U'/hc$ are the term values in cm^{-1} corresponding to the negative energy levels U, U'. Comparison of this principle with observed spectra shows that there are *selection rules* which limit the pairs of terms that may combine to give an observed emission line. These selection rules can be explained only on the basis of a full understanding of the quantization of electron orbits in atoms.

The explanation of nonclassical X-ray phenomena in terms of the photon leads to several new questions about atomic structure. The allowed electron orbits appear to be definitely quantized, which solves the problem of radiative stability by introducing a smallest orbit from which no transition to a lower energy (smaller) orbit is possible. On the other hand, some principle must be found that will lead to orbit quantization. There appears in addition to be some sort of unexplained *exclusion principle* operating on the electrons, so that only a limited number can occupy any particular orbit or shell. This exclusion principle is a determining factor in the structure of the periodic table.

REFERENCES

A. H. Compton and S. K. Allison, *X-rays in Theory and Experiment*, Van Nostrand, New York (1935).

W. Duane and F. L. Hunt, *Phys. Rev.*, **6,** 166, (1915).

J. W. M. DuMond and E. R. Cohen, *Revs. Modern Phys.* **25,** 691 (1953).

M. Planck, *Theorie der Wärmestrahlung*, Barth, Leipzig (1913).

D. Siegbahn, *The Spectroscopy of X-rays*, Oxford, London (1925).

A. Sommerfeld, *Atomic Structure and Spectral Lines*, Methuen, London (1923).

H. E. White, *Introduction to Atomic Spectra*, McGraw-Hill, New York (1934).

ILLUSTRATIVE PROBLEMS

1. What minimum potential must be applied to an X-ray tube to obtain Bragg reflection at 90° to the incident beam, if the beam is incident parallel to the cube axis of a crystal of NaCl?

Solution. The lattice spacing of NaCl is $d_0 = 2.81$ A, and the 90° reflection described will involve the (110) planes, with a spacing of $d = d_0/\sqrt{2} = 2.0$ A. The Bragg condition is $n\lambda = 2\,d\sin\theta$, where here $\theta = 45°$. The maximum λ is given by $n = 1$, or $\lambda = 2\,d\sin\theta = 2.81$ A. This is the longest wavelength for which the specified reflection can occur; it will be the short wavelength limit of the continuous spectrum for the minimum voltage V on the X-ray tube. Using (6.7) and (6.8), we have V (kilovolt) $= 12.4/2.81 = 4.41$ kv.

2. The wavelengths in X units (10^{-11} cm) of the K absorption limit and the three L absorption limits of four elements are

	K	L_{III}	L_{II}	L_{I}
$_{47}$Ag	485.2	3684.4	3504.7	3260.5
$_{55}$Cs	344.5	2467.8	2307.3	2160.5
$_{78}$Pt	158.2	1070.9	952.1	892.1
$_{82}$Pb	141.0	950.0	813.6	780.6

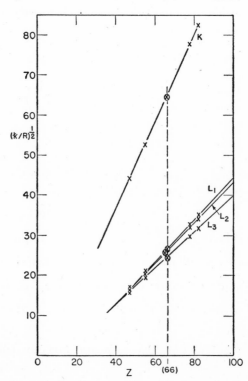

Fig. 6.6. Moseley diagram of K and L absorption limits.

The subscripts of the elements are their atomic numbers Z.
Construct a Moseley diagram using $\sqrt{k/R}$ for the four limits and identify the element with the following absorption limits in X.U.:

K	L_{III}	L_{II}	L_I
229.4	1587.0	1441.4	1364.8

Solution. The Moseley diagram is shown in Fig. 6.6. The unknown element is dysprosium ($Z = 66$).

PROBLEMS

1. Using the values $h = 6.625 \times 10^{-27}$ erg sec, $e = 1.602 \times 10^{-19}$ clb, $c = 2.998 \times 10^{10}$ cm/sec, construct a table of conversion factors, to four significant figures, for the following computations in cgs units:

(a) Given the energy E of an electron in ergs, find

    (1) the frequency of the radiation emitted when the energy E is transformed into radiation;

    (2) the wave number in cm^{-1} of this light;

    (3) the wavelength in vacuum of this light.

(b) Given the energy V of an electron in electron volts, find 1, 2, 3 as in (a).

(c) List the conversion factors for the reverse transformations; i.e., find E and V when frequency, wave number, or wavelength are given.

2. Derive a formula for the minimum potential in kilovolts to be applied to an X-ray tube in order to produce radiation for Bragg reflection of jth order on a set of lattice planes of d Angstroms spacing. Apply the equation for the first three diffraction orders of calcite with a spacing of 3.03 A.

3. From measurements of the wavelengths of K, L, M absorption limits of various elements one finds the following abbreviated table of $(k/R)^{1/2}$ for the elements of order number Z.

	Z	K	L_1	L_2	L_3	M_1	M_2	M_3	M_4	M_5
Ca	20	17.245								
Zn	30	26.677								
Zr	40	36.410	13.70	13.03	12.80					
Sn	50	46.363	18.14	17.51	17.01					
Nd	60	56.587	22.94	22.26	21.39					
Yb	70	67.232	27.83	27.12	25.67					
Hg	80	78.22	33.05	32.35	30.07			14.49	13.32	13.07
Th	90	89.92	38.82	38.08	34.64	19.53	18.86	17.24	16.02	15.65

(a) Construct a Moseley diagram for the K and L limits, plotting $(k/R)^{1/2}$ versus Z.

(b) When a certain white powder is placed in front of the photographic film of an X-ray spectrograph, absorption limits are observed at the following wavelengths (one X unit $= 10^{-11}$ cm)

4483.8 X.U.,   344.04 X.U.,   2160 X.U.,   2307 X.U.,   2467 X.U.

Identify the chemical composition of the powder.

4. What voltages must be applied to the X-ray tube with suitable anticathodes to excite the K emission lines of the five elements in illustrative problem 2? The strongest lines of this spectrum are called K_{α_1} and K_{α_2} and correspond to transitions from L_{III} and L_{II}, respectively, to the K level. Compute the wavelengths of these lines from the data in illustrative problem 2 and compare the result with the following experimental data.

	K_{α_1}	K_{α_2}
Ag	558 X.U.	563 X.U.
Cs	400	404
Pt	182	190
Pb	165	170
Dy	269	274

5. The k/R values of some of the strongest K series emission X-ray lines of various elements are as follows:

Ca	Zn	Zr	Sn	Nd	Yb	Th
271.62	634.59	1155.68	1844	2712	3781	6661
271.88	636.29	1161.89	1861	2751	3856	6888
272.85	637.79	1300.28	2095	3104	4356	7795
273.46	696.32	1301.29	2098	3113	4373	8036
273.65		1323.56	2144	3189	4484	

(a) Using the data of problem 3, determine the L and M levels (i.e., whether L_1, L_2, L_3, M_1, etc.) from which the electron must jump into the K level to give the observed lines of Th and of Sn. Verify for the other elements that it is always the same L level which does not combine with K.

(b) At what wavelengths should one expect to find the L absorption edges of calcium? Why are they not listed in the table of problem 3?

6. The following is a complete list of the L emission series of Th, including both strong and weak lines (forbidden by selection rules):

$(k/R) =$

1068.59	1353.18	1429.67	1193.45	1398.16	1443.86	958.38
818.93	1102.62	1179.22	943.49	955.16	1147.78	1155.57
1150.71	1250.72	1262.46	844.93	903.11	1175.47	1157.14
1209.80	1422.11	1437.05	1490.93	1495.03	1507.15	1458.61

Which ones of these lines can be accounted for as combinations between some L and some M level, using the data of problem 3?

7. Make a rough estimate of the number of electrons N_L and N_M required to fill the L- and M-shells. When all the absorption edges of a shell are observed, we can assume that shell to be filled. Calculate the screening constant σ from the L_1 and M_1 values in problem 3; take σ to equal the number of electrons in the shell under consideration plus all inner shells. These values of N_L and N_M will be a little too large because the electrons do not really occupy circular orbits, and there is additional screening by electrons that are nominally outside the shell but actually penetrate it to some extent. The values of N_L and N_M obtained here are of the correct order of magnitude, however.

Chapter 7

OPTICAL SPECTRA

The X-ray spectra of the previous chapter correspond to transitions of the inner atomic electrons. We expect that similar laws apply to the outermost electrons. The term values and wave numbers associated with the outer electrons will be on the order of $T_i = -U_i/hc = \frac{1}{2}Z_i e^2/r_i hc$, where $Z_i \approx 1$ because the outermost electron sees the nuclear charge Z as screened by $Z - 1$ other electrons. If we take the outer radius as $r_i = 2 \times 10^{-8}$ cm, then $T_i \approx 3 \times 10^4$ cm^{-1}. This corresponds to a wavelength of $1/T_i \approx 3300$ A, which is in the ultraviolet range. Certain transitions will involve energies less than hcT_i, and the photons will have longer wavelengths, corresponding to the visible region. Thus the radiation of visible light by any incandescent substance comes from the outermost electron or electrons. These are accordingly called the *optical* electrons.

The frequency distribution of radiation produced by the optical electrons is the *optical spectrum*. Because this light is in the visible or near-visible region, measurements of high precision and resolution are easier to achieve than with X-rays. The optical spectra themselves display a more complicated structure than the X-ray spectra. There is thus an abundance of experimental data on optical spectra, analysis of which should lead to further detailed understanding of how electrons behave in atoms. We expect the same principles to hold for optical as for X-ray spectra and the same questions to arise, such as orbit quantization and selection rules. Further nonclassical features may be revealed by the greater detail of the optical spectra.

In this chapter we discuss some empirical details of optical spectra. Many of the topics have exact analogies in X-ray spectra: the optical photoelectric effect is equivalent to X-ray ionization, the optical absorption and emission spectra resemble to some extent the X-ray absorption edges and the discrete (not the continuous) X-ray emission spectra.

There are some experimental precautions to observe if we want to study the outermost electron orbits of an atom. These orbits are subject to considerable distortion by the presence of neighboring atoms, so that we must study the spectra of monatomic gases at relatively low pressure. This difficulty is not present with X-ray spectra, because the inner electron orbits remain independent of the effects of chemical combination. Chemical effects involve only the outer electrons, as we have seen in Chapter 2, where the chemical measurements of atomic size always give values characteristic of the outermost orbits. Since optical spectra involve these same outer orbits, they are extremely sensitive to chemical effects. For example, molecules show characteristic optical spectra that extend from the ultraviolet into the far infrared. These spectra appear as "bands" of varying intensity that can be resolved into a large number of individual lines. In order to avoid confusion between molecular and atomic spectral lines, we must use gases that are normally monatomic or that can be made so. Fortunately, many molecules will dissociate into atoms at the very high effective temperatures produced in a spark discharge. Even under these conditions we do not obtain "pure" atomic spectra, for there is a considerable admixture of ionized atoms; positive ions have their own characteristic spectra, which differ from those of neutral atoms. The ionic spectra are similar in character to those of neutral atoms, however, and provide additional experimental data for analysis along with optical spectra (section 7.5).

If simple diatomic molecules do not make suitable sources for optical spectra, then we must expect liquids and solids to be even less suitable. Here an individual atom is in contact with something on the order of a dozen neighboring atoms. In solids the outermost electrons can become detached from the individual atoms and wander more or less freely throughout the entire volume of the solid. These freely wandering electrons can transport an electric current easily, so the solid is known as a *conductor*. Most metals have this property. An electric insulator or dielectric, on the other hand, is a solid in which the electrons remain more or less tightly bound to individual atoms. Even in these solids we do not expect the optical radiation to resemble that of free atoms.

In accordance with these arguments the following sections discuss phenomena related to individual atoms. The photoelectric effect is an exception because it is experimentally feasible only with solids.

7.1. The photoelectric effect

If the outermost electron in a neutral atom has a term value T_i, it can escape from the atom by absorption of any photon of wave number $k > T_i$. The example in the introductory paragraph suggests that ultraviolet light should be able to liberate electrons from many substances. This is indeed the case. The earliest observers recorded the emitted electrons directly instead of the residual ionized atoms—hence the name *photoelectric effect*. These measurements generally employ metal plates as sources of photoelectrons under irradiation with ultraviolet light. Since metals are conductors, the energy required for emission of an electron is characteristic of the conduction electrons in the metal as a whole, rather than of the individual atoms of the metal. The liberation of conduction electrons depends mainly on conditions at the surface of the metal. The minimum energy necessary to liberate an electron from a metal surface is called its *work function* $\varphi = hcT/e$, where φ has the dimensions of an electric potential and is generally on the order of a few volts. Some typical values of φ appear in Table 2.2, and the accompanying text contains some further discussion of the work function concept.

Although we cannot use the photoelectric effect on metal surfaces to learn about the outer electron orbits of free atoms, the observations do emphasize strongly the necessity of describing this process in terms of photons rather than continuous electromagnetic waves. The experiments of Millikan with visible light on the alkali metals Li, Na, and K provide examples of this necessity. In these experiments the illuminated plate is in a vacuum and is opposite to a collecting electrode. An electrometer measures the electron current to the collector when the metal plate is illuminated. A retarding potential V is applied between the plate and the collector, which means that the measured current comes only from electrons that leave the illuminated plate with kinetic energies $\frac{1}{2}mv^2$ exceeding eV. The collector current varies with the retarding voltage V; and if the illuminating light is monochromatic of wave number k, the current falls to zero at a well-defined "cutoff" potential $V(k)$ that depends on the wave number k.

A simple scheme for determining the cutoff potential is indicated in Fig. 7.1. The collecting electrode and photoelectric plate are connected to an electrometer. As the current flows, it charges the electrometer until the system reaches the cutoff potential $V(k)$. Then the current ceases and $V(k)$ registers directly on the electrometer.

The measurements show that the cutoff potential for any particular metal varies with the wave number of the light according to

$$V(k) = C(k - k_0) = Ck - \varphi$$
$$C = 12.4 \text{ kv - A} = hc/e$$

(7.1)

The constant C in (7.1) is the same as that of Eq. (6.5) for the short wavelength limit of the continuous X-ray or *Bremsstrahlung* spectrum; and φ is the work function of the metal surface. Equation (7.1) tells us that for each surface there is a characteristic wave number $k_0 = e\varphi/hc$, such that light of wave number less than k_0 does not produce photoelectrons. This is in accord with all observations.

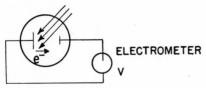

Fig. 7.1. Measurement of photoelectric stopping potential.

Equation (7.1) is immediately interpretable in terms of photon absorption, which turns (7.1) into a simple equation of energy conservation upon multiplication by the electron charge e. The term $eV(k) = \frac{1}{2}mv^2$ is the total kinetic energy with which an electron emerges from the surface. The term $eCk = hck = W$ is the energy of a single incident photon of wave number k. And $e\varphi = B$ is the binding energy of the electron in the surface. Thus (7.1) reads

$$\frac{1}{2}mv^2 = W - B \tag{7.1a}$$

which is just the energy conservation equation for complete absorption of a single photon by a bound electron, resulting in ejection of the electron.

In contrast to the success of the photon concept, the wave theory of light is helpless to explain the empirical facts of the optical photoelectric effect. It cannot interpret the variation of the effect with wave number of the incident light and in particular fails to explain why the emission should cease entirely for $k < k_0$. Also, an increase in light intensity means in the wave picture an increase in amplitude E_0 of the electric vector of the light wave. This correspondingly increases the amplitude of oscillation of an absorbing electron or hence the energy with which the electron is finally ejected. The observations show, however, that $\frac{1}{2}mv^2$ is independent of intensity and dependent only on frequency ν of the incident light—both features in accord with the photon interpretation, which regards increase in intensity simply as an increase in the density of photons of energy $h\nu$.

The optical photoelectric effect thus provides the most direct and palpable evidence for the existence of the photon.

7.2. Ionization potentials

Photoionization of an isolated, neutral atom of monatomic gas can proceed by removal of any one of its electrons. Ionization by X-rays generally involves one of the inner electrons, while ionization by visible and ultraviolet light can affect only the outermost electrons. Measurement of optical photoionization would give the binding energy B_i or corresponding term value $T_i = B_i/hc$ of the outermost electron. We frequently express those quantities in terms of the equivalent *ionization potential*

$$V_i = B_i/e = hcT_i/e = (12.4 \text{ kv-A})T_i \tag{7.2}$$

measurement of V_i will give us some quantitative information about the outer electron orbits in atoms, just as the X-ray measurements (6.11) gave information about the inner orbits.

Unfortunately, the photoelectric effect in solids is not a suitable means for determining V_i, as discussed above. To obtain V_i for a "normal" atom, we could in principle perform a photoelectric experiment on a gas of free, monatomic molecules. In practice this involves some complications because the source of photoelectrons no longer forms a natural electrode. Another experimental technique for measuring V_i is to induce ionization of gaseous atoms by electron bombardment. If an electron impinges on an atom with a kinetic energy that equals or exceeds eV_i, it can transfer this energy to the optical electron, which then escapes from the atom. Since the incident electron loses an appreciable part of its energy, the electron impact is called *inelastic*. If the incident electron energy is too small to effect any internal changes in the atom, all collisions will be *elastic* (conserving kinetic energy).

A schematic diagram of the procedure for measuring V_i by inelastic collisions is shown in Fig. 7.2. The gas to be measured fills at a pressure of about 10 cm of mercury a tube containing a filament, grid, and plate. A variable potential V maintained between the filament and the grid accelerates electrons emitted by the filament toward the grid. The net potential acting on the electrons is $V' = V - \Delta\varphi$, where $\Delta\varphi$ is the contact potential difference between the filament and grid. The plate is maintained slightly negative with respect to the filament and hence collects no electrons. When $V' < V_i$, no electron ever has enough energy to ionize a gas atom by collision, and no current flows in the plate circuit. As we increase V, some of the electrons on nearing the grid have enough energy to ionize gas atoms. The positive ions travel to the plate and cause a current in the plate circuit. The value of V at which the plate current starts to increase is then $V = V_i + \Delta\varphi$. Independent knowledge of $\Delta\varphi$ permits us to determine V_i.

Atoms may show several ionization potentials in such an experiment. The second, third, ... potentials correspond to removal of a second, third, ... electron, forming more highly positive ions. The first or normal ionization potential varies regularly with position of the atom in the periodic table. It is lowest for the alkali metals, ranging around 4 to 6 volts. It increases with elements in successive columns of the periodic table and has the largest value for the inert gases. Helium with $V_i = 24.6$ volts has the highest ionization potential.

This striking behavior of the ionization potential, along with many other indications, suggests that the inert gases correspond to the closing of electron shells of the type discussed under X-ray

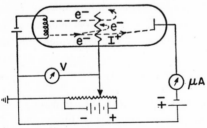

Fig. 7.2. Measurement of ionization potential by electron bombardment.

spectra. It is therefore natural to consider the alkali metals as having one additional electron outside such a closed shell. This outer electron is the *optical electron*, and the remaining $(Z - 1)$ electrons form the *core*, which generally remains undisturbed by visible and ultraviolet light. In corresponding fashion the alkaline earths have two optical electrons outside the core, and atoms in the following rows of Fig. 1.1 have even more optical electrons. Clearly the simplest cases to consider are the alkali metals (including hydrogen) and we shall therefore draw most of our detailed examples from this group.

The ionization potentials of the alkali metals and hydrogen are shown in Table 7.1. The third column of this table lists the orbit radius of the optical electron as calculated from Eq. (6.10) with $Z_i = 1$, since the core presumably shields $(Z - 1)$ of the Z units of positive charge on the nucleus. Note that except for hydrogen there is relatively little increase in atomic size as we go from the lightest to the heaviest elements in the series. These outer orbit radii are the same order of magnitude as the atomic sizes deduced in Chapter 2.

TABLE 7.1.

IONIZATION POTENTIALS AND ORBIT RADII OF OPTICAL ELECTRONS

Element	H	Li	Na	K	Rb	Cs
V_i (volts)	13.6	5.39	5.14	4.34	4.18	3.89
r_i (A)	0.53	1.34	1.41	1.67	1.73	1.86

TABLE 7.2.

IONIZATION POTENTIALS AND RADII OF NOBLE GAS ATOMS

Element	He	Ne	A	Kr	Xe
V_i (volts)	24.6	21.6	15.8	14.0	12.1
r_i (A)	0.29	0.33	0.46	0.51	0.59

It is of interest to compare the values of Table 7.1 with those for the noble gases, given in Table 7.2. The "radii" of the noble gas atoms average only about $\frac{1}{4}$ those of the immediately following alkali atoms in the periodic table. The optical electron in an alkali metal is hence quite well separated from its core and will presumably be alone responsible for ordinary optical phenomena. One check on this is provided by considering the second ionization potentials of the alkali metals. For Li, Na, K, and Rb they are respectively 75.6, 47.2, 31.8, and 27.5 ev. These ionization energies are very much larger than the energies of order 4 ev or less generally involved in optical transitions. This is another way of seeing that the core is unlikely to take part in the lowest energy optical phenomena: note that it is somewhat more unlikely for the light alkali atoms than for the heavier ones, where the second ionization potential becomes smaller. Further evidence for the presence of a single optical electron in neutral alkali atoms appears in section 7.5.

7.3. Critical potentials

Measurement of the ionization potentials in Table 7.1 determines the so-called *normal* energy level $U_i = -hcT_i = -eV_i$ in which the optical electron resides when the atom is undisturbed. Electron bombardment of gases can be made to yield information about other optical energy levels besides the normal one, as in the experiment of Franck and Hertz. In this experiment we observe directly the energy loss of electrons that bombard monatomic gas atoms, instead of looking for the positive ions produced. The experimental arrangement is the same as that shown in Fig. 7.2, except that the plate is connected over a small retarding potential to the grid instead of to the filament. The plate current then consists of electrons. The measurements record the variation of plate current versus accelerating grid voltage. At small voltages the current increases rapidly with voltage up to a certain critical voltage at which the current abruptly decreases. As the grid potential continues to increase, the plate current goes through a broad minimum and then rises to a second sharp peak at a second critical voltage. The curve of plate current against accelerating voltage has the form shown in Fig. 7.3. Further peaks also exist at higher voltages.

To interpret these peaks, it is helpful to keep in mind the physical processes discussed in the previous section on ionization potentials. The essential feature is that at sufficiently high accelerating voltages, an electron gains enough energy to engage in an inelastic collision with a gas atom. This collision leaves the electron with little or no energy, and in the discussion of the previous section the atom was ionized as a result. In the Franck-Hertz experiment we measure the electrons directly and would expect the electron current to fall off sharply when the electrons had just enough energy to make inelastic collisions with the gas atoms. Thus we might expect that the critical voltages observed equal V_i, $2V_i$, $3V_i$, $\cdots$, corresponding to the successive ionization of 1, 2, 3, $\cdots$ gas atoms by an electron as it accelerates towards the grid. Actually, the observed critical voltages have the values $(V_c - \Delta\varphi)$, $(2V_c - \Delta\varphi)$, $(3V_c - \Delta\varphi)$ $\cdots$ where $\Delta\varphi$ is a contact potential between the filament and grid. Then V_c represents the potential characteristic of the gas atoms. The remarkable feature of this measurement is that V_c is considerably smaller than V_i for all atoms studied!

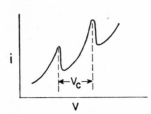

Fig. 7.3. Plate current in Franck-Hertz measurement of critical potential.

There is only one simple quantum mechanical explanation for this fact: there must be another energy level in the gas atom for the optical electron besides the normal level $-U_i$. This second energy level is somewhat higher than the normal level, and we call its energy $-U_2$, where $U_2 < U_i$. In accordance with the notion of quantized orbits that we found necessary in the previous chapter, we expect no orbits or energy levels to be permitted between $-U_i$ and $-U_2$. When the bombarding electrons attain an energy $E = -U_2 - (-U_i) = U_i - U_2$, they can undergo inelastic collisions in which the optical electron jumps to this upper state. The accelerating potential at which this first occurs is

$$V_c = \frac{E}{e} = \frac{U_i - U_2}{e} = \frac{hc}{e}(T_i - T_2) \tag{7.3}$$

where we have written $T_2 = -U_2/hc$ as the term value in cm^{-1} corresponding to the second level. The successive, evenly spaced current peaks in Fig. 7.3 therefore correspond to inelastic collisions of the bombarding electrons that leave 1, 2, 3, $\cdots$ gas atoms in this second level.

It is after all not surprising to find other energy levels besides the normal level for the optical electron. Consideration of X-rays in the last chapter showed us the existence in the atom of a number of different energy levels and corresponding quantized orbits. An exclusion principle was also necessary to limit the number of electrons that could occupy one single orbit. The optical electron normally occupies the lowest orbit in the atom that is not already filled, but we must expect that there will be other, higher energy levels that are not normally occupied. The optical electron can jump to these levels whenever it acquires the necessary energy.

These higher levels are called the *excited* states of the optical electron, as opposed to its normal or *ground* state. The excited level $-U_2$ is that of an optical electron which is still bound to the atom, because the energy eV_c necessary to reach $-U_2$ is considerably less than the energy eV_i necessary to liberate the electron from the atom. For example, in mercury $V_c = 4.89$ volts, $V_i = 10.43$ volts. Of course the optical electron does not remain long in the state $-U_2$ but rapidly returns to its normal state by emitting a photon of wave number $1/\lambda = k = T_i - T_2$. The experiments do indeed show that inelastic collisions are accompanied by the emission of radiation of this sharply defined wave number, which is called the *resonance* radiation. In the case of mercury it has a wavelength of 2537 A.

The Franck-Hertz experiment is another in the long list of atomic phenomena that require quantum concepts for their interpretation. Classically, the bombarding electrons can make inelastic collisions with the gas atoms at any energy, no matter how low. We can obtain a threshold eV_c for inelastic collisions only by postulating quantized orbits in the atom.

7.4. Optical absorption spectra

Electron bombardment mainly shows the existence of the first excited level $-U_2$. Measurement of the optical absorption spectrum reveals the presence of many higher excited (though still bound) levels. The "optical spectrum" covers the wavelength range from about 2000 A to about 10,000 A. Suppose that we have a source of radiation like an underwater spark gap with a spectrum that covers continuously the optical range. We analyze this radiation with a spectrograph, which spreads the spectrum out along a photographic plate. We now pass the radiation through a tube containing monatomic gas and examine the resulting spectrum in a spectrograph. At certain sharp, discrete frequencies ν_n the gas has absorbed the incident radiation, producing dark (unexposed) lines in the picture. The simplest type of absorption spectrum is that for an alkali atom, as shown in Fig. 7.4. The absorption lines plotted on a frequency scale start with some lowest frequency ν_2 and crowd closer and closer together at higher frequencies. These lines form a *series*, which converges on the *series limit*, ν_i. At frequencies above ν_i the sharp, discrete lines disappear, and absorption can occur over a continuous range of frequencies. For this reason it is customary to classify the regions below and above the series limit as the discrete and continuous absorption spectra, respectively. We shall concentrate exclusively on the discrete spectrum.

The absorption spectra find a ready interpretation on the quantum hypothesis. The optical electron exists in a normal state with term value $T_i = -U_i/hc$. Above this level exist many other unoccupied levels with term values T_2, T_3, $\cdots$, T_n, $\cdots$ and corresponding energies $-U_2$, $-U_3$, $\cdots$, $-U_n$, $\cdots$. The electron can jump from the normal to the nth excited state by absorbing a single photon of wave number

$$k_n = T_i - T_n = \nu_n/c \qquad (7.4)$$

where ν_n is the corresponding photon frequency. These frequencies ν_n appear in the absorption spectrum; their presence is direct evidence for

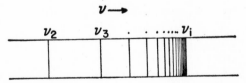

Fig. 7.4. Absorption spectrum of an alkali gas.

the existence of the energy levels $-U_n$ in the atom. Equation (7.4) is an example of the Ritz combination principle discussed in section 6.6, whereby all the lines of a spectral series can be represented as the differences of a set of term values.

The term values T_n deduced from the known ionization potential V_i and the measured absorption frequencies ν_n comprise a term level diagram, as shown in Fig. 7.5. The observed absorption frequencies correspond to the diagonal lines, which represent electron jumps from the normal state T_i to the excited states T_n. The absorption frequency that corresponds to the threshold for photoionization of the atom is

$$\nu_i = cT_i = eV_i/h \tag{7.5}$$

The ν_i as computed from (7.5) just equals the measured series limit, shown as ν_i in Fig. 7.4. The region $\nu > \nu_i$ corresponds to photoionization of the atom in which the liberated electron carries away the excess energy $\Delta E = (h\nu - h\nu_i)$ as kinetic energy. The orbits of the free electron are not quantized, so that ΔE may assume any value; hence the continuous nature of the absorption spectrum for $\nu > \nu_i$. On the other hand, absorption of any photon with $\nu < \nu_i$ leaves the electron still in a bound orbit in the atom. Bound orbits are always quantized, so the absorption spectrum for $\nu < \nu_i$ is discrete. One thing about the bound levels that we might not have guessed *a priori* but is evident from the absorption spectrum is that the discrete levels crowd closer and closer together as their term values T approach zero.

The optical absorption spectrum corroborates the electron bombardment experiments in that both lead to the same values of the ionization potential and of T_2 for the first excited level. The absorption spectrum yields a great deal of additional information about higher excited levels. We should like to express these data in systematic form. Figures 7.4 and 7.5 indicate that the term values T_n decrease rapidly with increasing order number n. The difference between successive term values

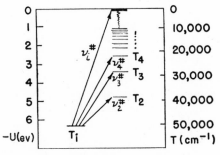

Fig. 7.5. Term or energy level diagram for optical absorption lines.
(The symbol v^{*} is used in place of k.)

decreases even more rapidly. In the case of an alkali spectrum with over 60 observed lines, we find that for large n,

$$T_{n-1} - T_n \approx T_n - T_{n+1} \approx 2R/n^3 \qquad (7.6)$$

where R is again Rydberg's constant, 1.097×10^5 cm^{-1}. Here n is the integer denoting the order of the term, counting in sequence from $n = 2$ for the first excited state. This integer is the *total quantum number* and is in some way related to the quantization of the corresponding orbits. Equation (7.6) suggests that the individual term values are of the form $T_n = R/n^2$, but this would imply that the optical absorption spectra for all alkali atoms are identical. This equality exists for large n values but not for small n, and we allow for this deviation by writing

$$T_n = R/(n - \Delta_n)^2 = R/(n')^2 \qquad (7.7)$$

The nonintegral quantity Δ_n is the *quantum defect*: it is largest in magnitude for lowest n, and $\Delta_n \to 0$ as $n \to \infty$. The quantum number n is still an integer, although the *effective quantum number* n' is not and becomes so only for large n.

To understand the origin of the quantum defect, consider the radii of the electron orbits corresponding to the term values T_n. The optical electron is in the electric field of a net charge of $+e$ from the nucleus plus core of inner electrons; the orbit radius corresponding to a term value T_n is

$$r_n = \frac{e^2}{2hcT_n} = \frac{e^2}{2hcR} (n')^2 = 0.53(n')^2 A \qquad (7.8)$$

For values of n' greater than about 3, r_n is considerably larger than the normal atomic radius, so that the orbit must lie entirely outside the core of inner electrons. For small values of n', however, r_n is not necessarily larger than the core itself—and it is just for these cases that the quantum defect is large. We are therefore led to associate the quantum defect with partial penetration of the electron core by the orbit of the optical electron.

We may compare (7.7) with the corresponding expression (6.16) for the term values of the inner electrons. These formulas have two striking features in common: the appearance of a universal constant R, which has no apparent connection with other physical constants of the electron, such as its charge and mass; the appearance of successive integers or quantum numbers in the denominator. The minor differences in form of (7.7) and (6.16) are all superficial and largely a matter of convention. In the X-ray formula (6.16) the quantities n are always integers, and any deviations are accounted for by varying the screening constant σ. The appearance of the factor $(Z - \sigma)^2$ simply reflects the fact that the inner electrons are not so completely screened from the nucleus as is the optical electron. In the optical formula (7.7) on the other hand, $(Z - \sigma)$ is conventionally taken to be exactly unity; for the penetrating orbits where this assumption fails, we adjust the values of T_n by inserting $n' = n - \Delta_n$ in place of n instead of trying to alter $(Z - \sigma)$, which does not appear explicitly. There is one other difference that is also a matter of convention: the inner K-, L-, M-, . . . shells have quantum numbers $n = 1, 2, 3, \cdots$ in Eq. (6.16). If the highest filled shell in the core has quantum number n_0, one can argue that the optical levels should start with $n_0 + 1$ for T_i, $n_0 + 2$ for T_2, etc. Many texts actually follow this system; but for purposes of comparing optical spectra of the alkali with each other and with hydrogen, it is convenient to adopt another point of view, already assumed above. We take the orbits of the optical electron to be those existing in the Coulomb field of a charge $+e$ and do not inquire into the exact structure of the source of this field. It is then logical to begin numbering the orbits with $n = 1$ for the normal state, $n = 2$ for the excited states.

7.5. *Optical emission spectra*

When the optical electron of an alkali atom jumps to an excited state, it does not remain there but jumps down into a lower state by emitting a photon of appropriate frequency. It very rapidly (in something like 10^{-8} sec!) returns to its ground state by one or more of these jumps in succession. The emission spectrum thus appears in a spectrograph as one or more series of sharp lines at discrete frequencies. The most immediately striking feature of even the most simple emission spectrum is its complexity. From the analysis of this complexity has come the detailed, quantitative information that gave rise to quantum mechanics and all its modern ramifications. Optical emission spectra are the experimental core of atomic physics.

One source of complexity in emission spectra is the fact that atoms can be forced to radiate by several different means. The radiating substance may be flame heated, placed on one of the carbons in an arc light, or placed on the electrodes of a spark gap. Different kinds of excitation usually produce different spectra from the same substance. The reason for this variation is evident. In flames and arcs the excitation of the optical electron comes from thermal impacts. The energies involved are usually too small to produce ionization, so that the spectrum is that of the neutral atom. In spark discharges the atom can become singly, doubly, or more highly ionized as the voltage of the spark is increased. For example, the arc spectrum of Be is that of the neutral Be atom, while the spark spectrum will contain in addition the lines of Be^+ and Be^{++}.

Comparative studies of the various spectra of many atoms and ions reveal a number of regularities known as the laws of *isoelectronic sequence*. We can summarize them as follows:

(1) Atoms in the same row of the periodic table, Fig. 1.1, like the alkalis, or the alkaline earths, or the halogens, have analogous spectra. By this we mean that the general appearance and properties of the lines, as well as their distribution in the spectrum, are similar for all atoms in the sequence. The lines appear in the same frequency range but do not have exactly the same frequencies for each spectrum.

(2) The spectrum of a singly charged positive ion has an analogous structure to that of the preceding neutral atom in the periodic table. Thus the spectrum of Mg^+ resembles that of Na. The principal difference is that the ionic spectrum appears at much higher frequencies than that of the neutral atom. More generally, the spectrum of a neutral atom with atomic number Z is similar to that of an ion of valence z and atomic number $(Z + z)$. The spectrum is shifted to higher frequencies for higher valences, the frequencies being proportional to $(z + 1)^2$. For example, corresponding lines of Na, Mg^+, and Al^{++} have an approximate frequency ratio $1:4:9$.

(3) We can generalize the above rules by stating that atoms with the same number of optical electrons have spectra with the same structure. We can obtain the frequency ratios $1:4:9: \ldots$ by inserting into Eq. (7.7) a factor $(z + 1)^2$ in analogy with the factor $(Z - \sigma)^2$ in the X-ray formula (6.16). The effective positive charge felt by the optical electrons in a z-valent positive ion is $(z + 1)e$, just as the charge felt by an inner electron is $(Z - \sigma)e$.

(4) It is reasonable to suppose that the simplest spectra are those due to one optical electron. These simple spectra occur for the atoms and ions H, He^+, Li, Li^{++}, Be^+, Na, K, Rb, Cs, Cu, Ag, Au, Mg^+, Ca^+. These single-electron spectra will form the basis of our discussion.

Even in single-electron spectra we encounter a complexity of spectrum lines. This complexity is not apparent with a spectrograph of low resolving power. Such an instrument usually shows a limited number, say 100, of sharp lines at intervals of several hundreds or thousands of wave numbers. With a better spectrograph, however, these single lines turn out to be groups of 2 or 3 with a spacing on the order of 1 to 10 wave numbers. These are the *multiplets* or *fine structure* of the lines. In an instrument of intermediate quality this fine structure, although not resolved, makes some of the lines appear fuzzy and has led to the distinction between "sharp" and "diffuse" lines. When the lines are observed with the highest resolving power, by means of an interferometer, the lines of the fine structure generally show a further splitting known as *hyperfine structure*.

We shall first concentrate on the gross structure of the spectral lines, leaving a discussion of the fine structure to a later chapter. We are thus

able to develop one at a time the basic principles involved. The chief
method used for the empirical analysis of emission spectra is to group
them into series of the same sort as found in optical absorption spectra.

7.6. Series analysis of spectra

The emission spectrum of an atom always shows the same series of
lines that appears in the absorption spectrum. This set of emission lines
is called the *principal series*. There appear in addition many other lines.
In one-electron spectra, which are the simplest, we find that most of the
remaining lines go to make up three other series, as shown in Fig. 7.6.
The lines of each series start with one of minimum wave number (frequency) and crowd together as they approach a maximum frequency,
the series limit. The four prominent series are named sharp, principal,
diffuse, and fundamental—frequently abbreviated by S, P, D, F. The
series limits of the sharp and diffuse series are identical. Their names
derive from the appearance of their lines in the early spectrographs.
Most lines of the fundamental series are in the infrared.

A common limit not only holds for the S and D series but has the
further remarkable property that its wave number is just equal to T_2,
the first and largest term value of the principal series. This fact, on comparison with Eqs. (7.4) and (7.5) for the absorption (P) series, shows that
we must consider the S and D series as arising from electron transitions
which end in the energy level $-U_2$. None of the principal term values,
however, can combine with T_2 to yield the observed lines of the S and
D series, which are different from each other. We must therefore assume
the existence of other excited levels in the atom besides those found in
absorption spectra. To distinguish these term values from those found
previously, they are denoted by S_n and D_n. Their values are given by
equations similar to (7.7),

$$S_n = R/(n - s_n)^2, \qquad n = 2, 3, \cdots \qquad (7.9)$$

$$D_n = R/(n - d_n)^2, \qquad n = 3, 4, \cdots \qquad (7.10)$$

The quantum defects s_n and d_n differ from Δ_n and from each other, so

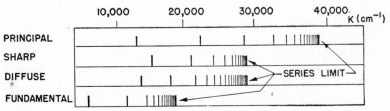

Fig. 7.6. Emission series of a one-electron spectrum. The principal
series is the same as found in the absorption spectrum.

that the term values $S_n \neq T_n \neq D_n$. Like the Δ_n, however, s_n and $d_n \to 0$ as $n \to \infty$: it is this feature that determines the appropriate starting number n. The wave numbers of the lines in the sharp and diffuse series are then given by

$$k_n(S) = T_2 - S_n, \qquad n = 2, 3, \cdots \qquad (7.11)$$

$$k_n(D) = T_2 - D_n, \qquad n = 3, 4, \cdots \qquad (7.12)$$

in analogy with (7.4).

In the same way the limit of the fundamental series corresponds to D_3, and we have

$$F_n = D_3 - k_n(F) = R/(n - f_n)^2, \qquad n = 4, 5, \cdots \qquad (7.13)$$

To write the principal series in the same notation, we put P_n in place of T_n. Moreover, we find by comparison with (7.9) that we could reasonably write the term T_i as S_1. Thus

$$P_n = S_1 - k_n(P) = R/(n - p_n)^2, \qquad n = 2, 3, \cdots \qquad (7.14)$$

It is conventional to write the subscript n in front of the term type designation, as nP, nD, etc. Thus the wave numbers of the various series are conventionally represented as

$$
\begin{aligned}
k_n(P) &= 1S - nP, & n &= 2, 3, 4, \cdots \\
k_n(S) &= 2P - nS, & n &= 2, 3, 4, \cdots \\
k_n(D) &= 2P - nD, & n &= 3, 4, 5, \cdots \\
k_n(F) &= 3D - nF, & n &= 4, 5, 6, \cdots
\end{aligned}
\qquad (7.15)
$$

Equation (7.15) contains all the lines usually seen in a one-electron spectrum, except perhaps for some infrared lines of the form $3D - nP$, $n = 4, 5, \cdots$. These transitions and the corresponding term values for sodium are shown in Fig. 7.7. If we arrange the columns in the order $SPDF$ as indicated, the transitions giving rise to emission spectra occur only between neighboring columns, S-P, P-D, D-F. Lines corresponding to S-D, S-S, P-F, P-P, S-F, etc., transitions usually are not found. This is direct evidence for *selection rules* of the sort mentioned previously in section 6.6. We may state the selection rule explicitly here: when we group the optical terms into series and order the series S, P, D, F, only neighboring terms can combine. This selection rule at once explains why the absorption spectrum is so much simpler than the emission spectrum of the same atom. For the alkali absorption spectrum the electron starts in the normal S level and hence can make transitions only to P levels. For emission spectra, however, the electron can start from any level, depending on its previous history.

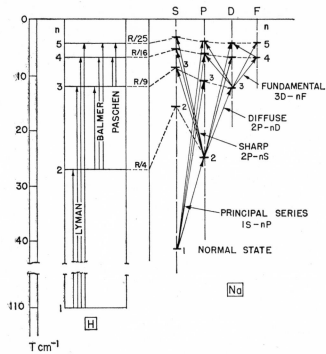

Fig. 7.7. Term diagram of sodium and hydrogen. The left-hand scale should be multiplied by a factor 10^3.

The quantum defects of all the terms vanish as n becomes large, which implies that all the terms become equal to R/n^2 in this limit. As discussed in section 7.4, we may attribute the quantum defects to penetration of the core by the optical electron. Hence the defects become smaller as the average radii of the orbits increase with n. Another way of reducing the quantum defect is to make the core smaller by going to lighter and lighter atoms. The ultimate limit is the hydrogen atom, which has no core at all but only an optical electron outside the nucleus. In this case, the *SPDF* terms are all identical for each value of n. When energy levels and term values are the same, even though they belong to different series, we call them *degenerate*. Figure 7.7 represents the hydrogen term scheme next to that of sodium and shows how the sodium diagram approaches the degenerate hydrogen terms for large n. For hydrogen the wave numbers of all lines are of the form

$$k = R\left(\frac{1}{n^2} - \frac{1}{m^2}\right), \qquad m > n \qquad (7.16)$$

where all possible integer n, m values can occur.

Historically, the hydrogen relations became evident earlier than the other laws for single electron spectra. As early as 1885 Balmer discovered that lines of the visible spectrum in hydrogen follow (7.16) with $n = 2$. This series, which corresponds to the sharp and diffuse series, is the *Balmer series* of hydrogen. In the ultraviolet region Lyman discovered the series with $n = 1$, corresponding to the principal series. Other series similarly bear the names of their discoverers: the Paschen, Brackett, and Pfund series have $n = 3$, 4, and 5, respectively.

The ions He^+ and Li^{++} exhibit spectra exactly resembling that of hydrogen, except that in place of the Rydberg constant R in (7.16) we must put $4R$ and $9R$, respectively. The entire spectrum accordingly shifts towards the ultraviolet region. The lines of He^+ found in the visible region form the Pickering series:

$$k = 4R(1/4^2 - 1/m^2), \quad m = 5, 6, \cdots \quad (7.17)$$

The striking whole-number relationships of the hydrogen series are the immediate source of modern atomic theory. Any acceptable explanation of atomic energy levels must account for the occurrence of these integers. It must also account for the universal appearance of the Rydberg constant R, which plays an important role not only in optical but also in X-ray spectra. The theory of wave or quantum mechanics fulfills both these requirements, and we will discuss it in Chapters 9 and 10.

SUMMARY

The photoelectric effect with visible or ultraviolet light provides direct evidence for the existence of the photon. The emission of photoelectrons is possible only above a certain threshold frequency for the incident light, $\nu_0 = e\varphi/h$, where φ is the work function of the metal surface. The kinetic energy of the emitted photoelectrons is $\frac{1}{2}mv^2 = h\nu - h\nu_0 = h\nu - e\varphi$ and is independent of the light intensity. Both of these facts contradict the expectations of the classical wave picture of light and are understandable only on the basis of the photon concept.

The optical photoelectric effect on a metal surface does not give us information about the electron orbits in free atoms. The orbits of the outermost or optical electrons are distorted in the metal, so that φ is a specific function of the surface. For this reason it is necessary to study free, gaseous atoms. Electron bombardment of gas atoms and measurement of the positive recoil ions determines the ionization potential V_i and the corresponding term value of the normal ground state $T_i = eV_i/hc$.

Electron bombardment of gas atoms and measurement of the electrons to determine their inelastic collisions (the Franck-Hertz experiment) shows the existence of an excited, bound level T_2, with $T_2 < T_i$.

The resonance radiation re-emitted from these atoms when the optical electron returns from this excited state to its normal state has wave number $k = T_i - T_2$. These electron bombardment experiments provide direct proof of the quantization of orbits and energy levels for the optical electrons.

The optical absorption spectrum shows the existence not only of T_2 but of an apparently infinite number of higher excited states, with $T_i > T_2 > T_3 > \cdots > T_n > T_m > \cdots > 0$. The term values are $T_n = R/(n - \Delta_n)^2$, where the universal Rydberg constant is $R = 1.097 \times 10^5$ cm^{-1}, $n = 2, 3, 4, \cdots$ is an integer, and Δ_n is the quantum defect. We can attribute the quantum defects to partial penetration of the core by the optical electrons; as $n \to \infty$, the optical orbits become very large and $\Delta_n \to 0$. The optical absorption spectrum appears as a series of discrete lines converging towards a series limit, $\nu_i = cT_i$. Beyond ν_i is a continuous absorption spectrum that corresponds to ionization of the atom with kinetic energy $\frac{1}{2}mv^2 = h\nu - h\nu_i$ carried away by the escaping electron.

Optical emission spectra are even more complicated than optical absorption spectra. There are generic similarities in the emission spectra of atoms or ions with the same number of optical electrons. The simplest spectra are those produced by substances with one optical electron: hydrogen, the alkalis, the singly charged positive ions of the alkaline earths, etc. These spectra fall into four main series: the sharp, principal, diffuse, and fundamental, labeled *SPDF*. A selection rule operates so that the only term combinations are *S-P*, *P-D*, and *D-F*. This selection rule and the fact that the principal series is identical with the absorption spectrum leads us to classify the normal term T_i as S_1 and the other T_n as P_n. The various series are given by

$$k_n(S) = 2P - nS, \qquad\qquad n = 2, 3, 4, \cdots$$
$$k_n(P) = 1S - nP, \qquad\qquad n = 2, 3, 4, \cdots$$
$$k_n(D) = 2P - nD, \qquad\qquad n = 3, 4, 5, \cdots$$
$$k_n(F) = 3D - nF, \qquad\qquad n = 4, 5, 6, \cdots$$

where the terms are of the form $nA = R/(n - a_n)^2$ for $A = S, P, D, F$. As $n \to \infty$, all the quantum defects $a_n \to 0$ and the *SPDF* terms for a given n become degenerate. In H, He$^+$, Li^{++}, where there is no core, this degeneracy is present for all values of n. This substantiates the argument that quantum defects arise from penetration of the core.

The most striking features of optical spectra to be explained by quantum theory are the incidence of integers n that are associated with the quantized orbits, and the invariable occurrence of the Rydberg constant R.

Table of conversion coefficients:

$$E \text{ (erg)} = 6.625 \times 10^{-27} \, \nu(\sec^{-1})$$
$$= 1.986 \times 10^{-16} \, k(\text{cm}^{-1})$$
$$= 1.986 \times 10^{-8}/\lambda(\text{A})$$
$$E \text{ (ev)} = 4.135 \times 10^{-15} \, \nu(\sec^{-1})$$
$$= 1.240 \times 10^{-4} \, k(\text{cm}^{-1})$$
$$= 1.240 \times 10^{4}/\lambda(\text{A})$$
$$\nu(\sec^{-1}) = 1.509 \times 10^{26} \, E \text{ (erg)}$$
$$= 2.418 \times 10^{14} \, E \text{ (ev)}$$
$$k(\text{cm}^{-1}) = 5.035 \times 10^{15} \, E \text{ (erg)}$$
$$= 8.066 \times 10^{3} \, E \text{ (ev)}$$
$$\lambda(\text{A}) = 1.986 \times 10^{-8}/E \text{ (erg)}$$
$$= 1.240 \times 10^{4}/E \text{ (ev)}$$

REFERENCES

A. E. Ruark and H. C. Urey, *Atoms, Molecules, and Quanta*, McGraw-Hill, New York (1930).

A. Sommerfeld, *Atomic Structure and Spectral Lines*, Methuen, London (1923).

H. E. White, *Introduction to Atomic Spectra*, McGraw-Hill, New York (1934).

ILLUSTRATIVE PROBLEMS

1. The limit of the principal series of lithium has the wave number $43,484.45 \text{ cm}^{-1}$. The following table gives the wave numbers of all absorption lines observed in lithium vapor:

$14,903.09 \text{ cm}^{-1}$	$43,055.25 \text{ cm}^{-1}$	$43,343.09 \text{ cm}^{-1}$
$30,924.52$	$43,103.52$	$43,354.55$
$36,467.46$	$43,144.45$	$43,363.20$
$39,011.60$	$x \; 43,179.85$	$43,371.10$
$40,390.00$	$x \; 43,209.71$	$43,377.87$
$41,215.53$	$x \; 43,235.88$	$43,384.27$
$41,749.30$	$43,256.45$	$43,389.73$
$42,112.3$	$43,277.04$	$43,394.81$
$42,371.0$	$43,295.78$	$43,399.91$
$42,567.63$	$43,308.90$	$43,404.06$
$42,713.12$	$43,323.93$	$43,408.02$
$42,826.55$	$43,335.20$	$43,411.76$
$42,924.00$		$43,416.31$
$42,994.17$		$43,420.27$
		$43,423.66$

(a) What is the ionization potential of Li in ev?

(b) Use Eq. (7.6) to determine the order numbers of the lines marked with x and assign the appropriate order numbers to the other lines.

(c) Compute the quantum defects of the first five lowest terms including the normal term.

(d) What is the limit of the diffuse and sharp series of Li? Give its wavelength.

Solution.

(a) $V_i = hc/eT_i = 1.240 \times 10^{-4} \times 43,484.45 \text{ cm}^{-1} = 5.39$ volts.

(b) $T_{n-1} - T_n \approx T_n - T_{n+1} \approx 2R/n^3$. By (7.4), $T_n = T_i - k_n$, so $2R/n^3 \approx k_n - k_{n-1} \approx k_{n+1} - k_n = 29.86 \text{ cm}^{-1} \approx 26.17 \text{ cm}^{-1}$. The average value is $2R/n^3 = 28.0 \text{ cm}^{-1}$, or $n = (1.097 \times 10^5/14)^{1/3} \approx 20$. This is the order number of the central line marked x: the other two are $n = 19$ and $n = 21$. The other lines run serially from $n = 2$ to $n = 42$.

(c) $T_n = T_i - k_n = R/(n - \Delta_n)^2$,

$$T_i = 43,484 \text{ cm}^{-1}, \qquad\qquad \Delta_1 = -0.59$$
$$T_2 = 43,484 - 14,903 = 28,581 \text{ cm}^{-1}, \qquad \Delta_2 = +0.04$$
$$T_3 = 43,484 - 30,925 = 12,559 \text{ cm}^{-1}, \qquad \Delta_3 = +0.05$$
$$T_4 = 43,484 - 36,467 = 7,017 \text{ cm}^{-1}, \qquad \Delta_4 = +0.05$$
$$T_5 = 43,484 - 39,012 = 4,472 \text{ cm}^{-1}, \qquad \Delta_5 = +0.04$$

(d) $T_2 = 28,581 \text{ cm}^{-1}$, $\lambda = 1/T_2 = 3519 \text{ A}$

2. The lowest term values for sodium are

1S	41,448 cm⁻¹	2P	24,484	3D	12,274	4F	6,858 cm⁻¹
2S	15,705	3P	11,180	4D	6,897		
3S	8,246	4P	6,407				

Describe the spectrum of sodium for the following excitation conditions:

(a) Bombardment with 2-volt electrons

(b) Bombardment with 4.2-volt electrons

(c) Illumination with light of 6159 A wavelength

(d) Illumination with light of 4123 A wavelength

(e) Illumination with light of 3303 A wavelength

Note that there are no selection rules for excitation by electron bombardment.

Solution. (a) $k = 8.066 \times 10^3 \times 2eV = 16,132 \text{ cm}^{-1}$. The $1S - 2P$ difference is $16,964 \text{ cm}^{-1}$, so that 2-volt electrons cannot produce any excited level at all. Hence no emission spectrum will appear.

(b) $k = 8.066 \times 10^3 \times 4.2eV = 33,877 \text{ cm}^{-1}$. Now $1S - 33,877 = 7571$ cm⁻¹. Since there are no selection rules for electron bombardment, the only limitations are imposed by energy restrictions. The levels excited are accordingly $2S$, $3S$, $2P$, $3P$, and $3D$. The subsequent emission

lines are $3P - 3S, 2P - 3S, 3D - 3P, 2P - 3D, 2S - 3P, 2P - 2S,$
$1S - 2P, 1S - 3P.$

(c) $k = 1/\lambda = 16{,}236$ cm^{-1}. Again the $2P$ state cannot be excited, and no emission spectrum appears.

(d) $k = 1/\lambda = 24{,}254$ cm^{-1}; $T_i - 24{,}254 = 17{,}194$. Since a partial photon is not absorbed, no excitation or emission occurs.

(e) $k = 1/\lambda \approx 30{,}270$ cm^{-1}; $T_i - 30{,}270 \approx 11{,}180$ cm^{-1}. The $3P$ level is therefore excited; the spectrum is the same as in part (b), omitting transition from the $3S$ level.

PROBLEMS

1. When the intensity of a light beam varies periodically with a frequency of 1 megacycle, it is found that the photocurrent excited by it in a vacuum photocell varies with the same frequency without any measurable phase lag. Hence the conversion of light energy into kinetic electronic energy must require less than 10^{-6} sec. To demonstrate the incompatibility of this result with classical electromagnetic theory, compute for how many seconds a beam of green light of 1 lumen/cm^2 intensity must fall on an atom of 1 A radius before the energy impinging on the atom amounts to one $h\nu$ (1 watt = 621 lumens).

2. The photocurrent of a photocell can be suppressed by application of a potential of -1 volt to the collector, when the illumination is monochromatic of 6000 A wavelength.

(a) What is the work function in ev of the photoelectric surface?

(b) What maximum wavelength can the monochromatic illumination have and produce any photocurrent in this cell?

(c) If an electrometer is connected across the cell, to what potential will it be charged when the illumination has a wavelength of 4000 A?

(d) To what minimum wavelength must the spectrum of a "white" beam of light extend to be able to charge the electrometer to a potential of 3 volts?

3. Using Eq. (6.10) with $Z_i = 1$, compute from the ionization potential the effective radius of the atom (optical electron orbit) for all the ionization potentials given in Appendix II. Plot the atomic radius versus the atomic number Z. Compare the results with the radii obtained from physical chemical methods (Table 2.1).

4. The first four lines and the series limit of the absorption spectrum of rubidium have the wave numbers (in 10^5 m^{-1})

$$12.8 \quad 23.8 \quad 27.8 \quad 29.8 \quad \text{limit } 33.7$$

(a) Find the ionization potential in volts.

(b) What is the excitation potential of Rb?

(c) What is the wavelength of the resonance line?

(d) What is the wave number of the series limits of the diffuse and sharp series?

(e) If Rb vapor is bombarded with electrons, what maximum energy in eV can the electrons have for elastic impacts?

(f) Compute the quantum defects of the first four P terms.

5. The first four lines of the sharp and diffuse series of rubidium have the wave numbers (in 10^5 m^{-1})

Sharp:	7.3	13.5	16.2	17.7
Diffuse:	6.5	12.9	15.9	17.5

Using the data from the preceding problem, determine

(a) The quantum defects of the first four S and D terms. Plot s_n and d_n in the same graph as p_n.

(b) What is the wave number of the limit of the fundamental series?

(c) What are the wave numbers of the lines of the fundamental series, if the quantum defect of the F terms is negligible? (The observed values are 7.4, 9.9, 11.3, 12.1 m^{-1})

(d) Construct a term level diagram for Rb, giving the values in m^{-1} and also in ev.

(e) The Rb spectrum also contains lines with the wave numbers 4.5, 7.7. What are the term notations of these lines? What minimum potential is required to excite these lines?

(f) What minimum potential is required to excite the first line of the fundamental series?

6. When Na vapor is bombarded with 4-volt electrons, it emits radiation of the following wavelengths:

$$\lambda_1 = 3,300 \text{ A} \qquad \lambda_4 = 11,400 \text{ A}$$
$$\lambda_2 = 5,900 \text{ A} \qquad \lambda_5 = 22,100 \text{ A}$$
$$\lambda_3 = 8,200 \text{ A} \qquad \lambda_6 = 91,500 \text{ A}$$

(a) Noting that the wave numbers of these spectra lines satisfy the relations

$$k_2 + k_4 + k_5 = k_1, \qquad k_4 + k_5 = k_3 + k_6$$

determine the term notation of these lines. From the data given two alternate designations of two pairs of lines are possible: give both.

(b) The ionization potential of Na is 5.14 volts. Using this and the above data compute the lowest five term values in cm^{-1} (slide rule accuracy) and plot the results in a term level diagram.

(c) What is the first excitation potential of Na?

(d) What must be the wavelength of the light which, when used to irradiate Na vapor, will excite the same six lines as are excited by the 4-volt electrons?

7. The first five lines of the sharp and diffuse series of Li have the wave numbers

sharp series	diffuse series
$k = 12{,}300.83$ cm^{-1}	$k = 16{,}378.86$ cm^{-1}
20,107.21	21,718.83
23,394.49	24,192.11
25,081.77	25,534.43
26,046.01	26,341.92

Use in addition the data of illustrative problem 1 if necessary.

(a) Construct a plot of $(1/\text{term})^{1/2}$ versus n for the various terms, and compute from it the value of the Rydberg constant.

(b) From the same plot show that the normal term is an S term.

(c) What is the first excitation potential of Li?

(d) Which ones of the above lines will appear in the emission spectrum when Li vapor is bombarded with 4.6-volt electrons, assuming no selection rules for electrons?

(e) Sketch the term level diagram of Li.

(f) What is the wave number of the limit of the fundamental series?

(g) Show that the emission spectrum can have a line of wave number 4085.78 cm^{-1}. What is its notation and what is the maximum wavelength of light that can excite it by irradiation?

Part II

THEORETICAL INTERPRETATION OF THE FACTS

By using the photon to interpret atomic spectra, we can relate the major nonclassical phenomena of Part I to one central problem of atomic structure. This problem is to understand why the orbits of electrons in atoms appear to be quantized, with a smallest orbit for each atom and a limited capacity for electrons in each orbit.

Quantum mechanics successfully explains this fact, and Part II (Chapters 8–12) is concerned with working out the major aspects of this explanation. A revolution in the philosophy of physics was required, however, before quantum mechanics could replace classical physics. This revolution was begun in Einstein's theory of relativity, which insisted on taking into account the experimental limitations of any possible measurement. The theory of relativity also suggested that certain questions in physics may turn out to be meaningless and hence unanswerable; e.g., the motion of the earth relative to the ether.

A similar insistence on the limitations inherent in experimental measurements leads to the uncertainty principle, which states that it is meaningless to ask for a precise simultaneous knowledge of a particle's position and momentum. This principle can be developed mathematically into the full formulation of quantum mechanics.

Chapter 8

SPECIAL THEORY OF RELATIVITY

Chapters 1 through 7 have reviewed the primary experimental facts concerning atoms. In these chapters we described the atoms entirely in classical terms—as hard spheres, or as miniature solar systems with the electrons revolving in circular orbits, or in terms of a static model with fixed elastic constants for each electron. In dealing with light and its interaction with atoms, we were forced to introduce the nonclassical concept of the photon or light quantum. According to this concept, atoms can emit or absorb light of frequency only in discrete, indivisible quanta of energy $E = h\nu$.

Although we have introduced quantization for light, we have not considered any nonclassical innovations for the structure of the atom itself. The experimental facts, however, give abundant evidence that some non-classical ideas are necessary. The quantization of electron orbits is the most outstanding feature of atomic structure that is inexplicable on a classical basis. This quantization is essential to save atoms from the classical catastrophe of radiative collapse. The existence of discrete energy levels in atoms, with a lowest or ground level, is another manifestation of orbit quantization. Not only are the orbits quantized, but a certain exclusion principle acts to prevent all the electrons in an atom from occupying the same orbit. The capacity of each orbit to hold electrons appears to be strictly limited, although it is larger than unity. The K-shell orbit has a capacity of 2 electrons, for example, and the L- M- $\cdots$ shell orbits can hold increasing but finite numbers of electrons. This exclusion principle has a direct connection with the build-up of the periodic table of chemical elements. Another nonclassical phenomenon is the existence of well-obeyed selection rules that forbid certain radiative transitions in atoms, even when sufficient energy is available.

The solution of all these mysteries lies in the development and application of a suitable quantum mechanics to the motion of electrons in atoms. This quantum mechanics will have the same underlying principles as that for light. For example, we must somehow regard light as consisting simultaneously of wave motion (crystal diffraction) and of indivisible corpuscles or photons (photoelectric effect). It will turn out that we must do the same thing for electrons: regard them not only as particles, but as simultaneously possessing wavelike properties. From this more general point of view electrons and photons are just two special examples of an all-inclusive quantum mechanics.

Chapters 8 through 12 are concerned with setting up the quantum mechanical description of the atom and verifying that it satisfactorily accounts for the observations. This will require a fairly radical departure from the philosophy of classical physics. Historically and logically, the first point of this departure is Einstein's special theory of relativity. The relativistic formulas established in the present chapter provide a suitable vehicle for the introduction of de Broglie's wave mechanical postulate (Chapter 9). Under this postulate, electrons and photons appear as special cases of a more general formalism.

8.1. The Michelson-Morley experiment

To appreciate the need for the theory of relativity, consider one of the outstanding problems of classical physics at the turn of the twentieth century. The brilliant success of Maxwell's theory of light left little doubt that the velocity of light in free space should be

$$c = q \text{ (esu)}/q \text{ (emu)} = 2.998 \times 10^{10} \text{ cm/sec} \qquad (8.1)$$

where the q's refer to the same charge, measured in electrostatic and electromagnetic units, respectively. To a classical physicist nothing was more natural than the assumption that the velocity of light must be measured relative to the medium through which the light propagates. For light this medium bore the name of the *ether*, imagined as a massless, frictionless fluid filling all space uniformly. Even if the ether has a uniform motion in space, the surface of the earth cannot always be at rest relative to the ether because of the earth's revolution around the sun and its rotation about its own axis. In fact, from astronomical observations we expect the velocity v of the earth's surface relative to the ether to be of order

$$v/c \approx 10^{-4} \qquad (8.2)$$

over at least part of the earth's orbit about the sun. Therefore very precise measurements of the velocity of light relative to the earth's surface should reveal the velocity v of the earth's surface relative to the ether. The purpose of the Michelson-Morley experiment was to determine v in this way. The negative result of the experiment stimulated the development of the theory of relativity.

The basic plan of the experiment is as shown in Fig. 8.1. Monochromatic light of wavelength λ from a source L passes to a semisilvered mirror M, where the beam splits into two parts. One part passes straight ahead to a mirror a distance l_1 away; the other goes at right angles to the original direction and is reflected by a mirror at a distance l_2. The reflected beams recombine at M and pass to an interferometer at I. The entire apparatus can rotate through 90°, and any relative phase shift of the two beams upon this rotation is observable in the interferometer. The light paths are entirely in vacuum.

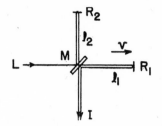

Fig. 8.1. Scheme of the Michelson-Morley experiment.

Let the initial velocity v of the apparatus through the ether be parallel to l_1, as in Fig. 8.1.

If c and v combine like classical velocities, the time required for the beam to go from M along l_1 and back should be

$$t_1 = \frac{l_1}{c - v} + \frac{l_1}{c + v} = \frac{2l_1/c}{1 - v^2/c^2} \tag{8.3}$$

For the beam along l_2, on the other hand, the mirror moves sidewards so that the light beam through the ether must follow a diagonal path. Since the velocity along this path is c, the component in a direction perpendicular to v is $\sqrt{c^2 - v^2}$. The time required to go from M to the mirror and back is accordingly

$$t_2 = \frac{2l_2/c}{\sqrt{1 - v^2/c^2}} \tag{8.4}$$

When the two beams recombine in the interferometer, they will be shifted relative to each other by a number of wavelengths

$$n = \frac{(t_1 - t_2)c}{\lambda} = \frac{2/\lambda}{\sqrt{1 - v^2/c^2}} \left(\frac{l_1}{\sqrt{1 - v^2/c^2}} - l_2 \right) \tag{8.5}$$

After a 90° rotation the shift of the beams becomes

$$n' = \frac{2\lambda}{\sqrt{1 - v^2/c^2}} \left(l_1 - \frac{l_2}{\sqrt{1 - v_2/c^2}} \right) \tag{8.6}$$

The change in the beam shift in this process is

$$\Delta n = n - n' = \frac{2}{\lambda} \frac{l_1 + l_2}{\sqrt{1 - v^2/c^2}} \left(\frac{1}{\sqrt{1 - v^2/c^2}} - 1 \right) \approx \frac{l_1 + l_2}{\lambda} \frac{v^2}{c^2} \tag{8.7}$$

where the last expression in the equation is an approximation valid when $v/c \ll 1$.

By using multiple reflections in the paths l_1 and l_2, Michelson and Morley achieved a total path length of about 20 meters. With visible light of about 5000 A wavelength and $v/c \approx 10^{-4}$ as expected for the earth moving through space, the fringe shift would be on the order of $\Delta n \approx 1$.

The actual displacement that Michelson and Morley observed was certainly less than $\frac{1}{20}$, probably less than $\frac{1}{40}$ the expected amount, and was entirely attributable to experimental errors.

The negative result of this experiment, repeated several times at in, tervals of weeks or months, occasioned a great deal of speculation. A simple hypothesis that fitted this particular experiment was the Fitzgerald-Lorentz contraction. According to this hypothesis distances measured along the direction of v shrink by a factor $\sqrt{1 - v^2/c^2}$, which is just sufficient to account for the experimental result that $\Delta n = 0$. This explanation is purely *ad hoc*, however, and bears no logical relationship to any other physical phenomena.

Einstein on the other hand took a philosophically much more far-reaching step and assumed the null result of the Michelson-Morley experiment as a postulate. That is, the vacuum velocity of light is assumed to be a constant c in any possible measurement, and never $\sqrt{c^2 - v^2}$. This essential assumption leads to the special theory of relativity. This theory encompasses not only the Michelson-Morley experiment but also a host of other experimental facts. Its agreement with observation is so universal that we cannot doubt its correctness.

8.2. The Lorentz transformation

A single phrase suffices to present the entire postulational basis of relativity, although that phrase requires a paragraph or two of interpretation. The relativity postulate is that

$$\text{all inertial systems are equivalent} \tag{8.8}$$

Here "inertial" means that the systems are moving relative to one another with uniform, straight-line velocities; "equivalent" means that all the laws of physics have identical formulations in the two systems. The general postulate (8.8) may be subdivided into two special postulates:

$$\text{all inertial systems have equivalent laws of mechanics,} \tag{8.8a}$$
all inertial systems have equivalent laws of electromagnetism
and optics: in particular, the velocity of light is a constant,
$$\text{independent of the system} \tag{8.8b}$$

The postulate (8.8a) is nothing new, for it obtains in classical mechanics also. The real innovation in relativity was the extension of the postulate to cover electromagnetic phenomena.

Consider the relativity postulate for mechanics (8.8a), and let S and S' be two inertial systems. In Fig. 8.2, S' is moving relative to S with a constant velocity v parallel to the x-direction; the coordinate axes xyz and $x'y'z'$ are parallel in the two systems. According to (8.8a), if

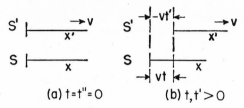

(a) $t = t'' = 0$ (b) $t, t' > 0$

Fig. 8.2. Relatively moving systems.

we establish the law of mechanics $F = ma$ in system S, then the law $F' = m'a'$ must hold in system S'. The equivalence of all inertial systems implies that we must be able to describe any physical phenomenon equally well in the coordinates of any inertial system. Shifting from one system to another is simply a matter of convenience, and for this purpose we must establish the *transformation laws* between the coordinates of system S and system S'. These tranformation laws give x', y', z', t' as functions of x, y, z, t:

$$x' = f_1(x,y,z,t)$$
$$y' = f_2(x,y,z,t)$$
$$z' = f_3(x,y,z,t)$$
$$t' = f_4(x,y,z,t)$$

(8.9)

We have included the time t as a coordinate because the laws of mechanics involve t in such quantities as $a = d^2x/dt^2$. The postulate (8.8a) requires that the transformations (8.9) be *linear*; that is, the functions f involve x, y, z, and t only to the first power and contain no products of two or more quantities x, y, z, t. Otherwise the equations for force-free motion, $d^2x/dt^2 = d^2y/dt^2 = d^2z/dt^2 = 0$ would not be the same in all inertial systems.

Classical mechanics yields a linear set of transformations (8.9), in accordance with (8.8a). For the systems of Fig. 8.2, supposing that at time $t = t' = 0$ the origins of coordinates in S and S' coincide, we have

$$x' = x - vt$$
$$y' = y$$
$$z' = z$$
$$t' = t$$

(8.10)

This classical transformation is known as a *Galilean* transformation. It leads to the conclusion that the Michelson-Morley experiment should give a nonvanishing result, as discussed in section 8.1. It is thus incompatible with postulate (8.8b). The question naturally arises whether there exists any transformation law (8.9) compatible with both (8.8a) and (8.8b). If not, the general relativity postulate (8.8) must be abandoned. It turns out that there is just one transformation, known as the Lorentz transformation, which satisfies (8.8a) and (8.8b). The Lorentz transformation is thus prescribed by the postulate of relativity.

To allow for a more general transformation than (8.10) between the systems S and S' ,we write

$$x' = \gamma(x - vt)$$
$$y' = y$$
$$z' = z \qquad\qquad (8.11)$$
$$t' = ax + bt$$

Here γ, a, b are constants to be determined; the requirement of linearity assures us that they are constants. Since the relative motion is in the x-direction, we have no reason to alter the classical equivalence of the coordinates perpendicular to the x-direction. In the expression for x' and t' there are no constant terms because we have taken $x = x' = 0$ at $t = t' = 0$. The factor $(x - vt)$ in the expression for x' comes from the fact that the point $x' = $ constant in S' corresponds to a point moving with uniform velicity v in S. We wish to choose γ, a, b in order to satisfy (8.8b). Suppose that at time $t = t' = 0$ a light ray starts from the (then coincident) origins of coordinates, $x = x' = y = y' = z = z' = 0$. At some later instant we measure the distance traveled by the light ray. Since the velocity of light must equal c in both systems, we have

$$x^2 + y^2 + z^2 = c^2t^2 \qquad\qquad (8.12a)$$
$$x'^2 + y'^2 + z'^2 = c^2t'^2 \qquad\qquad (8.12b)$$

Now substitute (8.11) in (8.12b), obtaining

$$\gamma^2(x^2 - 2xvt + v^2t^2) + y^2 + z^2 = (c^2)(a^2x^2 + 2abxt + b^2t^2) \qquad (8.13)$$

Rearranging terms yields

$$(\gamma^2 - a^2c^2)x^2 + y^2 + z^2 = (c^2b^2 - \gamma^2v^2)t^2 + 2xt(abc^2 + v\gamma^2) \qquad (8.14)$$

If the transformation laws (8.11) really carry us from system S' to S, then (8.14) must be identical with (8.12a) for arbitrary x, y, z, and t. This means that the coefficients in (8.12a) and (8.14) must be identical for each of the independent terms x^2, y^2, z^2, t^2 and xt. That is,

$$\gamma^2 - a^2c^2 = 1$$
$$c^2b^2 - \gamma^2v^2 = c^2 \qquad\qquad (8.15)$$
$$abc^2 + v\gamma^2 = 0$$

Putting $ac = A$ and $v/c = \beta$, we have

$$\gamma^2 - A^2 = 1 \tag{8.16a}$$

$$b^2 - \beta^2\gamma^2 = 1 \tag{8.16b}$$

$$Ab + \beta\gamma^2 = 0 \tag{8.16c}$$

Eliminating A between (8.16a) and (8.16c) yields

$$\gamma^2 - \frac{\beta^2\gamma^4}{b^2} = 1 = \frac{\gamma^2}{b^2}\,(b^2 - \beta^2\gamma^2) \tag{8.17}$$

Comparison of (8.17) and (8.16b) shows that

$$\gamma^2 = b^2 \tag{8.18}$$

Substitution of this result in (8.16b) yields

$$\gamma^2 = b^2 = 1/(1 - \beta^2) \tag{8.19}$$

And substitution of (8.19) in (8.16a) leads to

$$A^2 = \gamma^2 - 1 = \beta^2/(1 - \beta^2) \tag{8.20}$$

In taking the square roots to obtain γ, b, and A, some ambiguities of $\pm$ signs appear. We resolve these by choosing the signs to be compatible with (8.16c) and to lead to the necessary result $x' = x$ and $t' = t$ when $v = 0$. The coefficients are now uniquely determined and the transformations (8.11) read

$$x' = \frac{x - \beta(ct)}{\sqrt{1 - \beta^2}}, \qquad (ct') = \frac{(ct) - \beta x}{\sqrt{1 - \beta^2}}$$

$$y' = y, \qquad z' = z \tag{8.21}$$

Here we write the coordinate (ct) instead of t to make all quantities have the same physical dimensions. Formula (8.21) are the *Lorentz transformations*. We can reverse them by solving algebraically for x, t in terms of x', t', in which case (8.21) yields

$$x = \frac{x' + \beta(ct')}{\sqrt{1 - \beta^2}}, \qquad (ct) = \frac{ct' + \beta x'}{\sqrt{1 - \beta^2}}$$

$$y = y' \qquad z = z' \tag{8.22}$$

Equations (8.22) are exactly similar in form to (8.21), as we expect from the equivalence of the systems; the only difference is that the velocity of S' relative to S is $+v$, while that of S relative to S' is $-v$.

We may give a physical interpretation of the Lorentz transformation in terms of contraction and dilation factors. Suppose that an object is at rest in system S' and is of length $\Delta x' = x_2' - x_1'$. An observer in S

instantaneously measures the end points of the object to be x_2 and x_1, so that the length is $\Delta x = x_2 - x_1$ in S. Here "instantaneous" implies that the corresponding times are identical, $t_2 = t_1$, or $\Delta t = t_2 - t_1 = 0$. To relate $\Delta x'$ with Δx, we can take differences of the right-hand equation of (8.21) or (8.22):

$$\Delta x' = \frac{\Delta x - \beta c\,\Delta t}{\sqrt{1 - \beta^2}} \tag{8.21a}$$

$$\Delta x = \frac{\Delta x' + \beta c\,\Delta t'}{\sqrt{1 - \beta^2}} \tag{8.22a}$$

We cannot use (8.22a) because $\Delta t'$ is unknown and does not in general equal Δt. From (8.21a) with $\Delta t = 0$ follows

$$\Delta x = x_2 - x_1 = \sqrt{1 - \beta^2}\,\Delta x' \tag{8.23}$$

Equation (8.23) states that an object which is moving relative to an observer appears to be contracted in the direction of motion by a factor $\sqrt{1 - \beta^2}$. If we reverse the situation and let an observer in S' measure an object in S, the prime would shift to the other side of Eq. (8.23), but the physical meaning would be the same. This apparent contraction in the direction of motion was introduced as an *ad hoc* postulate by Fitzgerald and Lorentz in the years before the announcement of the relativity principle.

We obtain a similar effect with the time coordinate. Suppose that an event occurs in S' at a fixed position $x_1' = x_2'$ and is of duration $\Delta t' = t_2' - t_1'$. An observer in S measures this interval as $\Delta t = t_2 - t_1$. In relating t and t', the question again arises of using (8.21) or (8.22). Since we know nothing about x_1 and x_2, we must use (8.22), obtaining

$$\Delta t = t_2 - t_1 = \Delta t'/\sqrt{1 - \beta^2} \tag{8.24}$$

In this case $1/\sqrt{1 - \beta^2}$ is a factor of dilation, by which the time interval in a system appears to lengthen when measured by a relatively moving observer.

Note that these equations all imply that $v < c$. Otherwise $\sqrt{1 - \beta^2}$ becomes imaginary, and we have no physical interpretation for imaginary distances and time intervals. The restriction that no measurable entity can travel faster than light can also serve as an alternative postulate from which to derive the formulas of special relativity. It is of interest to observe that the relations resulting as $v \to c$ are sometimes qualitatively the same as in classical motion when $v \to \infty$. For example, (8.23) implies that as $v \to c$, an object of fixed length in S' can pass an observer in S in an arbitrarily short time. This would be true classically as $v \to \infty$.

8.3. Addition of velocities and Doppler effect

The conclusion that all material velocities in relativity must not exceed the limit c contradicts the classical law for addition of velocities, according to which the addition of two parallel velocities like $\frac{7}{8}c$ and $\frac{9}{10}c$ would yield a resultant velocity considerably exceeding c. The proper relativistic law for velocity addition follows from (8.21) or (8.22). We may anticipate that it will approach the classical addition as $v \to 0$, and that it will never yield resultant velocities greater than c.

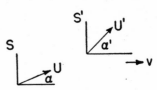

Fig. 8.3. Relativistic addition of velocities.

In the simplest case, consider a body in system S' moving in the x-direction with a velocity $u' = dx'/dt'$. What is the velocity $u = dx/dt$ seen in system S? From Eqs. (8.22) we have

$$dx = \gamma(dx' + \beta c\, dt'), \qquad c\, dt = \gamma(c\, dt' + \beta\, dx')$$

$$dx/dt = u = \frac{c(dx'/dt' + v)}{c + v/c\; dx'/dt'} = \frac{u' + v}{1 + u'v/c^2} \qquad (8.25)$$

The reader can easily convince himself that if u' and v are both less than c, then u must also be less than c, as expected. Moreover, (8.25) reduces to the classical law $u = u' + v$ when u' and v are much smaller than c.

In case the velocity u' is not parallel to v, we can follow a similar procedure. Suppose the velocity is U' at an angle α' as shown in Fig. 8.3. Then we have Eq. (8.25) with $u' = U' \cos \alpha'$ for the component of U' parallel to v; and for the component of U' perpendicular to v we have

$$dy = dy', \qquad w' = dy'/dt' = U' \sin \alpha'$$

$$w = \frac{dy}{dt} = \frac{dy'/\gamma}{dt' + v/c^2\, dx'} = \frac{w'}{\gamma(1 + u'v/c^2)} \qquad (8.26)$$

Then the total velocity in the system S is

$$U = \sqrt{u^2 + w^2}$$

$$= \frac{\sqrt{U'^2 + v^2 + 2U'v \cos \alpha' - (U'v \sin \alpha')^2/c^2}}{1 + (U'v \cos \alpha')/c^2} \qquad (8.27)$$

and the angle with the x-axis is given by

$$\tan \alpha = \frac{w}{u} = \frac{w'}{\gamma(u' + v)} = \frac{U' \sin \alpha'}{(U' \cos \alpha' + v)} \qquad (8.28)$$

An interesting special case occurs when U' is perpendicular to v, and $\cos \alpha' = 0$. Then from (8.26),

$$w = w'/\gamma = U'\sqrt{1 - \beta^2}, \qquad u = v \qquad (8.29)$$

Equation (8.29) comes directly from applying the time dilation factor (8.24) and noting that the perpendicular space coordinates in (8.21) suffer neither contraction nor dilation.

These formulas and all others in relativity theory reduce to those of classical physics for velocities much smaller than c. The phenomena of everyday observation are the basis of the laws of classical physics and are hence well described by these laws. Only highly advanced techniques of measurement like those of optics uncover the need for improved laws. Furthermore, these improvements do not deny the formulas of classical physics that have proved so useful, but merely extend them to domains where they have never been considered before. The two prime examples of this continuous extension are relativity and quantum mechanics, which apply to the domains of very high velocities and very small quantities of energy, distance, and momentum. Relativity reduces to classical equations for $v \ll c$, and quantum mechanics "corresponds" to classical physics for high quantum numbers (large electron orbits).

We can apply the transformations (8.25) − (8.27) and (8.22) to obtain the relativistic Doppler effect of a light wave. Suppose that a source of light in system S' has a frequency ν' when measured in S'. We define the light ray to be in the $x'y'$-plane and to make an angle α' with the x'-axis. An observer in S sees this light ray, and we inquire what angle α it makes with his x-axis and what frequency ν he ascribes to the light. Since $z = z'$ in (8.22), a light ray with no z' component has no z component and hence lies in the xy-plane.

The light wave is a periodic disturbance, so that its E or H vector in system S' is proportional to $\sin [2\pi(\nu't' - s'/\lambda')]$, where s' is the distance from the source measured along the path of the light ray and $\lambda' = c/\nu'$ is the wavelength. If the light source is at the origin of coordinates in S' and the light ray is in the $x'y'$-plane, then $x' = s' \cos \alpha'$ and $y' = s' \sin \alpha'$, or hence $s' = x' \cos \alpha' + y' \sin \alpha' = s' (\sin^2 \alpha' + \cos^2 \alpha')$. Thus the E or H vector is proportional to $\sin [(2\pi/c)\nu'(ct' - x' \cos \alpha' - y' \sin \alpha')]$ in the original system S', and is proportional to $\sin [(2\pi/c)\nu(ct - x \cos \alpha - y \sin \alpha)]$ in the observation system S. The quantity inside the brackets is the phase of the light wave. The phase is a physical quantity that must have one single numerical value at any point in space and instant of time, which numerical value cannot depend in any way on the coordinate system used to describe space and time. This is one way of restating the basic postulate of relativity. Hence for all corresponding points xyt and $x'y't'$ we have

$$\nu(ct - x \cos \alpha - y \sin \alpha) = \nu'(ct' - x' \cos \alpha' - y' \sin \alpha') \quad (8.30)$$

The velocity of light c is the only quantity in (8.30) that is the same for both systems. From (8.25) with $u' = c \cos \alpha'$, $u = c \cos \alpha$,

$$u/c = \cos \alpha = (\cos \alpha' + \beta)/(1 + \beta \cos \alpha') \tag{8.31}$$

and from (8.26) with $w' = c \sin \alpha'$, $w = c \sin \alpha$,

$$w/c = \sin \alpha = \sin \alpha'/\gamma(1 + \beta \cos \alpha') \tag{8.32}$$

Equation (8.31) relates the direction of the light ray in S to that in S'. We now substitute (8.31), (8.32) and (8.22) on the left-hand side of (8.30), obtaining

$$\nu \left[\gamma(ct' + \beta x') - \frac{\gamma(\cos \alpha' + \beta)(x' + \beta ct')}{(1 + \beta \cos \alpha')} - \frac{y' \sin \alpha'}{\gamma(1 + \beta \cos \alpha')} \right]$$

$$= \left(\frac{\nu/\gamma}{1 + \beta \cos \alpha'} \right) [\gamma^2(1 - \beta^2) ct' - \gamma^2(1 - \beta^2)x' \cos \alpha' - y' \sin \alpha']$$

$$= \frac{\nu}{\gamma(1 + \beta \cos \alpha')} (ct' - x' \cos \alpha' - y' \sin \alpha') \tag{8.33}$$

$$= \nu'(ct' - x' \cos \alpha' - y' \sin \alpha')$$

Thus the relativistic Doppler transformation is

$$\nu = \nu' \frac{(1 + \beta \cos \alpha')}{\sqrt{1 - \beta^2}} \tag{8.34}$$

We can write this in the form

$$\nu = \nu'[(1 + \beta \cos \alpha') + (1/\sqrt{1 - \beta^2} - 1)(1 + \beta \cos \alpha')]$$

$$= \nu'(1 + \beta \cos \alpha' + \tfrac{1}{2}\beta^2 + \dots \text{(higher powers in } \beta)) \tag{8.35}$$

by making an expansion valid for $\beta < 1$. The second term in the final bracket is the classical Doppler shift. The third is a specifically relativistic Doppler term, which has the feature of being independent of the angle α'.

8.4. Relativistic transformation of mass and energy

We have seen above how relativity implies contraction and dilation factors in distance and time proportional to $\sqrt{1 - \beta^2}$. A similar factor occurs in the mass of a particle in relativity. Suppose that observers in systems S and S' have identical balls of mass m as measured by each observer in his own system. Each observer throws his ball in a direction perpendicular to the direction of the relative velocity v. The balls make a perfectly elastic collision and return to the observers. The situation as seen by observer S is shown in Fig. 8.4. His own ball has velocity w, and the ball

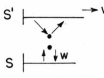

Fig. 8.4. Elastic collision as seen from S.

from S' has an x-velocity of v, and a y-velocity of $w'\sqrt{1 - \beta^2}$ according to (8.29). Here w' is the velocity of the S' ball as seen by the observer in S'. Since the balls are identical and the whole system is perfectly symmetric, we must have

$$w = w' \tag{8.36}$$

Now define the momentum of a ball to be mU, where m is a parameter that reduces to the actual mass of the ball as $U \to 0$ but may in general be a function of velocity, $m(U)$. For the collision of Fig. 8.4, conservation of the y-momentum would read (as seen from S)

$$wm(w) = \sqrt{1 - \beta^2}\, wm(\sqrt{w^2(1 - v^2/c^2) + v^2}) \tag{8.37}$$

Now dividing both sides by w and taking the limit as $w \to 0$, we have

$$m(0) = \sqrt{1 - \beta^2}\, m(v)$$
$$m = m_0/\sqrt{1 - \beta^2} \tag{8.38}$$

In (8.38) m is the mass at velocity v, and m_0 is the so-called *rest mass*, which is a characteristic of the body under consideration. This equation indicates explicitly that no material body can have a velocity greater than c.

The momentum of a body in relativity is given by the classical formula

$$p = mv \tag{8.39}$$

except that now m is given by (8.38). The first direct experimental verification of the relativistic variation of mass was provided by Bucherer in 1909. Since then repeated confirmation and refinement of his results by other experiments, some similar in technique and some different, have left no doubt that the basic relation (8.38) is correct. A direct method of measuring the change in mass (8.38) is to determine e/m for very fast electrons by the parabola method, Eq. (3.6). The rest energy of an electron is only $m_0c^2 = 0.51$ mev, so that an accelerating potential of 500 kev will produce electrons with $\beta > 0.8$. Modern accelerating machines can easily produce voltages of this order and higher. Another source of high-speed electrons is the naturally radioactive elements, whose nuclei spontaneously emit α, β, and γ rays. The β rays have been identified as electrons with very high velocities, up to $\beta \approx 0.98$. Bucherer used a β ray source in his early parabola experiment. The results of all such measurements are that the apparent e/m value for very fast electrons deviates systematically from the e/m_0 value for slow electrons. These deviations accurately follow the formula

$$e/m = (e/m_0)\sqrt{1 - \beta^2} \tag{8.38a}$$

in verification of (8.38). For $\beta = 0.98$ the effect is quite pronounced, since $\sqrt{1 - \beta^2} = \frac{1}{5}$.

In this connection we should note that (8.38) holds for uniform motion in a circle, such as described by a charged particle in a constant magnetic induction. Although the particle is under constant acceleration, the acceleration is always perpendicular to v and does not affect the mass-velocity relationship.

Suppose now that we accelerate a body of rest mass m_0 by application of a force F. We assume that the body is originally at rest and that F is constantly in the x-direction. The total amount of work done on the body by the external force is

$$T = \int_0^x F\, dx = \int_0^t Fv\, dt \tag{8.40}$$

The relativistic form of Newton's law is the same as Newton's original statement of it—not $F = ma$, but

$$F = dp/dt = (d/dt)(mv) \tag{8.41}$$

This equation reduces to $F = ma$ only in case m is a constant, which is no longer true in relativity. From (8.38–8.41) we have, performing an integration by parts,

$$\begin{aligned}
T &= \int_0^t v\frac{dp}{dt}\, dt = \int_0^p v\, dp = vp \Big]_0^p - \int_0^v p\, dv \\[6pt]
&= \frac{m_0 v^2}{\sqrt{1 - \beta^2}}\Big]_0^v - \int_0^v \frac{m_0\, d(\frac{1}{2}v^2)}{\sqrt{1 - v^2/c^2}} \\[6pt]
&= m_0 c^2 \left(\frac{\beta^2}{\sqrt{1 - \beta^2}} + \sqrt{1 - \beta^2}\right)_0^v = m_0 c^2 \left(\frac{1}{\sqrt{1 - \beta^2}}\right)_0^v \tag{8.42} \\[6pt]
&= \frac{m_0 c^2}{\sqrt{1 - \beta^2}} - m_0 c^2
\end{aligned}$$

One of the basic laws of physics, which cannot be altered by relativity for any inertial systems is that of the conservation of energy. Therefore the work T must equal the kinetic energy of the body moving at its final velocity v, and this kinetic energy must be convertible back into work when the body comes to rest. We can check this interpretation by considering the limit of (8.42) as $v/c \to 0$, which should equal the classical, nonrelativistic expression for the kinetic energy. For $\beta \ll 1$, we can approximate $(1 - \beta^2)^{1/2}$ by means of a binomial expansion, $(1 - \beta^2)^{-1/2} = 1 + \frac{1}{2}\beta^2$. .... Then (8.42) becomes

$$T = m_0 c^2(1/\sqrt{1 - \beta^2} - 1) \approx m_0' c^2(\tfrac{1}{2}\beta^2) = \tfrac{1}{2}m_0 v^2 \tag{8.43}$$

This is indeed the classical expression for kinetic energy, so that we may call the right-hand side of (8.42) the relativistic kinetic energy of a body of rest mass m_0.

We can also write (8.42) in the form

$$T = \text{K.E.} = E(v) - E(0) \tag{8.43b}$$

$$E(v) = m_0 c^2 / \sqrt{1 - \beta^2} = mc^2 \tag{8.44}$$

That is, the energy of motion (kinetic) is the difference of an energy $E(v)$ characteristic of the body at velocity v and an energy $E(0)$ characteristic of the body at rest. This characteristic energy $E(v)$ should have a name, and the most reasonable one is the total energy of the body. The energy

$$E(0) = m_0 c^2 \tag{8.45}$$

is the rest energy or rest-mass energy of the body. Thus (8.43b) states that the total energy of a body at a velocity v equals its kinetic energy plus an invariant rest-mass energy that is always present and is not ordinarily convertible into any other form of work or energy. Nuclear reactions, however, can accomplish the direct conversion of rest mass into heat or other useful energy. These reactions have provided experimental proof of Eqs. (8.45) and (8.44), which are Einstein's celebrated mass-energy relationship. Another form of (8.44) is

$$E^2 - m_0^2 c^4 = m_0^2 c^4 [1/(1 - \beta^2) - 1]$$
$$= m_0^2 c^2 v^2 / (1 - \beta^2) = p^2 c^2 \tag{8.44a}$$

The relation of mass and energy provides a direct physical interpretation of the classical electron radius r_0, Eq. (4.42). If the electron were a perfectly conducting sphere of radius r_0 and charge $-e$, its electrostatic energy would be e^2/r_0. If we set this electrostatic energy equal to the observed rest-energy $m_0 c^2$, we obtain

$$r_0 = (e^2 / m_0 c^2) = 2.82 \times 10^{-13} \text{ cm} \tag{8.46}$$

It should be emphasized, however, that present electromagnetic theories suggest that the electron rest energy is not entirely electrostatic in character. One cannot speak of "deriving" the relation (8.46). The simple physical interpretation serves merely as an aid to remembering the relations between physical constants.

8.5. Four-vectors

In classical mechanics, the position coordinates x, y, and z form a vector in three dimensions; the time t appears as a nonvector (scalar) quantity quite different from the space coordinates. The Lorentz transformation (8.21) shows that in relativity time is on an equal footing with the space coordinates. This suggests that a particle in relativity must be specified by four equivalent coordinates, x, y, z, ct. Since the number of independent coordinates equals the number of dimensions of the space in which the particle moves, this is a 4-dimensional representation of the particle's behavior. The coordinates x, y, z are said to form a 3-vector, and x, y, z, and ct compose a 4-vector.

A second example of a common physical 4-vector may help to make the concept clear. Consider a particle of rest mass m_0 moving parallel to the x-axis. In system S it has velocity u, in S' it has velocity u'. The corresponding momenta and total energies are

$$p_x = m_0 u / \sqrt{1 - u^2/c^2}, \qquad p_x' = m_0 u' / \sqrt{1 - u'^2/c^2}$$
$$E_0 = m_0 c^2 / \sqrt{1 - u^2/c^2}, \qquad E' = m_0 c^2 / \sqrt{1 - u'^2/c^2} \qquad (8.47)$$

From Eq. (8.25) for the addition of velocities it follows that

$$1 - u^2/c^2 = \frac{(1 - u'^2/c^2)(1 - v^2/c^2)}{(1 + u'v/c^2)^2}$$

$$\frac{1}{\sqrt{1 - u^2/c^2}} = \frac{1 + u'v/c^2}{\sqrt{1 - u'^2/c^2}\ \sqrt{1 - v^2/c^2}} \qquad (8.48)$$

Multiplying by (8.25), we have

$$\frac{u}{\sqrt{1 - u^2/c^2}} = \frac{u' + v}{\sqrt{1 - u'^2/c^2}\ \sqrt{1 - v^2/c^2}} \qquad (8.49)$$

Thus

$$cp_x = \frac{m_0(u' + v)c}{\sqrt{1 - u'^2/c^2}\ \sqrt{1 - v^2/c^2}}$$

$$= \frac{1}{\sqrt{1 - \beta^2}} \left(\frac{m_0 u' c}{\sqrt{1 - u'^2/c}} + \frac{v}{c} \frac{m_0 c^2}{\sqrt{1 - u'^2/c^2}} \right)$$

$$= \frac{cp_x' + \beta E'}{\sqrt{1 - \beta^2}}$$

$$E = \frac{m_0 c^2 (1 + u'v/c^2)}{\sqrt{1 - u'^2/c^2}\ \sqrt{1 - v^2/c^2}} \qquad (8.50)$$

$$= \frac{1}{\sqrt{1 - \beta^2}} \left(\frac{m_0 c^2}{\sqrt{1 - u'^2/c^2}} + v \frac{m_0 u'}{\sqrt{1 - u'^2/c^2}} \right)$$

$$= \frac{E' + \beta(cp_x')}{\sqrt{1 - \beta^2}}$$

where $\beta = v/c$.

Equations (8.50) exactly resemble the Lorentz transformations (8.22) for x and ct. The reverse equation expressing cp_x' and E' in terms of cp_x and E are obtained in the same way and are the analogues of the first Lorentz transformations (8.21). By carrying through similar arguments for the perpendicular components of momentum p_y and p_z, we find that

$$cp_y = cp_y', \quad cp_z = cp_z' \tag{8.51}$$

One therefore concludes that the 3-vector of momentum $c\boldsymbol{p}$ and the total relativistic energy E build a 4-vector in the same way as $\boldsymbol{r}$ and ct.

The factors c are inserted in cp and ct in order to make the transformation equations perfectly symmetric. All the quantities in the transformation now have the same physical dimensions—length (x, y, z, ct) and energy (cp_x, cp_y, cp_z, E). From these examples we arrive by induction at the general rule that any 4-vector (A_1, A_2, A_3, A_4) obeys the transformation law

$$A_1 = \frac{A_1' + \beta A_4'}{\sqrt{1 - \beta^2}}, \qquad A_2 = A_2'$$
$$A_3 = A_3', \qquad A_4 = \frac{A_4' + \beta A_1'}{\sqrt{1 - \beta^2}} \tag{8.52}$$

where the system S' moves relative to S in the 1-direction at a uniform velocity $v = \beta c$ and the 4-direction is the timelike axis. Equation (8.52) is the definition of a 4-vector; from it we can derive the basic property of 4-vectors that

$$A_1^2 + A_2^2 + A_3^2 - A_4^2 = A_1'^2 + A_2'^2 + A_3'^2 - A_4'^2 \tag{8.53}$$

The quantity $(A_1^2 + A_2^2 + A_3^2 - A_4^2)$ is therefore *invariant* under Lorentz transformations. In analogy with the three-dimensional case, this quantity can be called the square of the magnitude of the 4-vector. Thus a 4-vector has the property that its magnitude is invariant under Lorentz transformation.

The squared magnitude of a 4-vector, unlike that of a 3-vector, may be positive, negative, or zero. If the squared magnitude is positive, the vector is called *spacelike* because it resembles the first three terms of (8.53); if the squared magnitude is negative, the vector is *timelike* in agreement with the last term of (8.53). For the coordinate vector of a light beam in vacuum the magnitude is zero,

$$x^2 + y^2 + z^2 - (ct)^2 = 0 \tag{8.54}$$

The Lorentz invariance of this quantity is just another way of stating the postulate that the velocity of light is the same in all systems. The momentum-energy 4-vector of a material particle is timelike, for according to (8.44a)

$$p_x^2 + p_y^2 + p_z^2 - (E/c)^2 = -(m_0 c)^2 \tag{8.55}$$

Here Lorentz invariance is equivalent to the statement that m_0 and c are constant for all systems, so that m_0 must be an intrinsic characteristic of the body under consideration.

8.6. The electromagnetic field

We conclude by mentioning one or two properties of the electromagnetic field in relativity, without giving derivations or a treatment that is in any way complete. From Maxwell's equations we can deduce the transformation laws for the fields in empty space:

$$E_{y-z} = \left(E' + \frac{v \times H'}{c} \right)_{y-z} \bigg/ \sqrt{1 - \beta^2}, \quad E_x = E_x'$$
$$H_{y-z} = \left(H' - \frac{v \times E'}{c} \right)_{y-z} \bigg/ \sqrt{1 - \beta^2}, \quad H_x = H_x' \tag{8.56}$$

where v is in the x-direction. It is of interest to note that, apart from the factor $\gamma = 1/\sqrt{1 - \beta^2}$, the first Eq. (8.56) when multiplied by q (esu) is just the classical force on a charged particle in combined electric and magnetic fields. The second Eq. (8.56) is its counterpart demanded by the symmetry of all relativistic transformations. In relativity there is no clear distinction between electric and magnetic fields, which are combined into a single electromagnetic field. This field has 6 independent components and is something mathematically more elaborate than a 4-vector. It is a *tensor* of a certain type (antisymmetric) in four dimensions, and its closest analogue in three dimensions is the cross product of two vectors. In three dimensions this cross product is equivalent to another vector, but in four dimensions it is not.

Using equations like (8.56), Einstein considered the energy content of an electromagnetic (light) wave in a certain volume. In system S' let the energy contained in a volume V' be equal to W'. Then the energy W contained in the corresponding volume V in S is

$$W = W' \frac{(1 + \beta \cos \alpha')}{\sqrt{1 - \beta^2}} \tag{8.57}$$

where α' is the angle that the direction of the light ray in S' makes with the direction of v, the relative velocity of S' and S. The transformation law (8.57) for the energy content of a light wave is remarkable for being identical with (8.34), the transformation law for the frequency, although the derivation of (8.57) in no way invokes the frequency. From (8.57) and (8.34) we obtain

$$W/\nu = W'/\nu' = h \tag{8.58}$$

where h is a constant of proportionality. This is just the familiar quantum condition (6.2)! It is indeed remarkable that the relativity theory, which treats light exclusively as electromagnetic waves, should lead directly to the idea of the quantum. Relativity itself of course gives no indication of the actual magnitude of h but lends strong support to the quantum concept in general. In the next chapter we shall see how relativistic formulas provide a starting point for further development of quantum mechanics.

SUMMARY

The theory of relativity rests on the postulate that all systems of reference are equivalent if they are inertial; i.e., differ only by motion with a uniform velocity. This means that there is no absolute system of coordinates nor any way for determining an *absolute* velocity for any system S. In particular, we cannot specify any velocity for S by observations made on S alone.

The relativity postulate includes electromagnetic phenomena, so that the velocity of light is a constant for all inertial systems. This hypothesis is in accord with the null result of the Michelson-Morley experiment. From this axiom we can obtain the Lorentz transformation. The transformation is physically equivalent to the apparent shortening of a rod moving with velocity $v = c\beta$ by a factor $\sqrt{1 - \beta^2}$ known as the *Lorentz contraction*. A time interval in a system S' moving with velocity v relative to an observer appears to have lengthened by a corresponding factor $1/\sqrt{1 - \beta^2}$.

This Lorentz factor also appears in the relativistic transformation of mass: a particle of rest mass m_0 has an effective mass $m = m_0/\sqrt{1 - \beta^2}$ when traveling with velocity c. Its total energy at this velocity is mc^2, of which m_0c^2 is rest-mass energy and the remainder is kinetic energy. This kinetic energy $m_0c^2(1/\sqrt{1 - \beta^2} - 1) \approx \frac{1}{2}m_0v^2$ when $v/c = \beta \ll 1$. The rest-mass energy is not ordinarily converted into work or heat, but such conversion occurs in nuclear reactions. The rest energy of an electron is $m_0c^2 = 0.51$ mev.

The Lorentz transformation can be used to define a 4-vector as any four quantities that transform like x, y, z, ct in going from system S to S'. An example is the energy-momentum vector cp_x, cp_y, cp_z, E. The magnitude of a 4-vector is invariant under a Lorentz transformation.

A 4-vector is spacelike or timelike according as its squared magnitude is positive or negative.

The relativistic law for addition of parallel velocities becomes

$$u = (u' + v)/(1 + u'v/c^2)$$

For u', $v \ll c$, this reduces to the classical law of simple addition; but as u' or $v \to c$, the addition formula is such that u can never exceed c, even when u' or $v = c$. Similar formulas exist for the relativistic addition of nonparallel velocities, and for the transformation of the directions of u and u'. The net result of these formulas is the impossibility of achieving any velocity greater than that of light.

The relativistic Doppler effect formula is

$$\nu = \nu' \frac{1 + \beta \cos \alpha'}{\sqrt{1 - \beta^2}}$$

The same transformation law holds for the energy content W of a given volume of a light wave. This implies that

$$W = h\nu$$

Although relativity does not determine the constant h, it gives remarkable support to the quantum hypothesis of light.

REFERENCES

P. G. Bergmann, *Introduction to the Theory of Relativity*, Prentice-Hall, New York (1942).

A. Einstein and others, *The Principle of Relativity*, Dover Publications, New York.

W. Pauli, *Encyclopädie der mathematischen Wissenschaften*, **5** (3), 539 (1921).

ILLUSTRATIVE PROBLEMS

1. If classical theory were valid, what accelerating voltage would be required to produce electrons with the velocity of light? What is, according to relativistic mechanics, the actual velocity of the electrons for this potential? By what fraction has their mass increased?

Solution. Classically, $eV = \frac{1}{2}m_0v^2$, even for $v = c$. Thus $eV = \frac{1}{2}m_0c^2 = 0.25$ mev, or $V = 250$ kv. Relativistically, the kinetic energy is (8.43),

$$T = m_0c^2 \left(\frac{1}{\sqrt{1 - \beta^2}} - 1 \right) = 0.25 \text{ mev} = \frac{1}{2}m_0c^2$$

or $1/\sqrt{1 - \beta^2} = \frac{3}{2}$, so that the velocity is $v = \beta c = \frac{1}{3}\sqrt{5}c = 0.75c$. Their mass is $m_0/\sqrt{1 - \beta^2} = \frac{3}{2}m_0$, an increase of 50% over the rest-mass value.

2. The special theory of relativity is of importance for bodies that move with velocities approaching that of light. Electrons in atomic orbits frequently do have $v \to c$, so that we should incorporate relativistic mechanics into any complete theory of the atom. Estimate v/c for the K electrons in lead.

Solution. According to (6.10) and (6.12) $\frac{1}{2}mv^2 = -U_i = B_i = hcR(Z - \sigma)^2/n^2$, where $Z = 82$, $\sigma = 1$, $n = 1$ and m is the electron mass. Thus

$$\frac{v}{c} = \left(\frac{2hR}{mc}\right)^{1/2} \left(\frac{Z - \sigma}{n}\right)$$

$$= \left(\frac{2 \times 6.62 \times 10^{-27} \times 1.097 \times 10^5}{9.1 \times 10^{28} \times 3 \times 10^{10}}\right)^{1/2} = 0.42$$

On a classical basis we expect these electrons to have 40% of the velocity of light, so that relativistic corrections should be appreciable. Not all atomic electrons move so rapidly; for example, the electron in a hydrogen atom with a radius of 0.53 A has a velocity $v = c/137$. Although this electron velocity is rather small relative to that of light, we must remember that optical measurements are of extremely high precision and will reveal even very small relativistic effects.

PROBLEMS

1. (a) Derive (8.22) from (8.21). (b) Show that the Lorentz contraction (8.23) will account for the null result of the Michelson-Morley experiment.

2. β rays from radium C are deflected in a circle of 16 cm radius by an induction of 121 gausses. They then enter the space between the place parallel plates of a capacitor, which is also in the magnetic field. The capacitor plates are $\frac{1}{4}$ mm apart. Find the velocity v of the electrons, their total energy E, and kinetic energy T in ev, and the potential V on the capacitor plates necessary to pass the electrons.

3. What is the energy in ergs corresponding to 1 gram of rest-mass energy? How does this compare with the energy to be obtained from chemical combustion of a gram of coal? Before the equivalence of mass and energy was realized, a serious problem in astrophysics was the question of why the sun did not rapidly burn itself out. Compare the rates of chemical and "rest-mass" burning of the sun.

4. The elastic impact of two identical particles with rest mass m_0 is described by an observer R as follows:

(i) before impact $m_1 = m_2$, $v_1 = -v_2 = v$,

(ii) after impact $m_1' = m_1 = m_2'$, $v_1' = -v = -v_2'$

(a) What are the total momentum P, total energy E, and total kinetic energy T of the system (of both particles together) for observer R? Give all answers in terms of m_0, v, and c.

(b) How will an observer S, moving with the velocity v (i.e., with m_1 before impact) describe this impact? Give the values of m_1, m_2, v_1, v_2 before and after the impact.

(c) What are the total momentum P_s and the total energy E_s of the system for observer S?

5. In the prerelativity ether theory the ether was supposed to be dragged along to some extent by a moving, transparent medium whose index of refraction differs from unity. Measurements first made by Fizeau on the velocity of light in streaming liquids indicated that the velocity of light is

$$c' = c/n - v(1 - 1/n^2) \qquad (8.59)$$

where v is the streaming velocity of the liquid (directed opposite to c and c') and n its refractive index. Show that (8.59) agrees with the relativistic law (8.25) for the addition of velocities, provided that small terms proportional to $(v/c)^2$ and higher powers are neglected.

The explanation of "ether drag," as well as the negative Michelson-Morley experiment, by the hypothesis that the velocity of light is c for all systems has deprived the concept of the ether of all usefulness. It is now generally discarded.

6. The relation $E = mc^2$ can be used to compute the "effective mass" of a photon. What is this mass for a photon of wavelength 6000 A?

7. Make a rough estimate of how relativity affects the binding energy of atomic electrons. To first approximation show that if the nonrelativistic binding energy is B, the relativistic binding energy is $B(1 + B/2m_0c^2)$ where m_0 is the electron rest mass.

Proceed as follows: Equation (6.10) expresses B and the orbit radius in terms of the electron mass. Classically this mass is m_0, relativistically it is (8.38). The corresponding change in B is evaluated by using the classical value for v^2 as an approximation in $1/\sqrt{1 - \beta^2} \approx 1 + v^2/2c^2$.

How large is this relativistic effect for a K electron in Pb, which has a K absorption edge at 0.141 A?

Chapter 9

WAVE MECHANICS

In the preceding chapters we have encountered a number of phenomena that require quantum mechanics for their explanation. These quantum phenomena scarcely appeared when we viewed the atom from the outside as a classical hard sphere; but as we penetrate into the interior of the atom they become more and more important. The two chief quantum phenomena that we have encountered are the photon, or light quantum, and the quantization of electron orbits in atoms. In previous chapters we simply introduced these ideas as working hypotheses to account for the observations of atomic spectra. We now begin the study of the details of quantum mechanics itself, which also goes under the equivalent title of wave mechanics.

The detailed theory of wave mechanics involves a number of new and at first sight quite striking hypotheses. The statement of these postulates is necessarily rather mathematical in character, and their application to physical phenomena involves considerable mathematical technique. We shall attempt to stress the main physical features of wave mechanics, developing the necessary mathematical apparatus as we go along. Our discussion starts from the formulas of relativity.

9.1. The photon as a particle

Consider the properties of the photons that we suppose to constitute the elements of a light beam in quantum mechanics. They travel in vacuum with the velocity of light and have total energy $E = h\nu$. According to relativistic Eq. (8.44), we can associate this energy with a mass $m = E/c^2 = hc/\lambda$. The rest mass is

$$m_0 = \sqrt{1 - \beta^2}\, m \equiv 0 \qquad (9.1)$$

for any finite energy E of the photon, since $\beta = 1$. Thus a photon behaves like a nonmaterial particle whose energy is entirely kinetic. The momentum associated with this energy is, by (8.44a),

$$p = \frac{1}{c}\sqrt{E^2 - m_0^2 c^4} = \frac{E}{c} = \frac{h}{\lambda} \qquad (9.2)$$

It is frequently convenient to think of the photon as a real particle, even in macroscopic applications where the wave picture of light is also adequate. For example, from (9.2) we can deduce that a light beam of energy density $u = n_v E$ has associated with it a momentum density

$$g = n_v p = u/c \qquad (9.3)$$

Here n_v, the number of photons per unit volume, does not appear explicitly in the final relation (9.3); thus we expect that (9.3) is of general validity for both the particle and wave pictures of light. This is in fact the case, but the derivation of (9.3) from the wave picture alone is considerably more complicated than (9.2) and does not involve so immediate a physical picture of the situation. In the wave theory the momentum of light is associated with the Poynting vector, which represents energy flow (Appendix IV); but it is not simple to give a rigorous proof of this association.

The linear momentum of light is observable through the pressure that it produces. Suppose a beam of light containing (n_v) photons of energy E per unit volume impinges normally on a plane surface. If the surface completely absorbs the photons, it also absorbs momentum at the rate

$$cn_v p = F/A = P \qquad (9.4)$$

per unit area of its surface. A rate of change of momentum is equivalent to a force F; and the force per unit area is the pressure P on the surface, as given by (9.4). Comparison with (9.3) shows that

$$P = u \qquad (9.5a)$$

If the surface is totally reflecting, the photons bounce off and reverse their incident momentum, so that the momentum change at the surface is twice as great as for absorption. Then

$$P = 2u \qquad (9.5b)$$

As before, relations (9.5) are derivable from the wave theory of light, but a rigorous derivation is more difficult and physically less immediate. The pressure (9.5) was directly measured by Lebedev and by Nichols and Hull, shortly before the special theory of relativity appeared. Highly polished mirrors were hung on a delicate torsion balance, in which oscillations were excited by periodic illumination of the mirrors with strong artificial light. The observations confirm (9.5b) within experimental error.

9.2. The angular momentum of light

In addition to its linear momentum, light also possesses an angular momentum. This angular momentum is predictable from the classical, wave picture of light and has been measured in a macroscopic experiment by Beth. The classical theory and the experiment involve the torque produced by light in a doubly refracting medium. This is an optical medium like calcite, which has different refractive indices in different directions. We can choose a set of *principal axes* in the material such that the relationship $D = \epsilon E$ of a simple refractive medium (Eq. 6a, Appendix IV) becomes

$$D_x = \epsilon_x E_x, \quad D_y = \epsilon_y E_y, \quad D_z = \epsilon_z E_z \tag{9.6}$$

where ϵ_x, ϵ_y, ϵ_z are not all equal. In spite of this asymmetry, relation (IV-7a) still holds for the polarization P per unit volume. We can regard P as representing the number of electric dipoles per unit volume; according to (IV-13a) the total torque per unit volume is

$$N = P \times E = \frac{1}{4\pi} (D - E) \times E = \frac{1}{4\pi} D \times E \tag{9.7}$$

since $E \times E \equiv 0$. In an ordinary medium where $D = \epsilon E$, N would also vanish identically, but in a doubly refracting medium it does not.

Suppose that a slab of doubly refracting material is cut so that two of its principal axes are parallel to the plane faces of the slab, and the third axis (z-axis) is perpendicular. Let a plane-polarized light wave be incident along the z-axis. The incident E vector of amplitude E_0 makes an angle θ with the principal x-axis of the medium. The components of E after passing through a thickness z of the crystal are

$$E_x = E_0 \cos \theta \cos \frac{ct - n_x z}{\bar{\lambda}}$$
$$E_y = E_0 \sin \theta \cos \frac{ct - n_y z}{\bar{\lambda}} \tag{9.8}$$

where $n_x = \sqrt{\epsilon_x}$, $n_y = \sqrt{\epsilon_y}$ (we take the magnetic permeability of the medium to be $\mu = 1$), and $\bar{\lambda} = \lambda/2\pi = c/\omega$. We shall call both λ and $\bar{\lambda}$ the "wavelength" and avoid confusion by writing the appropriate symbol.

From (9.6)–(9.8) we calculate the torque per unit volume at a depth z in the slab:

$$N = N i_z = \frac{i_z}{4\pi} E_0^2 \sin \theta \cos \theta (\epsilon_x - \epsilon_y) \cos \frac{ct - n_x z}{\bar{\lambda}} \cos \frac{ct - n_y z}{\bar{\lambda}} \tag{9.9}$$

The axis of the torque is the direction of propagation of the light beam. To take the time average of (9.9), we note that

$$\cos (\omega t + A) \cos (\omega t + B) = \tfrac{1}{2}[\cos (2\omega t + A + B) + \cos (A - B)].$$

The first term in the brackets averages to zero, and the second term is a constant. From the second term the magnitude of the torque per unit volume at depth z is

$$N(z) = \frac{E_0{}^2}{16\pi} (\sin 2\theta)(\epsilon_x - \epsilon_y) \cos\left[\frac{(n_x - n_y)z}{\lambda}\right] \qquad (9.10)$$

The total torque per unit area exerted on the slab is the integral of (9.10) over the entire thickness z_0 :

$$T/A = \int_0^{z_0} N \, dz \qquad (9.11)$$

$$= (E_0/4\pi)^2 n\lambda \sin 2\theta \sin (\Delta n z_0/\lambda)$$

where $n = \frac{1}{2}(n_x + n_y)$, $\Delta n = n_x - n_y$.

The sign and magnitude of the torque (9.11) depend on the thickness of the slab. A maximum torque occurs for a slab of thickness

$$z_0 = (\pi/2)(\lambda/\Delta n) = \tfrac{1}{4}(\lambda/\Delta n) \qquad (9.12)$$

Such a slab is called a *quarter-wave plate* because of the factor $\frac{1}{4}$ occurring in (9.12). A quarter-wave plate has the property that it turns plane-polarized light into circularly polarized, and vice versa, as can be seen from manipulating Eqs. (9.8). Suppose now that we combine two quarter-wave plates to make a total thickness twice that given by (9.12), and that circularly polarized light is incident on the first plate. It produces in this plate a torque per unit area (T/A) given by (9.11) and emerges plane-polarized. In the second plate it also produces a torque T/A and emerges circularly polarized in the opposite sense from the incident beam. Thus this *half-wave plate* reverses the circular polarization of the incident light, suffering in the process a torque $2(T/A)$. When the angle θ is adjusted to be 45°, this torque takes its maximum value

$$2(T_0/A) = 2n\lambda(E_0/4\pi)^2 \qquad (9.13)$$

By reflecting the transmitted beam on a mirror and passing the reflected beam back through the plate, Beth was able to increase (T/A) by another factor of 2 over (9.13). The half-wave plate was hung on a fiber to form a torsion pendulum. The equilibrium position of the pendulum was determined by measuring its free oscillations: first with no light passing through the plate, then with right circularly polarized light, and finally as a check with left circularly polarized light. The shift of the equilibrium position under these different circumstances measures the torque (9.13). The observations confirm not only the existence of the torque but also its predicted magnitude.

We can associate this torque directly with angular momentum of the light beam. According to Newton's law of action and reaction the torque T/A on the crystal implies an equal and opposite torque $-T/A$ on the light beam itself. The mechanical definition of torque is that $T = \Delta L/\Delta t$, where ΔL is the change in angular momentum of the system to which the torque is applied, and Δt is the time interval during which ΔL occurs. If the thickness of the half-wave plate is l, the time during which $-T$ acts on any part of the beam is $\Delta t = l/v = ln/c$. Here $v = c/n$ is the velocity of the light through the plate. Let $\Omega = L/V$ be the angular momentum per unit volume in the beam. Then

$$T/A = \frac{\Delta L}{A \, \Delta t} = \frac{c \, \Delta L}{(lA)n} = \Delta\Omega c/n \qquad (9.14)$$

where $lA = V$. The total change in angular momentum density on passage through the half-wave plate is, from (9.13) and (9.14),

$$\Delta\Omega = \frac{n}{c}\frac{T}{A} = \frac{2n^2}{c}\left(\frac{E_0}{4\pi}\right)^2 \lambda = \frac{2\epsilon\lambda}{c}\frac{E_0^2}{8\pi}$$
$$= 2\lambda u/c \qquad (9.15)$$

Here $n^2 = \mu\epsilon = \epsilon$, and the energy density of the light beam in the medium, according to (IV-14a) is $U = \epsilon E_0^2/8\pi$.

A light beam experiences the change $\Delta\Omega$ when its circular polarization reverses its direction. The simplest and most direct interpretation of (9.15) is that right (left) circularly polarized light has an angular momentum density

$$\Omega = \pm\lambda u/c \qquad (9.16)$$

The change when right circularly polarized light is converted to left circular polarization is $\Delta\Omega = [+\lambda u/c - (-\lambda u/c)] = 2\lambda u/c$ as in (9.15). The angular momentum density (9.16) is really a vector, $\boldsymbol{\Omega}$, directed parallel or antiparallel to the direction of propagation of the beam. Unpolarized and plane-polarized light have no net angular momentum density: they contain equal numbers of right and left circularly polarized components. Any light beam can be decomposed mathematically into circularly polarized components, regardless of whether the original beam has any net polarization.

The association of angular momentum density with circular polarization is a fundamental aspect of light. On a classical picture the production of a circularly polarized beam of light requires an atomic electron moving in a circle. As the electron loses energy by radiation, it spirals towards the center of the atom, thus losing angular momentum. The total angular momentum of the system must be conserved, however, according to the general principles of mechanics. This implies that the circularly polarized radiation carries off angular momentum.

The photon interpretation of light describes circularly polarized light as a stream of circularly polarized photons. Beth's experiment indicates that each photon carries an angular momentum by rotating about its direction of propagation as an axis.

Consider a circularly polarized, monochromatic light beam containing n_v photons per unit volume, and denote by L_z the magnitude of the angular momentum of each photon about the z-axis (direction of propagation of the beam). Then (9.16) becomes

$$n_V L_z = \Omega = \pm \lambda u/c = \pm (\lambda/c) n_V h\nu$$

$$L_z = \pm h/2\pi = \pm \hbar \qquad (9.17)$$

The quantity $h/2\pi$ occurs so often in quantum mechanics that we use the special symbol $\hbar$ for it. Equation (9.17) states that the z-component of a photon's angular momentum must have one of the two specific values $\pm \hbar$. This statement is important in two respects: it shows that the quantum mechanical unit for angular momentum is $\hbar$; and, more essential, it exemplifies the principle of *space quantization*. The angular momentum component L_z of a photon is strictly quantized, for it can take one of only two discrete values. This principle of space quantization, if extended to material particles like atoms, exactly explains the observations of Stern and Gerlach (section 3.7). The details of this explanation will be developed in Chapters 10 and 11. The space quantization principle can even be made to yield the quantization of orbits in atoms (section 9.6)!

9.3. The Compton effect

The preceding sections have discussed the macroscopic evidence for the linear and angular momentum of light. The microscopic evidence gives more detailed support to these concepts. "Microscopic" processes here are those involving one photon at a time. The Compton effect, first studied in 1923, provides striking experimental proof of the reality of the linear momentum of individual photons. In this experiment X-ray photons, which have relatively short wavelengths and hence large momenta, scatter from electrons bound in atoms. The outermost optical electrons have binding energies of only a few electron volts, which is negligible in comparison with the energy of an X-ray photon, some 10^4 to 10^5 electron volts. That is, the effect is practically the same as if the electron were free and at rest. We shall therefore consider the mathematically simpler probem of photon scattering by a free and initially stationary electron.

This case is an example of a procedure that repeatedly proves very useful in physics. When a physical problem appears too difficult to solve directly, we try instead to find an artificial problem that is readily soluble and is as much like the given problem as possible. After solving the artificial problem, we can frequently improve the solution to resemble more closely that of the real problem. The chief skill involved is to formulate a soluble problem that closely resembles the original problem.

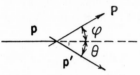

Consider the elastic scattering of a photon from a free electron at rest. We take the photon to be a particle with definite energy and momentum. The collision is like that of two perfectly elastic billiard balls, and the laws of conservation of energy and momentum should apply. In Figure 9.1 the initial and final photon momenta are p, p' with corresponding energies E, E'. The electron momentum after collision is P, and its kinetic energy is $T = mc^2 - m_0c^2$. Now we have

Fig. 9.1. Compton collision.

$$p - p' = P \qquad \text{(conservation of momentum)} \qquad (9.18)$$

$$E - E' = T \qquad \text{(conservation of energy)} \qquad (9.19)$$

$$P^2c^2 = (T + m_0c^2)^2 - m_0^2c^4$$

$$= T^2 + 2m_0c^2T \qquad (9.20)$$

$$\text{(momentum-energy relation for the electron)}$$

$$pc = E, \qquad p'c = E' \qquad (9.21)$$
$$\text{(momentum-energy relation for photons)}$$

The boldface type indicates 3-dimensional vectors; the same symbols in ordinary type are the magnitudes of these vectors.

If θ is the angle between initial and final photon directions,

$$P \cdot P = P^2 = (p - p') \cdot (p - p')$$
$$= p^2 + p'^2 - 2pp' \cos \theta \qquad (9.22)$$

From (9.19) and (9.21) we have

$$T = E - E' = (p - p')c \qquad (9.23)$$

and from (9.20) and (9.23),

$$P^2 = (1/c^2)T^2 + 2m_0T$$
$$= (p - p')^2 + 2m_0c(p - p') \qquad (9.24)$$

Combining (9.22) and (9.24), multiplying by h, and using (9.2), we have

$$2m_0c(p - p') = 2pp'(1 - \cos \theta)$$

$$h(1/p' - 1/p) = h/m_0c(1 - \cos \theta) \qquad (9.25)$$

$$\lambda' - \lambda = 2\pi\lambda_0(1 - \cos \theta)$$

Equation (9.25) is the basic relation of the Compton effect. It states that in scattering by a free electron an X-ray photon will increase its wavelength by an amount that depends on the angle of scattering. The only other quantity appearing in the final equation is the *Compton wavelength* of the electron,

$$\lambda_0 = 2\pi\lambda_0 = h/m_0c = 2.426 \times 10^{-10} \text{ cm} \qquad (9.25a)$$

which depends only on the fundamental constants h, m_0, c.

Experiments verify all the features of (9.25), providing the most direct possible evidence for the existence of light quanta. Paradoxically, the Compton effect occurs in crystals together with Bragg reflection, a phenomenon that we can explain only by treating light as continuous wave motion. This is a primary example of the wave-particle duality that is an inherent feature of wave mechanics. There seems in fact to be no way to resolve the dilemma. Physicists are now accustomed to describing phenomena alternatively in terms of particles or of waves, whichever seems best suited to the purpose.

Although the Compton and photoelectric effects both reveal the photon character of light, there is an important physical difference between them. In the Compton effect, momentum and energy are conserved between the photon and electron alone. In the photoelectric effect, the photon is entirely absorbed and gives up all its energy to the ejected electron. The student can readily prove for himself that the photon and electron alone cannot conserve momentum in this case. Conservation of momentum is, however, one of the few principles of classical mechanics that carry over absolutely without modification into wave mechanics. In the photoelectric effect, therefore, we must recall that the electron is originally bound by electric forces to a nucleus much heavier than itself. The binding forces serve as a means for transmitting momentum to the nucleus. If the nuclear recoil momentum is P, its energy is $P^2/2M$; therefore if the nuclear mass M is very large, the nucleus can absorb a large amount of momentum without acquiring much energy. The photoelectric effect would be impossible without the nuclear recoil. For a free electron only the Compton effect can occur, and for this reason it was appropriate to neglect the binding energy in the discussion above. This qualitative argument indicates that the photoelectric effect is most important for photon energies of the same order as the electron binding energy. The Compton effect is dominant for higher photon energies.

9.4. de Broglie's hypothesis

The particle attributes of light were known from the early days of quantum theory around 1905. During the same period the theory of relativity gave additional evidence that the Lorentz transformation properties of a light wave were those of a particle with zero rest mass. On the whole, however, light was regarded as wavelike in character.

If a wave motion had certain particle-like properties, it might have seemed natural to ask whether nature was symmetrical in this regard—whether particles might not have certain wavelike aspects. Eventually such a hypothesis was indeed made and became the cornerstone of wave mechanics. In 1924 de Broglie postulated that material particles as well as light quanta have associated with them an intrinsic frequency ν and wavelength λ, given by

$$\nu = E/h, \qquad \lambda = h/p \tag{9.26}$$

where p and E are, respectively, the momentum and total energy of the particle. The medium in which this wave motion exists is not specified, since the ether postulated for that purpose in the case of light turns out to be illusory.

In the case of a photon with zero rest mass, $pc = E$, so that de Broglie's relations yield $\lambda\nu = E/p = c$ which is indeed true for light. For a material particle with $m_0 \neq 0$ the relation is more complicated, and we must discuss *group* and *phase* velocities. Consider a superposition of two almost identical waves moving along the x-axis, represented by

$$\varphi_1 = A \cos \left[2\pi(\nu_1 t - x/\lambda_1)\right]$$
$$\varphi_2 = A \cos \left[2\pi(\nu_2 t - x/\lambda_2)\right] \tag{9.27}$$

The superposition is a wave

$$\begin{aligned}
\Phi &= \varphi_1 + \varphi_2 \\
&= 2A \cos \left\{2\pi \left[\frac{\nu_1 - \nu_2}{2} t - \frac{x}{2}\left(\frac{1}{\lambda_1} - \frac{1}{\lambda_2}\right)\right]\right\} \\
&\quad \times \cos \left\{2\pi \left[\frac{\nu_1 + \nu_2}{2} t - \frac{x}{2}\left(\frac{1}{\lambda_1} + \frac{1}{\lambda_2}\right)\right]\right\}
\end{aligned} \tag{9.28}$$

If $\lambda_1 \approx \lambda_2 \approx \lambda$ and $\nu_1 \approx \nu_2 \approx \nu$, we can write the second factor of (9.28) as $\cos\left[2\pi(\nu t - x/\lambda)\right]$. This represents a wave motion with velocity

$$v = \lambda\nu \tag{9.29}$$

which is the *phase velocity*. The first factor of (9.28) is a much more slowly varying amplitude function that represents wave motion with a velocity

$$w = \frac{\Delta \nu}{\Delta(1/\lambda)} = \frac{d\nu}{d(1/\lambda)} = -\frac{\lambda^2 \, d\nu}{d\lambda} = v - \lambda \frac{d\nu}{d\lambda} \qquad (9.30)$$

The velocity w is the *group velocity*, a term readily understood from Fig. 9.2. The wave motion (9.28) consists of a rapid oscillation enclosed by more slowly varying envelopes. The solid lines in Fig. 9.2 progress with the phase velocity v, generally greater than the group velocity w of the envelopes. Thus the wave train appears to be constantly moving through the slower envelopes without distorting their shape.

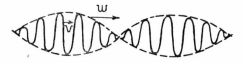

Fig. 9.2. Phase velocity v and group velocity w of wave packets.

We can obtain some intuitive notion of the wave-particle duality from this picture. Each of the envelopes of Fig. 9.2 forms a "wave packet," which we must clearly associate with the particle aspect, while the waves of phase velocity v represent the wave aspect. For a material particle, the phase and group velocities are

$$v = \lambda \nu = E/p = c\sqrt{1 + (m_0 c/p)^2} \qquad (9.31)$$

$$w = d\nu/d(1/\lambda) = dE/dp = c/\sqrt{1 + (m_0 c/p)^2} \qquad (9.32)$$

$$vw = c^2 \qquad (9.33)$$

The group or particulate velocity is always less than c, as is required by relativity. Conversely, the phase velocity is always greater than c, for a material particle. In the light of relativity we must simply interpret this to mean that we cannot experience such wave motion directly. For a photon with $m_0 = 0$, $w = v = c$.

Figure 9.2 also applies to the photon versus wave picture of light. Under the de Broglie hypothesis, the distinction between material particles and photons largely disappears: they are distinguished mainly by nonvanishing and zero values for their rest masses.

9.5. Crystal diffraction of electrons

The first direct demonstration of the wave motion associated with particles was the experiment of Davisson and Germer (1927). In the chapter on X-rays we noted that interference phenomena can be interpreted only in terms of waves and not in terms of particles. Thus diffraction by crystals proves the wave nature of X-rays. Davisson and Germer tried the same measurement with electrons instead of X-rays and looked for something similar to Bragg reflection.

The experiment consists of shooting a beam of electrons from an electron "gun" at a nickel crystal. If the wave hypothesis is valid, the electrons should show interference maxima at glancing angles given by Bragg's relation

$$n\lambda = 2\, d \sin \theta \qquad (9.34)$$

The effective spacing of the planes in nickel is $d = 2.15$ A, and the first question in the experiment is what energy of electrons to use. The energy must be such that the de Broglie wavelength λ is less than $2\,d$; it should not be too much smaller than d, however, in order to make the maxima for different n widely spaced and easily distinguishable. Using (9.26) and the nonrelativistic momentum-energy relation valid for a slow electron, we obtain

$$\lambda = h/p = h/\sqrt{2mT} = 12.26 \text{ A}/\sqrt{V} \qquad (9.35)$$

where T is the kinetic energy of the electron, m its mass, and V the accelerating voltage in volts of the electron gun. In the case of nickel it is necessary to use $V > 9$ volts, say up to V around 100 volts— voltages easily obtainable in the laboratory.

The measurement was first performed with electrons of about 50–60 electron volts energy. Peaks appeared that correspond to diffraction of the electron waves not only from the Bragg planes in the crystal, but also from the lattices of the surface planes. The surface diffraction follows Eq. (5.15), where b is the lattice constant. The positions of the peaks and their variation with V confirmed (9.35) within the experimental error. This provided a striking validation of de Broglie's hypothesis. We have many indirect proofs which support the hypothesis to a much higher degree of precision than that attainable with such a direct experiment.

9.6. The Bohr atom

The high-precision confirmations of de Broglie's hypothesis come mainly from optical spectra, where extremely accurate measurements are possible. In this section we shall see how the hypothesis (9.26) provides a natural basis for the quantization of electron orbits in an atom. It also introduces the integer quantum numbers n that characterize the term values of these orbits, and provides a theoretical formula for the Rydberg constant R in terms of fundamental constants e, h, c, and m_0, the electron rest mass. The simple pictorial model used here is due to Bohr (1913).

Suppose that an electron is moving in a circular orbit with constant velocity—what becomes of its associated wave motion? The associated waves of wavelength $\lambda = h/p$ must also follow the circular path. In order for the electron motion in the orbit to be stable, the wave train must form a *standing wave*. Imagine that we try to wrap an infinitely long wave train of wavelength λ around a circular orbit of radius r. The total wave at any position on the circumference represents a sum over many different points on the original train. Unless the original wave is exactly in phase at all these corresponding points, destructive interference will exist and the net total wave on the circular orbit will be zero. If the original wave is exactly in phase at all points that correspond to a single position on the circle, the interference is constructive and a nonvanishing standing wave is set up. This phase condition is

$$2\pi r = n\lambda \tag{9.36a}$$

where n is an integer. Substituting (9.26), we have

$$L = mvr = n(h/2\pi) = n\hbar \tag{9.36}$$

where L is the angular momentum of the electron in its orbit.

The form (9.36), without the physical interpretation (9.36a), was introduced by Bohr a decade before de Broglie's hypothesis, as an *ad hoc* assumption to help explain atomic spectra. It is interesting to note that (9.36) is a generalization of Eq. (9.17) for the angular momentum of a photon. The photon can have as its z-component of L only one unit of $\hbar$, while according to (9.36) the electron in an atomic orbit can have any integral multiple of $\hbar$ for its angular momentum.

Equation (9.36) provides the quantization of atomic orbits that spectroscopic observations show to be necessary. The integer n in (9.36) plays the role of the principal quantum number in the empirical formulae for atomic spectra. To see in detail how this comes about, consider the equations for an electron in a circular orbit about a central charge $+Ze$. From (6.10),

$$mvr = pr = Ze^2/v \tag{9.37}$$

and by (9.36),

$$Ze^2/\hbar v = pr/\hbar = n \tag{9.38}$$

Equation (9.38) relates the quantum number n to the orbital velocity v and hence to the electron energy. The binding energy in the orbit is

$$B = -U = +\frac{1}{2}m_0 v^2 = +\frac{1}{2}(m_0 c^2)\frac{(\alpha Z)^2}{n^2} \tag{9.39}$$

$$\alpha = \frac{e^2}{\hbar c} = \frac{1}{137} \tag{9.40}$$

Equation (9.39) expresses the electron binding energy in terms of the rest mass energy $m_0 c^2$ of the electron, the effective charge Z at the center of the orbit, the quantum number n, and the quantity α defined in (9.40). This quantity α is the "fine structure constant" of Sommerfeld: it is a number without physical dimensions, as the reader can check for himself, taking e to be in esu. The best numerical value of $1/\alpha$ at present is not quite the integer 137, but deviates by less than 0.1% from this number, which we can use as a good approximation.

The term value corresponding to (9.39) is

$$T = \frac{B}{hc} = \frac{B}{2\pi\hbar c} = \frac{1}{4\pi}\left(\frac{m_0 c}{\hbar}\right)\frac{\alpha^2 Z^2}{n^2} = \frac{RZ^2}{n^2} \qquad (9.41)$$

$$R = \frac{\alpha^2}{4\pi\lambdabar_0} \qquad (9.42)$$

where $\lambdabar_0 = \lambda_0/2\pi$ is the electron Compton wavelength appearing in (9.25). The quantity R defined by (9.42) turns out to have the same numerical value as the spectroscopically measured Rydberg constant, $R = 1.097 \times 10^5$ cm^{-1}. Equation (9.42) represents a great triumph for the quantum theory in relating the optical constant R to the physical constants e, m, c, and h. Equation (9.41) explains the term values (6.16) observed for the X-ray shells. The K-, L-, M-, $\cdots$ shells correspond to quantum numbers $n = 1, 2, 3, \cdots$ as expected for the lowest and next lowest energy levels. The factor $(Z - \sigma)$ in (6.16) is the effective central positive charge seen by the electrons in any shell: it is the total charge $+Ze$ on the nucleus minus the screening by an average of σ negative electrons. For optical spectra the term values (7.7) follow from (9.41) by assuming the nucleus is completely shielded by the other $Z - 1$ electrons. By convention we express any failure of the shielding for the optical electron by changing n to $n' = n - \Delta_n$ instead of altering $Z_{\text{eff}} = 1$.

If, however, we remove one electron from an atom with two optical electrons, the remaining positive ion has one optical electron with $Z_{\text{eff}} = 2$. Using this picture and (9.41), we can readily understand the laws of isoelectronic sequence in section 7.5.

For the hydrogen atom there is no "core" of electrons inside the optical electron, and Eq. (9.41) should hold with $Z = 1$ and $\Delta_n = 0$. Since this is the ideal case to which formula (9.41) applies, it is instructive to consider some of the magnitudes associated with the hydrogen atom. The binding energy in the ground state is

$$B = hcR = 13.6 \text{ ev} \qquad (9.43)$$

The binding energies of the $K(n = 1)$ electrons in heavier elements increase roughly as Z^2, so that for an element like lead the K shell energy is on the order of 100 kev, as indicated by X-ray absorption edges. For L electrons the binding energies are less by a factor $\frac{1}{4}$ = $1/n^2$ in addition to the reduction caused by screening of the nucleus.

The radius of the smallest orbit for the hydrogen atom, corresponding to the ground state energy (9.43) is by (6.10) for $Z = 1$,

$$r = e^2/2B = a_0 = 0.53 \text{ A} \tag{9.44}$$

For the K orbits of heavier atoms we have $r = Ze^2/B$, where B increases as Z^2, so that the net effect is to reduce r as $1/Z$. The K shells of heavy elements thus have radii on the order of 10^{-10} cm. The radius of the hydrogen ground orbit serves as a sort of secondary standard of length for some atomic problems, since all atoms have exterior dimensions on the order of 1 A. The conventional symbol for this "Bohr orbit radius" is a_0, as in (9.44). The radii of higher orbits increase as $n^2 a_0$.

We have by this time introduced four different lengths to characterize electrons in atoms: $1/R$, a_0, λ_0, and r_0. It is interesting to note that these quantities differ essentially by powers of α; using the definitions (9.42), (9.44), (9.25a), and (4.42), the reader can readily verify that

$$\frac{1}{4\pi R} = \frac{a_0}{\alpha} = \frac{\lambda_0}{\alpha^2} = \frac{r_0}{\alpha^3} \tag{9.45}$$

Relation (9.38) is useful for estimating the importance of relativistic corrections for an electron in a particular orbit. We have

$$\beta = v/c = \alpha Z/n \tag{9.46}$$

For the lowest orbit of hydrogen, $v = c/137$, so that relativistic corrections are not large. In the K shell of lead, however, $v \approx 0.6c$, so that relativistic corrections are appreciable. They become rapidly smaller with increasing n, since the corrections are generally of order β^2.

9.7. Further details of the Bohr-Sommerfeld atom

We must emphasize that the simple model used here is no longer regarded as giving a completely correct picture of the atom. It was historically the first successful attempt to explain orbit quantization in atoms, however, and still remains conceptually the simplest way of doing so. For this reason we have discussed it briefly. Because of its inadequacies this "old quantum mechanics" has now been entirely replaced by the "new quantum mechanics," which was developed after de Broglie's hypothesis and is the subject of Chapter 10.

Many of the conclusions obtained from considering the old quantum mechanical model remain nonetheless true in the new quantum mechanics. Because of its pictorial simplicity we use the quasi-classical Bohr model in this section to obtain a few generally valid results. In Chapter 4, an electron circulating in any orbit with a constant angular momentum L produces a constant magnetic dipole moment, given by $\mathbf{\mu} = GL$, where $G = e/2mc$ is the gyromagnetic ratio, Eq. (4.4). Relations (9.17) and (9.36) strongly suggest that all angular momenta in atoms are of the order of magnitude of $\hbar$, say

$$L = l\hbar \tag{9.47}$$

where l is a fairly small, physically dimensionless number. It becomes convenient to express the magnetic moment in terms of $\hbar$ also:

$$\mu = GL = g_L\mu_0 l \tag{9.48}$$

$$\mu_0 = e\hbar/2m_0c = 0.927 \text{ erg/gauss} \tag{9.49}$$

$$g_L = 1 \tag{9.50}$$

Here μ_0 is the *Bohr magneton*. Its order of magnitude is as expected from paramagnetic measurements. We have also added for convenience in later applications a dimensionless "g factor."

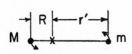

Fig. 9.3 Rotation of atom about center of gravity

In the case of orbital angular momentum L, the g factor is $g_L = 1$, so its insertion is superfluous. It will be useful in Chapter 11, where we encounter cases where $g \neq 1$.

We obtain a further confirmation of the model on which we deduced the expression (9.42) for R by considering the effect of nuclear motion. In deriving (6.10), we implicitly assumed that the nucleus was a fixed center; i.e., that it was infinitely heavy relative to the electron. This is not literally true. For the lightest elements the nucleus is around 10^4 times as heavy as the electron, so that its motion will have an effect of order 10^{-4} on the Bohr orbits and energies. Fractions like 10^{-4} are readily measurable in spectroscopy, however, which is a principal reason for the great fruitfulness of this field. In a precise treatment of the one-electron atom, both electron and nucleus should be considered as rotating about their common center of mass, as indicated in Fig. 9.3. The center of mass is defined by $MR = mr'$; the total radius is $r = R + r'$, or hence

$$r' = \left(\frac{M}{M + m}\right)r \tag{9.51}$$

Here m and M are the respective electron and nuclear masses. By repeating the arguments that lead to (9.41), we find that the net result of the nuclear motion is to reduce E by the same factor as r in (9.51). Thus

$$E_n = -\frac{1}{2}\frac{(\alpha Z)^2}{n^2}\left(\frac{mM}{m+M}\right)c^2 \qquad (9.52)$$

The factor $mM/(m+M)$ is the "reduced mass" of the electron in the center of mass system.

From (9.52) we see that the Rydberg constant of (9.42) is really R_∞, corresponding to infinite nuclear mass M. Then

$$R_M = (M/M + m)R_\infty \qquad (9.53)$$

The difference between R_M and R_∞ is greatest for hydrogen, where

$$R_\infty = 109,737.3 \text{ cm}^{-1}, \qquad R_H = 109,677.6 \text{ cm}^{-1} \quad (9.54)$$

From these experimental values and (9.53) we can deduce the ratio M/m for the hydrogen nucleus and electron. It is found to be $M/m = 1836$, in excellent agreement with the deflection measurements of e/m for electrons and hydrogen ions.

The simple circular orbits of section 9.6 may be generalized to elliptical orbits with the nucleus at one focus, a step first taken by Sommerfeld. Although this development encompasses some further details of atomic structure, it belongs to the now discarded old quantum theory and will not be discussed here.

9.8. The correspondence principle

Quantum mechanics, in its "old" or "new" form, represents a radical departure from classical theory. The question then arises, how can the laws of classical mechanics and electrodynamics be valid for large-scale phenomena when they fail so badly in application to atoms and electrons? The answer is that quantum mechanics is fundamental and correct in every situation, while classical mechanics is only an approximation valid under conditions generally satisfied in the macroscopic world. In quantum mechanical terms we can state these conditions rather precisely: quantum mechanics approaches infinitesimally close to classical mechanics in the limit as the quantum numbers $n \to \infty$. This is the *principle of correspondence* between classical and quantum mechanics enunciated by Bohr for the old quantum mechanics; it is equally valid for the new. It strongly resembles the theorems in mathematics that a series like $1/n$, where x takes only integer values, is well approximated by the continuous function $1/x$, when $x, n \gg 1$. The difference between quantum (integer) and classical (continuous) formulas is most pronounced for low values of n.

As an illustration of this correspondence, consider the frequencies of light emitted by the hydrogen atom from orbits of large n. The frequency for a transition from n_1 to n_2 is

$$\nu = kc = Rc(1/n_1^2 - 1/n_2^2) \qquad (9.55)$$

If the change $\Delta n = (n_2 - n_1) \ll n_1$, n_2, this expression becomes approximately

$$\nu \approx (2Rc/n^3)\,\Delta n = \nu_0\,\Delta n$$

$$n \approx n_1 \approx n_2 \qquad (9.56)$$

Since $\Delta n = 1, 2, 3, \cdots$, the frequencies (9.56) are just the harmonics of a fundamental frequency $\nu_0 = 2Rc/n^3$. The frequency of rotation of the electron in its orbit is, from (9.37–39), (9.41),

$$\nu_r = \frac{v}{2\pi r} = \frac{1}{\pi}\frac{(\tfrac{1}{2}mv^2)}{mvr} = \frac{1}{\pi}\frac{B}{n\hbar} = \frac{1}{\pi n\hbar}\frac{hcR}{n^2} = \frac{2Rc}{n^3} \qquad (9.57)$$

Thus the fundamental frequency of radiation equals the frequency of electron rotation in its orbit, which is just the classical result. Note that (9.56) is an approximation valid only if $\Delta n \ll n$. Thus a second requirement for quantum mechanics to approach classical mechanics is that in any transition $\Delta n \ll n$.

9.9. The uncertainty principle

The stationary orbits for atomic electrons that follow from de Broglie's hypothesis combine some features of the static and dynamic models. This is why each of these classical models could lead in some instances to correct conclusions. In the quantum mechanical picture of an atomic state, the wave packet of the electron is distributed over the entire region occupied by the classical orbit. This distribution can be regarded as a standing wave that does not vary with time; in this way we can understand how such states can exist without radiating. On the other hand, this description does not permit us to specify exactly the position or velocity of the electron in the atom. Thus to obtain the advantages of a wave packet picture of stationary states, we must abandon the idea of classical kinematics, where the position and velocity of a point particle (electron) can always be specified exactly.

This sacrifice of classical kinematics is not peculiar to the problem of the atom but is a fundamental, general feature of wave mechanics. In fact, one statement of the basic postulates of the new quantum mechanics is that a classical, completely determined motion cannot be ascribed to any mechanical system, including atoms. This is the *uncertainty principle*. Its discussion here will serve to introduce the philosophy of the new quantum mechanics, which is the basis for the treatment of the atom in Chapter 10.

The philosophy of the uncertainty principle is directly akin to that underlying the theory of relativity. Relativity insists on considering physical situations only in relation to their possibilities of measurement. There is no such thing as an absolute measurement of length or of a time interval.

In specifying a length or time interval, it is always necessary to specify in addition the relative motion of the observer. The observer and his limitations can never be divorced from the system under observation. For example, we could also derive the Lorentz transformations (8.21) on the assumption that two observers in S and S' can communicate by signals which travel only with the speed of light and no faster. In quantum mechanics a similar insistence on taking into account the means of measurement in any situation leads to Heisenberg's uncertainty principle.

To state this principle, we may return to Fig. 9.2, in which the envelopes represent the particle aspect of a wave train. From this picture it is clear that we cannot localize an individual particle in position closer than a distance of order $\Delta x \approx \frac{1}{2}D$, where D is the length of an envelope. According to (9.28), this distance is

$$D = \frac{1}{\Delta(1/\lambda)} \tag{9.58}$$

Substituting (9.26), we have

$$\Delta x \, \Delta p \approx h/2 \approx \hbar \tag{9.59}$$

Here Δp represents an uncertainty in the particle momentum, which gives rise to the spread in wavelength $\Delta(1/\lambda)$. Since (9.59) is only an order of magnitude estimate, we can write $\hbar$ instead of h on the right-hand side.

Equation (9.59) is Heisenberg's famous uncertainty relation. It states that the uncertainty in the simultaneous knowledge of the position and momentum of a particle can never be less than a certain amount. For example, if we know the position exactly, $\Delta x = 0$, $\Delta p \to \infty$, and we can say nothing at all about the momentum. Conversely, if $\Delta p = 0$, $\Delta x \to \infty$, so that a perfect knowledge of momentum implies a complete ignorance of position in space. When $\Delta p = 0$ the wave train in Fig. 9.2 is of constant amplitude and contains just one wavelength, corresponding to envelopes that have become infinitely long. A beam of monochromatic light provides a physical example of this situation: the photons all have the exactly known momentum $p = h/\lambda$, but their position is unknown within infinite limits.

This uncertainty in knowledge of the position and momentum (velocity) of a particle implies that we cannot predict exactly where it will be at some later time or exactly how it will be moving. Thus we must abandon the absolute predictability of classical physics, much in the same way as relativity abandons the classical idea of absolute motion. It is useless to try to measure the position and momentum of a particle more accurately than allowed by (9.59). For suppose that we attempt to measure the position with great precision. To do this we must be able to see the particle, which involves reflection of light from the particle. The smallest unit of light that can be reflected is one photon, and we have seen in the Compton effect how such a reflection behaves like a billiard ball collision. Reflection of the photon would impart to the particle a certain recoil momentum. That is, the very act of measuring the particle position would make our knowledge of its momentum less precise. A second measurement to redetermine the momentum would disturb the position, etc. A physical argument of this sort, based on the limitations in measuring technique available to an observer, can be carried through to yield just the relation (9.59).

The wave train in Fig. 9.2 proceeds along the x-axis, so that the uncertainty relation actually holds between Δx and Δp_x, the component of momentum in the x-direction. Similar relations of course hold between Δy and Δp_y, Δz and Δp_z. Now we wish quantum mechanics to be in addition relativistically invariant, and the discussion of 4-vectors shows that the (ct) bears the same relation to x, y, z as (E/c) does to p_x, p_y, p_z. Therefore a corresponding uncertainty relation must exist between t and E;

$$\Delta(ct) \, \Delta(E/c) = \Delta t \, \Delta E \approx \hbar \qquad (9.60)$$

Uncertainty relations of the type (9.59) and (9.60) exist in fact between all pairs of "canonically conjugate" variables in classical mechanics. The only other such pairs that will be of importance to our discussion are the angular momentum L and angular position φ, for which

$$\Delta L_z \, \Delta \varphi_z \approx \hbar \qquad (9.61)$$

Here φ_z is the angle of rotation about the z-axis; and similar rules pertain to the x- and y-axes.

We can apply the uncertainty principle to obtain a physical interpretation of the Compton wavelength $\lambdabar_0$ (9.25a). Consider the relativistic momentum-energy equation $p^2 + (m_0c)^2 = (E/c)^2$. Here m_0c has the dimensions of a momentum, but it is a quantity intrinsic to the particle and Lorentz invariant. If we insert $\Delta p = m_0c$ in (9.59), the corresponding uncertainty in position is

$$\Delta x \approx \hbar/\Delta p = \lambdabar_0 \qquad (9.62)$$

Thus the Compton wavelength represents a sort of inherent uncertainty in position or "spread" of a particle, which it should exhibit even when at rest.

Relation (9.62) points out an interesting contrast between classical and quantum mechanics. Any estimate of the size of an electron by classical means always leads to a radius on the order of $r_0 = e^2/m_0c^2 = 2.8 \times 10^{-13}$ cm. In quantum mechanics, however, we cannot localize the position of an electron at rest any closer than λ_0, regardless of what the intrinsic size of the electron may be. Thus in atomic phenomena the electron generally has an "effective" size on the order of λ_0, which is 137 times larger than the classical electron radius r_0.

The uncertainty relation makes it clear why classical mechanics is successful for macroscopic phenomena, while wave mechanics is necessary for atomic systems. Since $\hbar \approx 10^{-27}$ erg sec in cgs units, the uncertainty in position and momentum of a large-scale object is many orders of magnitude smaller than any measurement could show. We can then neglect the uncertainty relation and with it the essential wave structure of nature. The particle approximation of classical mechanics is sufficient. In atomic systems, however, the distances and momenta for light particles like electrons become extremely small and are comparable in magnitude with their uncertainties. The effects of the uncertainties then become very pronounced, as in the example of the electron radius discussed above.

SUMMARY

The formulas of relativity suggest considering the photon a particle of rest mass zero. The energy of the particle is $E = h\nu$, and the corresponding momentum is $p = E/c = h/\lambda$. Macroscopic experiments demonstrate the reality of this linear momentum. They also show an angular momentum for circularly polarized light, corresponding to $L_z = \pm\hbar = \pm h/2\pi$ for each photon. Thus angular momentum appears to be quantized in wave mechanics.

The Compton effect provides microscopic verification of the linear momentum as a property of individual photons. In this experiment a photon scatters elastically from an electron. The measured change in wavelength of the scattered photon agrees with the model of a billiard-ball collision and verifies the relation $p = h/\lambda$.

De Broglie's hypothesis is that material particles as well as photons have associated wave motions given by the same relations as for photons: $\nu = E/h$, $\lambda = h/p$, where p and E are, respectively, the momentum and total relativistic energy of the particle. We can associate these quantities with the phase and group velocities of a wave packet. The group velocity w of the wave packet is always $w < c$ for a material particle and is in fact the ordinary particle velocity. The phase velocity $v = \lambda \nu$ of the associated wave is $v = c^2/w > c$, so that according to relativity it is not directly observable. For the special case of a photon with zero rest mass, $v = w = c$.

The Davisson-Germer experiment of scattering electrons from a crystal provides direct evidence of the wave motion associated with particles. In this scattering interference maxima appear, which resemble the reflection of X-rays from the Bragg planes. Since the property of interference is a characteristic only of waves and not of particles as such, this experiment conclusively proves the existence of wave motion associated with particles like electrons. Quantitatively the measurements agree with the value $\lambda = h/p$ for the wavelength.

The application of de Broglie's hypothesis to motion in a circle leads immediately to the quantization of orbits, in agreement with the empirical evidence from atomic spectra. If a wave traveling in a circular orbit is to remain stable, it must not cancel itself out by destructive interference. Hence the only allowed orbits are those for which $n\lambda = 2\pi r$, or hence $L = n\hbar = nh/2\pi$, where $n = 1, 2, 3, \cdots$ is an integer. The corresponding electron binding energies are $B = (Z^2/n^2)hcR$, where $+Ze$ is the effective charge on the core and n is the quantum number. This is just the form of the observations discussed in Chapter 7, and the Rydberg constant is $R = (\frac{1}{4}\pi)\, \alpha^3/r_0$, where $\alpha = e^2/\hbar c = \frac{1}{137}$ and $r_0 = e^2/m_0 c^2$ is the classical electron radius. The success of this formula in interpreting atomic spectra and in predicting the numerical value of R lends strong support to de Broglie's hypothesis.

To specify the magnetic dipole moment μ associated with the orbital motion of the electron, it is convenient to introduce the Bohr magneton $\mu_0 = e\hbar/2m_0 c$. The magnetic moment for an angular momentum $L = l\hbar$ is then $\mu = g_L \mu_0 l$, where $g_L = 1$.

A physical interpretation of de Broglie's hypothesis is the *uncertainty principle*, which states that

$$\Delta p\,\Delta x \approx \Delta E\,\Delta t \approx \Delta L\,\Delta \varphi \approx \hbar,$$

where Δp is the uncertainty in the value of a particle's momentum and Δx the uncertainty in its corresponding position. Uncertainty relations exist between all pairs of "conjugate" variables such as E and t, L and φ. It is impossible to overcome this uncertainty by any series of measurements, since any measurement to fix x accurately will disturb p by an unknown amount, etc. This uncertainty is of no importance for macroscopic objects because $\hbar$ is so small, but for electrons in atoms the uncertainties are relatively large and a quantum mechanical treatment is necessary. Quantum mechanical formulas approach infinitesimally close to classical formulas in the limit of large quantum numbers, $n \rightarrow \infty$ (principle of correspondence). On the other hand, for small quantum numbers it is impossible to apply the deterministic formulas of classical mechanics, according to the uncertainty principle. For this reason the "old quantum mechanics" of the Bohr atom has been replaced by the "new quantum mechanics" incorporating de Broglie's hypothesis and the uncertainty principle (Chapter 10).

REFERENCES

R. A. Beth, *Phys. Rev.*, **50**, 115 (1936).

N. Bohr, *Phil. Mag.*, **26**, 1, 476 (1913).

A. H. Compton, *Phys. Rev.*, **21**, 483; **22**, 409 (1923).

C. J. Davisson and L. H. Germer, *Phys. Rev.*, **30**, 705 (1927).

L. de Broglie, *Phil. Mag.*, **47**, 446 (1924); *Annales de physique*, **3**, 22 (1925).

W. Heisenberg, *The Physical Principles of the Quantum Theory*, University of Chicago Press, Chicago (1930).

W. Heitler, *Elementary Wave Mechanics*, Oxford, New York (1945).

E. F. Nichols and G. F. Hull, *Phys. Rev.*, **17**, 26 (1903).

A. Sommerfeld, *Atomic Structure and Spectral Lines*, Methuen, London (1923).

H. E. White, *Introduction to Atomic Spectra*, McGraw-Hill, New York (1934).

ILLUSTRATIVE PROBLEMS

1. What is the maximum wavelength that a photon can have and be able to transfer half its energy to the recoil electron during a Compton impact? What are the direction and magnitude of the velocity of the recoil electron in this case?

Solution. The maximum change in wavelength or hence energy is given by (9.25) with $\theta = 180°$. The scattered photon emerges in the backward direction. Then $\lambda' - \lambda = 4\pi\lambda_0$. If we require that $\nu' = \nu/2$, $\lambda' = 2\lambda$; or hence $\lambda = 2\lambda_0 = 48.5$ XU. The electron recoils straight forward and has kinetic energy $h\nu/2 = hc/2\lambda = m_0 c^2/4$. According to the relativistic formula this is $m_0 c^2/4 = m_0 c^2 (1/\sqrt{1 - \beta^2} - 1)$ or hence $v/c = \beta = \frac{3}{5}$, $v = \frac{3}{5}c = 1.8 \times 10^{10}$ cm/sec.

2. A cubic crystal has a lattice constant of $a = 3A$. A beam of 36-volt electrons is incident upon the crystal. Locate the positions of the strongest two maxima as the crystal is rotated.

Solution. The wavelength of the electrons is by (9.35), $\lambda = 12.2/6 = 2.03$ A. The strongest maximum is from the $n = 1$ reflection on the (100) planes; the next strongest maxima are from $n = 1$ on the (110) planes and $n = 2$ on the (100) planes. For the (100) planes $d = a = 3$ A, for the (110) planes $d = a/\sqrt{2} = 2.12$ A. The corresponding values of θ are $\theta = \sin^{-1}(n\lambda/2\,d) = \sin^{-1}(0.34)$, $\sin^{-1}(0.48)$, $\sin^{-1}(0.68)$. The angles of deviation from the incident beam at which the diffracted electrons appear are $180° - 2\theta = 140°, 123°, 96°$.

3. (a) What minimum energy in ev must the electron in a spark discharge have to be able to strip a sodium ($Z = 11$) atom of its last electron, assuming that the other ten have already been removed? Is this energy smaller or larger than that required to excite the K radiation of the Na metal? (b) What is the wavelength of the first line of the "Lyman series" of a ten times ionized Na atom?

Solution. (a) $B = hcRZ^2/n^2 = (11)^2 \times 13.6$ ev $= 1.64$ kev. The formula for the X-ray K edges is $T = (Z - 1)^2 R$, indicating that for the K electrons in Na metal there is already some shielding of the nucleus. The energy to strip the last electron involves Z^2 instead of $(Z - 1)^2$ and is therefore larger than that required to excite K radiation. (b) The wave number is

$$1/\lambda = k = T - T' = RZ^2[(\tfrac{1}{1})^2 - (\tfrac{1}{2})^2]$$

$$= 1.00 \times 10^7 \text{ cm}^{-1}, \text{ or } \lambda = 10 \text{ A}$$

PROBLEMS

1. Derive the following alternative expressions for the group velocity in a dispersive medium.

$$w = \frac{d\nu}{d(1/\lambda)} = \frac{d\omega}{dk} \quad \text{where } \omega = 2\pi\nu, \, k = \frac{2\pi}{\lambda}$$

$$\frac{1}{w} = \frac{1}{c}\left(n + \nu\,\frac{dn}{d\nu}\right) = \frac{1}{c}\left(n - \lambda_0\,\frac{dn}{d\lambda_0}\right)$$

where λ_0 is the wavelength in vacuum, n the refractive index. Apply these relations to the velocity of X-ray photons for which $n = 1 - A/\nu^2$. Show the validity of the relation $1/w + 1/v = 2/c$ and show that the X-ray photons travel with a velocity smaller than c.

2. Using relativistic mechanics, find the voltage required for producing an electron for which the phase velocity is twice the electron velocity. Compute the frequency and the wavelength of this electron wave.

3. Determine the wavelength of X-rays for which the Compton scattering at 90° has twice the wavelength of the unmodified scattering in the forward direction.

4. Show that momentum and energy could not be conserved if a free electron were to absorb a quantum of any energy without re-emitting a second quantum or transferring recoil momentum to a nucleus. Reverse the argument to show that a freely moving electron of any energy cannot spontaneously emit radiation, and that it can convert some of its energy to photons only in a collision process. This is the quantum mechanical statement of the classical fact that a charge radiates only when accelerated but not during uniform motion.

5. An electron beam is incident normal to the lattice planes of a simple cubic lattice with a lattice constant of 2 A.

(a) Determine the electron energies in ev required to produce preferential reflection at the crystal surface at an angle of 150° with the incident beam.

(b) For what electron energies will a "Bragg reflected" beam at 90° to the incident beam occur?

6. An experiment is performed in which a beam of 100-volt electrons is incident at an angle of $i = 30°$ with the normal to the plane of a double grid. The two grids are electrically separate, and between them is a retarding potential V.

(a) What is the de Broglie wavelength of the incident beam of electrons?

(b) When $V = 36$ volts what is the wavelength for the beam transmitted through the grids?

(c) From these wavelengths compute the relative refractive index for the electron waves in the two spaces on both sides of the double grid.

(d) Using Snell's law compute the angle of refraction r of the refracted beam, relative to the normal to the plane of the grids, when $V = 36$ volts.

(e) For what voltage V will the electrons be totally reflected by the double screen? Use the optical condition $\sin r = 1$.

(f) Show that the results of (d) and (e) agree with the conclusions arrived at by computing the deflection of the electrons with classical particle mechanics.

7. Derive a relation for computing the mass m_0 of the electron from R_H, R_Z, m_H, and m_Z, where R_H is the Rydberg constant for hydrogen, m_H is the mass of a neutral hydrogen atom, and R_Z is the Rydberg constant for an atom composed of a single electron revolving about a nucleus of charge Ze, and m_Z is the mass of a neutral atom with this nucleus (and Z electrons). Compute m_0 (in amu) from the following data: $R_H = 109{,}677.58$ cm^{-1}, $R_{He} = 109{,}722.27$ cm^{-1}, $m_H = 1.00814$ amu, and $m_{He} = 4.00388$ amu.

8. A gas-discharge tube, driven at a high potential, contains H^1, H^2, He^3, He^4, Li^6, Li^7 ions or atoms, where the superscripts give the masses in amu.

(a) What is the minimum potential that must be applied to the tube to make all these ions emit a hydrogenlike spectrum?

(b) What is the wavelength of the spectrum line of highest frequency emitted by these hydrogenlike atoms?

(c) All the above atoms or ions will emit light of nearly the same wavelength as the first line of the Lyman series of H^1. Compute how much they differ in frequency and wavelength from this line and show in a sketch in the wavelength scale how the spectrum of the discharge would appear in the neighborhood of the first Lyman line.

9. In quantum mechanics the appearance of discrete energy levels is characteristic of any bound system. It is not peculiar to atoms with a potential varying as $1/r$. Using the old quantum mechanics approach— i.e., (9.36), find the energy levels of a harmonic oscillator in quantum mechanics. Proceed along the following line:

(a) consider a 3-dimensional harmonic oscillator, with potential energy $V = \frac{1}{2}kr^2$, kinetic energy $T = \frac{1}{2}mv^2$, and frequency of vibration $\omega_0 = \sqrt{k/m}$. Let the mass m be rotating in a stable orbit, in which the centripetal acceleration is provided by the spring force kr. Show that in this orbit $\omega = v/r = \omega_0$.

(b) Quantize the orbit by means of (9.36) and show that its total energy is $E = T + V = n\hbar\omega_0 = nh\nu_0$, where ν_0 is the classical linear frequency and $n = 0, 1, 2, 3, \cdots$ is an integer.

(c) A three-dimensional harmonic oscillation can be resolved into three independent one-dimensional oscillations (x-, y-, z- components). Each of these independent oscillations must be separately quantized and still satisfy $E_x + E_y + E_z = E$. The most general way of doing this is to take $E_x = n_x h\nu_0$, etc. so that $n_x + n_y + n_z = n$. Thus the one-dimensional harmonic oscillator has the same quantized energy levels as the three-dimensional oscillator.

In the new quantum mechanics the harmonic oscillator levels are more correctly given as $E_n = (n + \frac{1}{2})h\nu_0$. Note that this is just the energy (6.1) of a number of photons in an enclosure. The two problems are in fact the same: the electromagnetic field in an enclosure can be represented as a number of equivalent oscillators of various frequencies

ν. When these oscillators are quantized, the nth excited level of a particular oscillator corresponds to the presence of n photons of that frequency in the enclosure. We may ultimately allow the enclosure to become infinitely large, in which case the number of virtual field oscillators also becomes infinite.

10. The diffraction pattern produced by two slits of width "a" at a separation "d" has five strong maxima when $d/a = 3$. As a first approximation the intensity distribution can be assumed to consist of five sharp lines with the following diffraction angles θ and intensities I:

$$\text{central max:} \quad \theta = 0, \qquad I = 0.38 I_0$$

$$\text{first side max:} \quad \theta = \pm\lambda/d, \qquad I = 0.26 I_0$$

$$\text{second side max:} \quad \theta = \pm 2\lambda/d, \qquad I = 0.05 I_0$$

Note that $\sum I = I_0$. In terms of the photon theory this result can be interpreted as follows: the x-coordinates of the photons passing through the slits are known with an uncertainty $\Delta x = \frac{1}{2} d$; and since the x-component of their momentum is $h\theta/\lambda$, it is known with a mean-square uncertainty

$$\Delta p_x = \sqrt{\sum (h\theta/\lambda)^2 I/I_0}$$

because I/I_0 is the probability for occurrence of the deflection θ. Show that $\Delta p_x \, \Delta x = h(\text{constant})$ and find the value of the constant.

Chapter 10

THE SCHROEDINGER EQUATION

In the previous chapter we have discussed de Broglie's wave hypothesis and have made one simple application to the motion of an electron in an atomic orbit. This application is somewhat oversimplified, because it does not make use of all the properties of the associated wave motion, but only of the coincidence of the phase of the wave after completing a circuit of the orbit. To study the behavior of atomic electrons in further detail, we must treat the de Broglie waves with more complete and adequate mathematics. One of the most straightforward mathematical techniques is that of the Schroedinger equation (1926).

This chapter introduces the Schroedinger equation and the terminology used to relate it to physical interpretation. We apply it to the physically interesting case of the hydrogenlike atom.

10.1. The equation

In classical mechanics a system is completely described if we can set up and solve the equations of motion. These equations of motion are all applications of Newton's law $F = ma$ subject to the constraint of the particular system at hand; auxiliary laws like the conservation of energy simply represent integrals of $F = ma$. In wave mechanics we must likewise set up an equation of motion for the de Broglie waves associated with the particles. The solution of this equation then represents the complete wave mechanical description of the system. It contains all the information we can ever obtain about the system. If this wave mechanical solution allows a physical interpretation as particle motion in definite orbits, classical mechanics will be a valid approximation. This is the case for macroscopic bodies or for any system when the quantum numbers are large, according to the correspondence principle (section 9.8). For microscopic systems in states of low quantum number we cannot make the simple classical approximation of particles in definite orbits but must return to the basic, wave mechanical description.

The wave equation of motion is the *Schroedinger equation*. To set up this equation, consider the individual wave trains that combine to form the particle-like envelopes of Fig. 9.2. These wave trains are specified by a function of the form

$$\Psi = A \sin [2\pi(\nu t - x/\lambda)] + B \cos [2\pi(\nu t - x/\lambda)] \quad (10.1)$$

The *wave function* Ψ represents a periodic disturbance of some sort, but we cannot specify the exact nature of this disturbance nor of the medium in which it propagates. These questions are as meaningless as those relating to the absolute ether, which physicists in prerelativity days supposed to be the exclusive medium for the propagation of light. The wave function (10.1) actually represents a traveling wave that moves in the positive x-direction with a phase velocity $v = \lambda\nu$. Another type of wave function is the *standing wave*, given by

$$\Psi = (A' \sin 2\pi x/\lambda + B' \cos 2\pi x/\lambda) \sin 2\pi\nu t \qquad (10.2)$$

Standing and traveling waves are familiar in elementary physics from the discussion of acoustic vibrations in strings and air columns. The standing wave is most useful for our present purpose, which is ultimately to describe the states of an electron bound in an atom. A bound electron can certainly not travel to infinity as does the traveling wave (10.1).

As in the acoustical case, both traveling and standing waves satisfy the wave equation

$$\frac{\partial^2 \Psi}{\partial x^2} = \frac{1}{v^2} \frac{\partial^2 \Psi}{\partial t^2} \qquad (10.3)$$

If we now generalize the wave motion to three dimensions, (10.3) becomes

$$\frac{\partial^2 \Psi}{\partial x^2} + \frac{\partial^2 \Psi}{\partial y^2} + \frac{\partial^2 \Psi}{\partial z^2} \equiv \nabla^2 \Psi = \frac{1}{v^2} \frac{\partial^2 \Psi}{\partial t^2} \qquad (10.4)$$

The symbol ∇^2 is a conventional abbreviation for the differential operator $\partial^2/\partial x^2 + \partial^2/\partial y^2 + \partial^2/\partial z^2$.

We must now find a way of relating the wave equation (10.4) to the classical mechanical equation that would apply in this case. Then for any problem we can always find the correct wave equation by first setting up the classical equation and performing certain formal algebraic operations. To find these operations, we note that (10.4) is the wave equation for a free particle, for which by (9.31)

$$p_x{}^2 + p_y{}^2 + p_z{}^2 \equiv p^2 = E^2/v^2 \qquad (10.5)$$

where E is the total relativistic energy of the particle. Now (10.5) becomes just (10.4) if we multiply on the right by Ψ and make the substitutions

$$p_x, \quad p_y, \quad p_z \quad \rightarrow \quad -i\hbar\partial/\partial x, \quad -i\hbar\partial/\partial y, \quad -i\hbar\partial/\partial z \qquad (10.6)$$

$$E \rightarrow i\hbar\partial/\partial t$$

The factors $\hbar$ make the physical dimensions the same on both sides of (10.6); the other factors are thus far determined only to within a constant multiplier K. The choice of $K = \pm i$ is dictated by the following considerations: we want to be able to write

$$p\Psi = h/\lambda\Psi \qquad (10.7)$$

in accord with de Broglie's hypothesis (9.2). For this purpose we decompose Ψ into terms of the form $\Psi' = e^{\pm 2\pi i x/\lambda} e^{\pm 2\pi i \nu t}$ and consider a single one of such terms. Then if $p_x \to K\hbar \partial/\partial x$, we have

$$p_x\Psi' \to \frac{K\hbar\partial\Psi'}{\partial x} = \pm \frac{Ki2\pi\hbar}{\lambda}\Psi' = \pm \frac{Kih}{\lambda}\Psi' \qquad (10.8)$$

This is of the form (10.7) if $K = \pm i$. Thus we have established all the factors in (10.6), except for the $\pm$ signs, which are arbitrary. Equation (10.6) gives the standard sign convention.

We can write (10.5) in the form $p^2 + m_0^2 c^2 = E^2/c^2$. Substituting (10.6) and applying to Ψ yields

$$\nabla^2\Psi - \frac{1}{c^2}\frac{\partial^2\Psi}{\partial t^2} = m_0^2 c^2 \Psi \qquad (10.9)$$

This resembles an equation for a wave of velocity c, except for the addition of an extra term $m_0^2 c^2 \Psi$. For a photon with $m_0 = 0$, (10.9) becomes just the equation for a light wave, with $\Psi = E, H$, etc. Equation (10.9) is sometimes known as the *relativistic Schroedinger equation*, but it is the nonrelativistic form that we shall use. To obtain the nonrelativistic form, we write

$$E = m_0 c^2 + (W - V) \qquad (10.10)$$

where $m_0 c^2$ is the rest-mass energy, $W - V = T$ is the kinetic energy of the particle, V is its potential energy, and W is its total energy exclusive of rest mass. Then in the nonrelativistic case when $T \ll m_0 c^2$, we have

$$p^2 + m_0^2 c^2 = (E/c)^2 \approx m_0^2 c^2 + 2m_0(W - V) + \cdots$$

$$p^2/2m_0 + V = W \qquad (10.11)$$

The only quantity on the right-hand side of (10.10) that could replace E as a time derivative operator is W; in analogy with (10.6) we put

$$W \to i\hbar\partial/\partial t \qquad (10.12)$$

We are now in a position to write the usual nonrelativistic Schroedinger equation. The prescription is the following: write the classical Hamiltonian form (10.11) for the system, expressing the conservation of energy. In this form make the substitutions (10.6) and (10.12), applying the operators to the wave function Ψ. The resulting form

$$\left(-\frac{\hbar^2}{2m_0}\nabla^2 + V\right)\Psi = i\hbar\frac{\partial\Psi}{\partial t} \qquad (10.13)$$

is known as the time-dependent Schroedinger equation. For our application to electrons in atoms we shall mainly be interested in cases where W is a constant, corresponding to a definite discrete energy level. In this case

$$i\hbar \frac{\partial \Psi}{\partial t} = W\Psi \qquad (10.14a)$$

$$\Psi = \psi e^{-iWt/\hbar} \qquad (10.14b)$$

$$\left[\nabla^2 + \frac{2m_0}{\hbar^2} (W - V) \right] \psi = 0 \qquad (10.15)$$

Equation (10.15) with W a constant is the time-independent Schroedinger equation. This is the basic equation to solve in obtaining a wavemechanical description of the system.

10.2. The particle in a box

As an example of the explicit solution of (10.15) for a physical situation, consider a free particle in a box. The simplest possible case is a one-dimensional box of length D. We take the potential energy inside the box to be $V = 0$, and the Schroedinger equation (10.15) becomes

$$(\partial^2/\partial x^2 + k^2)\psi = 0 \qquad (10.16)$$

$$k = \sqrt{2m_0W/\hbar^2} \qquad (10.16a)$$

Here $k = 1/\lambda$ is called the *wave number* of the particle; it is related by a factor 2π to the wave number of spectroscopy (Chapters 6 and 7), $k = 2\pi k = 2\pi(1/\lambda)$. The general solution of (10.16) is $\psi = A \sin kx + B \cos kx$, which we can also write in the equivalent form

$$\psi = A \sin (kx + \delta) \qquad (10.17)$$

Since (10.16) is a second-order differential equation, the general solution (10.17) has two arbitrary constants. We can determine one of these from boundary conditions on ψ provided by the physical situation. The wave function ψ is somehow associated with the particle in the classical picture. Classically, the particle cannot be outside the box, so it is reasonable to suppose that $\psi \equiv 0$ in this region. Furthermore, since all wave motions that we know in nature are continuous, we expect the same of the de Broglie waves. This means that we should impose the boundary conditions $\psi = 0$ at both ends of the box. Let the positions of these ends be $x = 0, D$. Then

$$\psi(0) = A \sin \delta = 0, \quad \delta = 0 \qquad (10.18)$$

$$\psi(D) = 0 = A \sin kD \qquad (10.19)$$

In (10.18) $\delta = 0$ is the simplest solution of $\sin \delta = 0$. We cannot take $A = 0$, because then ψ would vanish everywhere, corresponding to the total absence of the particle. In (10.19) we have already inserted $\delta = 0$; if $A \neq 0$, the only solution is

$$k = n\pi/D, \qquad\qquad n = 1, 2, 3, \cdots \qquad (10.20)$$

We exclude $n = 0$ because this would again lead to identically vanishing ψ; and negative integer n are entirely equivalent to the positive integers.

Equation (10.20) is a quantization condition that introduces the quantum number n. It arises from the physical boundary conditions on ψ and leads to the quantized energies

$$W_n = \frac{1}{2m_0} \left(\frac{n\pi\hbar}{D} \right)^2 \qquad (10.21)$$

Thus the wave-mechanical particle in a box has discrete, quantized energy levels W_n. This is in contrast to the classical particle, which can have any energy. The corresponding wave functions ψ are plotted in Fig. 10.1 for the lowest values of n. Note that there are $(n - 1)$ interior positions in the box where $\psi = 0$. These are the *nodes* of the wave function.

Can we find any relation between this wave mechanical solution and the classical picture of a particle in a box? Classically, a particle in a one-dimensional box must continuously bounce back and forth between the ends of the box. Now consider the total wave function

$$\Psi = \psi e^{-iWt/\hbar} = A e^{-iWt/\hbar} \sin kx = \frac{A}{2i} \left(e^{i(kx-Wt/\hbar)} - e^{-i(kx+Wt/\hbar)} \right) \qquad (10.22)$$

The first term represents a wave traveling to the right, the second a wave traveling to the left. In this qualitative respect the wave mechanical solution (10.22) resembles the classical situation of a particle bouncing back and forth. The waves, however, obey a strict phase relation

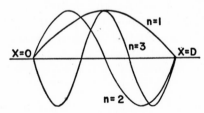

Fig. 10–1. Wave functions ψ_n of a particle in a one-dimensional box of length D.

such that the total ψ is always zero at the ends of the box and at the nodes.

It is a straightforward matter to extend the above formulas to the more realistic case of a particle in a three-dimensional box. In this case the Schroedinger equation becomes

$$\left(\frac{\partial^2}{\partial x^2} + \frac{\partial^2}{\partial y^2} + \frac{\partial^2}{\partial z^2} + k^2\right)\psi = 0 \qquad (10.23)$$

The general solution is

$$\psi = A \sin (k_x x + \delta_x) \sin (k_y y + \delta_y) \sin (k_z z + \delta_z) \qquad (10.24)$$

$$k_x{}^2 + k_y{}^2 + k_z{}^2 = k^2 = 2m_0 W/\hbar^2 \qquad (10.24a)$$

Using the same arguments as before about the boundary conditions $\psi = 0$ at the edges of the box, we obtain

$$\delta_x = \delta_y = \delta_z = 0 \qquad (10.25a)$$

$$k_x = \pi n_x/D_x, \quad k_y = \pi n_y/D_y, \quad k_z = \pi n_z/D_z \qquad (10.25b)$$

Here n_x, n_y, n_z are quantum numbers that can independently assume the values 1, 2, 3, $\cdots$; and D_x, D_y, D_z are the dimensions of the rectangular box. The nodes where $\psi = 0$ are now planes parallel to the sides of the box, instead of points as in the one-dimensional case.

The quantized energy values of the particle in the box are

$$W = \frac{(\pi\hbar)^2}{2m_0}\left[\left(\frac{n_x}{D_x}\right)^2 + \left(\frac{n_y}{D_y}\right)^2 + \left(\frac{n_z}{D_z}\right)^2\right] \qquad (10.26)$$

If D_x, D_y, D_z are incommensurate, no two values of W will be the same. When any two sides of the box are in the ratio of whole numbers,

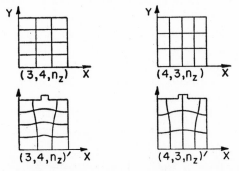

Fig. 10–2. Eigenfunction ψ corresponding to degenerate eigenvalues for $D_x = D_y$. The lines are the nodal positions where $\psi = 0$. In the two upper diagrams $W(3, 4, n_z) = W(4, 3, n_z)$ and a degeneracy exists. In the two lower diagrams a small perturbation has been introduced, which makes $W'(3, 4, n_z) < W'(4, 3, n_z)$ and hence removes the degeneracy.

however, there will be many cases where W is identical for two or more different sets of quantum numbers. Such energy levels are said to be *degenerate*. They correspond to wave functions that are geometrically different and just happen to have identical energies. In this situation a measurement of the energy alone would not be able to distinguish between the different possible geometrical configurations of the system. Actually this ideal condition of degeneracy is seldom fulfilled in practice: the box generally has some small irregularities which destroy the degeneracy, making the energy of each geometrical configuration (choice of n_x, n_y, n_z) slightly different. These irregularities cause a *perturbation* of the system that removes the degeneracy. Figure 10.2 illustrates this for a box with $D_x = D_y$. The $(3, 4, n_z)$ and $(4, 3, n_z)$ states are originally degenerate. The perturbation is a small dent in the side of the box, which splits the degenerate energies.

Equation (10.26) illustrates one way in which the wave mechanical solution approaches the classical situation for high quantum numbers (correspondence principle). The energy levels (10.26) are discrete, but as n_x, n_y, $n_z \rightarrow \infty$, the average spacing between successive levels decreases as $1/n^2$. Thus for high n the energy levels approach the continuous distribution of classical mechanics.

10.3. The hydrogenlike atom

A problem of greater physical importance than the rectangular box is the hydrogen atom. It was nevertheless worth while to discuss the rectangular box in some detail, because many general properties of its wave functions and quantized energy levels have close analogues in the atomic case. The rectangular box has the advantage of mathematical simplicity because $V = 0$; in the atom we must introduce the potential energy $V = -Ze^2/r$, which makes for mathematical complications in the solution. In this section we must carry through some of the mathematics in order to see that the Schroedinger equation gives physically sensible results. In particular, it must give the correct energy levels for hydrogenlike atoms, Eq. (9.39). The hydrogenlike spectrum is the basic problem of atomic physics and provides the crucial test of any theory.

Consider the nucleus as rigidly fixed and of charge $+Ze$ with a single electron of charge $-e$ outside. The classical expression for the total nonrelativistic energy of the electron is

$$W = p^2/2m_0 + V = p^2/2m_0 - Ze^2/r \qquad (10.27)$$

where r is the electron distance from the origin of coordinates located at the nucleus. The corresponding Schroedinger equation (10.15) is

$$\left[\nabla^2 + \frac{2m_0}{\hbar^2} \left(W + \frac{Ze^2}{r} \right) \right] \psi = 0 \qquad (10.28)$$

It is always simplest in solving wave mechanical problems to choose a coordinate system with the same symmetry properties as the potential.

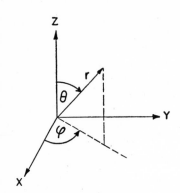

Therefore we measure the electron position in spherical polar coordinates r, θ, φ, illustrated in Fig. 10.3. The angle θ is conventionally measured from the z-axis, and φ from the x-axis. The relation between this coordinate system and the Cartesian coordinates is

$$x = r \sin \theta \cos \varphi$$

$$y = r \sin \theta \sin \varphi \qquad (10.29)$$

$$z = r \cos \theta$$

Fig. 10.3. Spherical polar coordinates.

By using these relations, we can establish the Laplacian operator ∇^2 in polar coordinates:

$$\nabla^2 = \frac{\partial^2}{\partial x^2} + \frac{\partial^2}{\partial y^2} + \frac{\partial^2}{\partial z^2} = \frac{1}{r^2} \frac{\partial}{\partial r}\left(r^2 \frac{\partial}{\partial r}\right) + \frac{1}{r^2 \sin \theta} \frac{\partial}{\partial \theta}\left(\sin \theta \frac{\partial}{\partial \theta}\right)$$
$$+ \frac{1}{r^2 \sin^2 \theta} \frac{\partial^2}{\partial \varphi^2} \qquad (10.30)$$

Equation (10.28) is solved by the method of separation of variables. This method is applicable only in a limited number of coordinate systems, which fortunately include those most often used in simple physical problems. Assume that the wave function can be written as a product of functions

$$\psi(r,\theta,\varphi) = R(r)\Theta(\theta)\Phi(\varphi) \qquad (10.31)$$

where each of the functions on the right-hand side involves only one variable, as indicated. Then if we divide Eq. (10.28) through by ψ, it becomes

$$\left[\frac{1}{R} \frac{1}{r^2} \frac{\partial}{\partial r}\left(r^2 \frac{\partial R}{\partial r}\right) + \frac{2m_0}{\hbar^2}\left(W + \frac{Ze^2}{r}\right)\right] + \frac{1}{r^2}\left[\frac{1}{\Theta} \frac{1}{\sin \theta} \frac{\partial}{\partial \theta}\left(\sin \theta \frac{\partial \Theta}{\partial \theta}\right)\right]$$
$$+ \frac{1}{r^2 \sin^2 \theta}\left(\frac{1}{\Phi} \frac{\partial^2 \Phi}{\partial \varphi^2}\right) = 0 \qquad (10.32)$$

Consider first the part $\left(\dfrac{1}{\Phi} \dfrac{\partial^2 \Phi}{\partial \varphi^2}\right)$. This is by definition a function of the variable φ only; but by comparison with (10.32) we see that it is equal to a quantity that is a function of r and θ only. This can be true only if the functions involved are constants. Thus we can set

$$\frac{1}{\Phi}\frac{\partial^2\Phi}{\partial\varphi^2} = -m^2 \tag{10.33a}$$

or hence

$$\Phi = e^{im\varphi}, \quad e^{-im\varphi} \tag{10.33}$$

where we have chosen the constant to be $-m^2$. This is a second-order differential equation and accordingly has two independent solutions. We have written these as $e^{\pm im\varphi} = \cos m\varphi \pm i \sin m\varphi$.

The value of the constant m is immediately limited by physical conditions. Since Φ is to be part of a physical wave function, it must have exactly the same value for the positions φ, $\varphi + 2\pi$, $\varphi + 4\pi$, $\cdots$, $\varphi + 2n\pi$, $\cdots$, where n is an integer. These mathematically different values all correspond to the same physical position. This constancy of Φ is possible only if $m = 0, 1, 2, \cdots$. To combine the two types of solution (10.33), we write

$$\Phi = e^{im\varphi}, \quad m = 0, \pm 1, \pm 2, \quad \cdots \tag{10.34}$$

Thus we have obtained our first quantum number m from physical restrictions on the wave function. It is known as the *magnetic* quantum number because it is important chiefly when the atom is in a magnetic field.

Having solved the equation for Φ, we may proceed a step farther and solve for Θ. The last two terms of (10.32) have the form

$$\frac{1}{r^2}\left[\frac{1}{\Theta}\frac{1}{\sin\theta}\frac{\partial}{\partial\theta}\left(\sin\theta\frac{\partial\Theta}{\partial\theta}\right) - \frac{m^2}{\sin^2\theta}\right] \tag{10.35}$$

By definition of Θ the expression in the brackets is a function of θ alone. but on comparison with (10.32) we see that it equals a function of r alone. Therefore this function must be another constant, which we shall with forehanded knowledge of the solution call $-l(l + 1)$. The resulting differential equation has solutions that are finite for all θ only if $l = 0, 1, 2, \cdots$. These solutions are well known as the *Legendre polynomials*,

$$\Theta(\theta) = P_l^m(\mu) = (1 - \mu^2)^{|m|/2}\frac{d^{|m|}P_l(\mu)}{d\mu^{|m|}}$$

$$P_l(\mu) = \frac{1}{2^l l!}\frac{d^l[(\mu^2 - 1)^l]}{d\mu^l} \tag{10.36}$$

$$\mu = \cos\theta, \quad P_0(\mu) \equiv 1$$

Thus the solutions Θ introduce a second or *azimuthal* quantum number. The absolute value signs on m in the definition of the polynomials mean simply that $P_l^{\,m} = P_l^{\,-m}$. From the definitions in (10.36), it is easy to see that $P_l^{\,m} \equiv 0$ for $|\,m\,| > l$. Therefore the two quantum numbers found so far satisfy the important relation

$$l \geq |\,m\,| \geq 0 \qquad (10.37)$$

Turning finally to the equation for R, we define the variables

$$\frac{2m_0 W}{\hbar^2} = -k^2, \qquad \eta = m_0 Z e^2 / \hbar^2 k$$

$$\qquad (10.38)$$

$$x = kr, \qquad \chi = R/r$$

Equation (10.32) becomes

$$\frac{d^2\chi}{dx^2} + \left[-1 - \frac{l(l+1)}{x^2} + \frac{2\eta}{x} \right] \chi = 0 \qquad (10.39)$$

We know that for a bound state the electron must remain in the immediate neighborhood of the nucleus; accordingly the wave function should vanish for large r, or $\chi \to 0$ as $x \to \infty$. A possible solution of this type is

$$\chi = A x^n e^{-x} \qquad (10.40)$$

Inserting this as a trial function in (10.39), we obtain

$$\left\{ \frac{1}{x^2} \left[n(n-1) - l(l+1) \right] + \frac{2}{x} (\eta - n) \right\} A x^n e^{-x} = 0 \quad (10.41)$$

This equation can be satisfied for $A \neq 0$ only if the coefficients of both the $1/x^2$ and the $1/x$ terms in the brackets vanish. This yields two conditions:

$$n = l + 1 \qquad (10.42a)$$

$$\eta = n = 1, 2, 3, \cdots \qquad (10.42b)$$

From (10.42b) we obtain the quantized energy levels. Substitution of (10.38) yields

$$W = -\hbar^2 k^2 / 2m_0 = -\frac{1}{2} m_0 \frac{Z^2 e^4}{\hbar^2 \eta^2} = -\frac{1}{2} (m_0 c^2) \frac{(\alpha Z)^2}{n^2} \qquad (10.43)$$

exactly as in (9.39). The wave mechanical solution therefore yields the correct energy levels for the hydrogenlike atom.

Actually, Eq. (10.39) has other bound solutions besides those of the form (10.40). These solutions can all be extracted by similar procedures. Since the mathematics becomes a little more involved, we shall merely state the conclusions: for all bound solutions of (10.39), Eqs. (10.42b) and hence (10.43) remain true. Equation (10.42a) is replaced by the more general form

$$n = l + 1 + \nu, \qquad \nu = 0, 1, 2, \cdots \qquad (10.42c)$$

The net effect of (10.42c) is to make n and l independent quantum numbers; they are non-negative integers satisfying the relation

$$n > l \geq 0 \qquad (10.42d)$$

Thus the total atomic wave function $\psi = R\Theta\Phi$ depends on three quantum numbers n, l, and m, which are independent except for the restrictions (10.37) and (10.42d). The wave function of a particle in a three-dimensional box also depends on three independent quantum numbers n_x, n_y, n_z. Comparison with the one-dimensional box leads us to conclude that the wave function of a quantized system has one quantum number for each independent coordinate.

The hydrogen atom is a doubly degenerate system because all wave functions with the same total quantum number n represent states of the same energy, regardless of l and m. The degeneracy with respect to l is peculiar to a potential with a strict $1/r$ dependence. It is removed if the potential deviates from a $1/r$ law. This is the case for alkali atoms with one optical electron outside a spherically symmetric core. In the region completely outside the core the optical electron moves in a $1/r$ potential; when the optical electron penetrates the core, however, the potential changes in form because the core no longer screens the nucleus so completely. This perturbation removes the degeneracy on l for alkali atoms. The m-degeneracy is removed only by a potential that is not spherically symmetric, as is characteristic of a uniform external magnetic or electric field.

In studying the alkali spectra (Chapter 7), we found a general formula for the optical energy levels:

$$W = Rhc/(n + a_n)^2 \qquad (10.44)$$

Here n is the same principal quantum number as in (10.42), (10.43); the quantum defect a_n varies not only with n but also with the different series S, P, D, F, $\cdots$. Since the energies (10.44) should depend on both n and l, we are led to associate the different series with different values of l. This idea finds further support in Eq. (7.15), where the principal quantum number begins with $n = 1, 2, 3, 4, \cdots$ for S, P, D, F, $\cdots$ terms. This is just the rule (10.42d), if we associate $l = 0, 1, 2, 3, \cdots$ with S, P, D, F, $\cdots$. The selection rule of section 7.6 for observed spectra then assumes the more mathematical form

$$\Delta l = \pm 1 \tag{10.45}$$

Figure 7.7 shows the one-electron energy levels for the case of degeneracy (no core).

As in the elementary de Broglie interpretation (Chapter 9) the wave functions $\psi(r, \theta, \varphi)$ represent standing waves. For a point-symmetric system (with a single center of symmetry) the nodal surfaces of the standing waves are a set of concentric spheres, a set of cones centered on the symmetry axis, and a set of planes through the symmetry axis. The "symmetry axis" is the one corresponding to the quantum number m; it is conventionally taken to be the z-axis. The total number of nodal surfaces for a wave function ψ_{nlm} is n. Since one of these is a sphere of radius $r \to \infty$, there are only $(n - 1)$ nodal surfaces at finite range from the nucleus. As the m-dependence of ψ can be written as a factor $\cos m\varphi$, we see that the quantum number $|m|$ represents the number of nodal planes through the symmetry axis. The polynomial $\Theta = P_l^{|m|} \cos \theta$ is of degree $(l - |m|)$ and therefore has $(l - |m|)$ zeros, all of which are real. They correspond to $(l - |m|)$ conical nodes. The remaining $(n - l - 1)$ nodes (if any) are concentric spheres of finite radius.

Table 10.1 catalogues the various nodes of the lowest one-electron wave functions.

TABLE 10.1. NODES OF LOWEST ONE-ELECTRON WAVE FUNCTIONS

Term	n	l	$\lvert m \rvert$	Spherical nodes	Conical nodes	Plane nodes
1S	1	0	0	0	0	0
2S	2	0	0	1	0	0
2P	2	1	0	0	1	0
	2	1	1	0	0	1
3S	3	0	0	2	0	0
3P	3	1	0	1	1	0
	3	1	1	1	0	1
3D	3	2	0	0	2	0
	3	2	1	0	1	1
	3	2	2	0	0	2
4F	4	3	0	0	3	0
	4	3	1	0	2	1
	4	3	2	0	1	2
	4	3	3	0	0	3

It is useful to consider the nodes in attempting to visualize the geometrical appearance of the wave function. For example, the two representations of a 2P state differ only in the orientations of their nodal plane, because the conical node corresponding to $m = 0$ is a cone with an angular aperture of 90°. It is hence a plane perpendicular to the z-axis. Nodes that are conical in appearance first occur for D-states.

10.4. Quantization of angular momentum

In the discussion of the hydrogen atom the quantum numbers l and m are associated only with the angular variables. The extraction of these quantum numbers would be unaltered for any potential $V(r)$ that is a function of r only. Such spherically symmetrical potentials give rise to *central* forces, which are always in the direction of the radius vector. In classical mechanics we have the theorem that angular momentum is always conserved by central forces. None of the principles of wave mechanics should upset this theorem, so we may anticipate that l and m are associated with angular momentum.

Let us return to the radial wave equation (10.39), writing it out in physical units:

$$\frac{d^2\chi}{dr^2} + \frac{2m_0}{\hbar^2}\left[W + \frac{Ze^2}{r} - \frac{\hbar^2 l(l+1)}{2m_0 r^2}\right]\chi = 0 \qquad (10.46)$$

Comparison with (10.15) indicates that in addition to the attractive coulomb potential $-Ze^2/r$, Eq. (10.46) contains an effective repulsive potential

$$V(r) = \frac{\hbar^2 l(l+1)}{2m_0 r^2} \qquad (10.47)$$

A similar repulsive potential also appears in the classical equations of motion: it is, in fact, the potential representing the centrifugal force on the particle. The centrifugal force is $F = m_0 r\omega^2 = L^2/m_0 r^3$, where $L = m_0 r^2 \omega$ is the constant angular momentum of the particle. This force is derivable from a potential

$$V(r) = L^2/2m_0 r^2 \qquad (10.48a)$$

$$F = -\partial V/\partial r = L^2/m_0 r^3 \qquad (10.48b)$$

Comparison of (10.48) with (10.47) shows that we must put

$$L^2 = \hbar^2 l(l+1) \qquad (10.49)$$

That is, in wave mechanics the angular momentum is inevitably quantized.

This procedure is superior to that of Chapter 9 in the following respects: here the quantization of angular momentum follows as a natural consequence from a rigorous mathematical solution based on the fundamental wave postulate of de Broglie. In Chapter 9 the quantization of angular momentum was an isolated, mysterious postulate justified only by the fact that it worked. Furthermore, (9.36) is not quite the same as (10.49), and the evidence leaves no question that (10.49) is right. An immediate physical advantage of the present treatment is that it allows states of zero angular momentum (*S* states) with the usual energy values (10.43). The simple model of section 9.6 always requires an angular momentum of one unit of $\hbar$ or more. In the days before the development of wave mechanics, modifications of the simple model were attempted in order to circumvent this difficulty. This Bohr-Sommerfeld atom was never entirely satisfactory, however; it has been entirely supplanted by the wave mechanical solution and its attendant condition (10.49).

Quantization affects not only the squared magnitude of the angular momentum but also its z-component. From the correspondences (10.6) we can derive the correspondence $L_z \rightarrow -i\hbar\partial/\partial\varphi$. Classically, $L = r \times p$, so that by use of (10.6)

$$L_z = xp_y - yp_x \rightarrow -i\hbar(x\partial/\partial y - y\partial/\partial x) = -i\hbar\partial/\partial\varphi \qquad (10.50)$$

by definition of φ. In wave mechanics we give meaning to these correspondences by inserting the wave function ψ on the right:

$$L_z\psi = -i\hbar\partial\psi/\partial\varphi \qquad (10.51)$$

For a hydrogen atom this becomes, according to (10.34)

$$L_z\psi = m\hbar\psi \qquad (10.52)$$

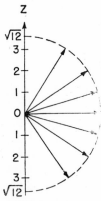

Fig. 10.4. Quantized angular momentum for $l = 3$. The projections of L on the z-axis in units of $\hbar$ can run from $m = -3$ to $+3$ as shown; the actual total magnitude of L is $\sqrt{12}\,\hbar$.

Thus the quantum number m represents the z-component of L in units of $\hbar$. The mathematical rule (10.37) now has a sensible physical interpretation: it merely states that the z-component of a vector cannot exceed the total magnitude of the vector! In fact, in quantum mechanics the z-component cannot even equal the total magnitude (unless both are zero). The various possible orientations of a nonzero angular momentum vector are illustrated in Fig. 10.4. This phenomenon of *space quantization* is in accord with the measurements of Stern and Gerlach (Chapter 3).

The results for L_z imply essentially that one component of L is quantized. By convention this is taken to be the z-component in the same way that the polar angle φ is conventionally defined about the z-axis. We could have chosen L_x or L_y to be the quantized component. Note, however, that only one component can be quantized: for since the magnitude L is quantized, and $L^2 = L_x^2 + L_y^2 + L_z^2$, quantization of more than one component would mean quantization of all three components. In this case, not only the magnitude but the direction of L would be absolutely fixed by the abstract principles of quantum mechanics, without reference to any physical problem! To avoid the possibility of such nonsense, we must realize that only one component of L can be quantized at a time. The other two components may range over all values consistent with

$$L_x^{\,2} + L_y^{\,2} = L^2 - L_z^{\,2} = [l(l+1) - m^2]\hbar^2 \qquad (10.53)$$

To form a physical picture of (10.53), it is sometimes convenient to think of the vector L as precessing continuously around its fixed z-component $L_z = m\hbar$.

Thus in wave mechanics neither the angular momentum nor its z-component can take arbitrary values, for both are quantized. The orbital angular momentum can assume only magnitudes given by (10.49); and for each value of l there are $(2l + 1)$ different possibilities for the z-component $m\hbar$,

$$m = l, l - 1, \cdots, -(l - 1), -l \qquad (10.54)$$

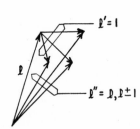

Fig. 10.5. Addition of quantized angular momenta.

The addition or subtraction of angular momentum vectors in quantum mechanics follows the usual rules of classical mechanics, except that the initial and final vectors are all quantized. If we add two angular momenta l and l' to make a resultant angular momentum l'', then

$$l + l' \geq l'' \geq |l - l'| \qquad (10.55a)$$

where l, l', and l'' are all integers. The same relation also holds if we subtract l from l' or vice versa. This is the quantum mechanical analogue of the classical rule that if $a + b = c$ is a vector sum, then the magnitudes satisfy the relation $a + b \geq c \geq |a - b|$. The quantum mechanical relation (10.55a) is illustrated for $l' = 1$ in Fig. 10.5. Note that although we specify the angular momenta by the integers l, the vectors in Fig. 10.5 are of lengths $\sqrt{l(l+1)}\,\hbar$. In classical vector addition, the z-components act like simple numbers, and this feature carries over to quantum mechanics:

$$m'' = m + m' \qquad (10.55b)$$

Equation (10.55a) is the basis of the vector model of the atom, which is a useful and relatively simple basis for understanding the details of more complex spectra than those so far discussed. We shall develop the vector model further in Chapter 11.

10.5. Parity

It is of interest to discuss at this point a quantum number that has no classical analogue. All the quantum numbers mentioned so far apply to properties well known in classical mechanics, like energy and angular momentum. The *parity* of a wave function ψ refers to its behavior upon simultaneous reflection of all the space coordinates: x, y, $z \rightarrow -x$, $-y$, $-z$. We may distinguish two ideal cases,

$$\psi(-x, -y, -z) = +\psi(x,y,z)$$
$$\psi(-x, -y, -z) = -\psi(x,y,z)$$
(10.56)

These can be combined in the form

$$\psi(-x, -y, -z) = P\psi(x,y,z) \tag{10.57}$$

where $P = +1$ or -1. Here P can be assigned the role of a quantum number. It is rather more restricted than the other quantum numbers we have found, since it ranges over just two values, $+1$ and -1. Nevertheless, we can treat it like a true quantum number. The physical property it defines is called the *parity* of the system; this parity is quantized and has the quantum number P. The names "even parity" and "odd parity" denote the respective cases $P = +1$ and $P = -1$. Parity is a concept that has no meaning in classical physics, because it is defined in terms of the Schroedinger wave function ψ.

Any solution of the Schroedinger equation where V is a function of the radius only, corresponding to a central force, satisfies (10.57). Consider the hydrogen atom wave function $\psi = R(r)\Theta(\theta)\Phi(\varphi)$. Under reflection of the coordinates, r, θ, $\varphi \rightarrow r$, $\pi - \theta$, $\pi + \varphi$. According to (10.34),

$$\Phi(\pi + \varphi) = e^{im\pi}e^{im\varphi} = (-1)^{|m|}\Phi(\varphi) \tag{10.58}$$

And $\theta \rightarrow \pi - \theta$ means $\mu \rightarrow -\mu$ in (10.36), so that

$$\Theta(-\theta) = (-1)^{l+|m|}\Theta(\theta) \tag{10.59}$$

Thus

$$\psi(-x, -y, -z) = R(r)(-1)^{l+|m|}\Theta(\theta)(-1)^{|m|}\Phi(\varphi)$$
$$= (-1)^l R(r)\Theta(\theta)\Phi(\varphi) \tag{10.60}$$
$$= (-1)^l \psi(x, y, z)$$

since $(-1)^{2|m|} \equiv 1$ for integer m. For a hydrogen wave function with quantum number l for orbital angular momentum, the parity is hence

$$P = (-1)^l \tag{10.61}$$

10.6. $|\psi|^2$ as probability

In wave mechanics our entire knowledge of a system is contained in its wave function ψ. We need some prescription for extracting from the mathematical function ψ the maximum possible amount of physical information about the system. The prescription that has proved most satisfactory, originally due to Born, is the following: if the wave function of a particle is $\psi(x,y,z)$, then $|\psi(x,y,z)|^2 \, dV$ is the probability of finding the particle in the volume element dV at the position (x,y,z). Since probability must always be real and non-negative, we take the absolute value squared, to allow for the possibility that ψ may be complex. We can always fix the constant A in expressions like (10.17), (10.24), and (10.40) to make this probability interpretation quantitatively exact. This process of fixing A is called *normalization* of the wave function. We normalize by requiring that

$$\int_V |\psi(x, y, z)|^2 \, dV = 1 \qquad (10.62)$$

which expresses the fact that there is one particle in the volume V. The choice of V varies with the problem at hand. For a bound state, where there is only one electron in the entire system, we take $V \to \infty$. For a free particle this is not possible, and V is some standard volume.

As an example, let us normalize (10.24) to represent one particle in a rectangular box. The volume V is then just that of the box, and (10.62) reads

$$1 = \int |\psi|^2 \, dV$$

$$= |A|^2 \int_0^{D_x} dx \int_0^{D_y} dy \int_0^{D_z} dz \, \sin^2 \frac{2\pi x n_x}{D_x} \sin^2 \frac{2\pi y n_y}{D_y} \sin^2 \frac{2\pi z n_z}{D_z} \qquad (10.63)$$

$$= |A|^2 \left(\frac{1}{2}\right)^3 D_x D_y D_z$$

where V is the volume of the box. The normalization determines only the absolute magnitude of A. It will never be necessary to know the real and imaginary parts of A separately. In this particular problem the normalization constant A happens to be the same for all sets of quantum numbers (n_x, n_y, n_z). In most physical problems this is not the case, and A is a function of these quantum numbers.

This interpretation indicates information we can obtain about a system in wave mechanics. An electron in a hydrogen atom, for example, can never be specified to run in a particular orbit as in the Bohr model of Chapter 9. Fig. 10.6 shows the probability distributions $|\psi|^2$ for some hydrogen wave functions. In general, we must be satisfied to know average values of any mechanical quantities such as position, momentum, etc. After normalizing so that $|\psi|^2$ represents the true probability, we have for the average value of any quantity q,

$$\langle q \rangle = \int_V |\psi|^2 q \, dV = \int_V \psi^* q \psi \, dV \qquad (10.64)$$

In the second part of (10.64) we have replaced $|\psi|^2$ by the mathematically identical $\psi^* \psi$ (where ψ^* is the complex conjugate of ψ), with the modification that q appears between ψ^* and ψ. This form is the more general one, because it allows q to be a quantity that involves derivatives, like $p_x \rightarrow -i\hbar\partial/\partial x$, $L_z \rightarrow -i\hbar\partial/\partial\varphi$, etc.

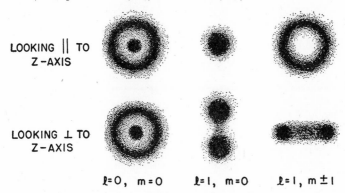

LOOKING $\parallel$ TO Z-AXIS

LOOKING $\perp$ TO Z-AXIS

$\ell=0$, m=0 $\ell=1$, m=0 $\ell=1$, m$\pm$1

Fig. 10.6. Particle density distribution $|\psi|^2$ for $n = 2$.

In quantum mechanics the average value $\langle q \rangle$ is frequently called the "expectation value" in accord with the following idea. We envision a large number of independent measurements on the system to determine q: they yield the values q_1, q_2, $\cdots$, q_n, $\cdots$. These values are in general all different, but the expected average of all the measurements is the expectation value $\langle q \rangle$, which we can calculate from (10.64).

There is one special case in which the individual measurements show no fluctuation at all. Every measurement yields precisely $q_n \equiv \langle q \rangle$. This is the case in which the quantity q is quantized. Consider, for example, $q = L_z$. Any individual measurement of L_z yields exactly the value $m\hbar$; and by (10.64),

$$\langle L_z \rangle = \int_V \psi^* L_z \psi \, dV = m\hbar \int_V \psi^* \psi \, dV = m\hbar \qquad (10.65)$$

by use of (10.62). The expectation value of a quantized property, which is the identical result of every measurement, is called the *eigenvalue*. For example, the eigenvalue of L_z is $m\hbar$, and Eq. (10.43) gives the eigenvalues of the energy W for a hydrogen atom.

10.7. The uncertainty principle

The discussion of the preceding section in terms of probability is closely akin in spirit to the uncertainty principle of section 9.9. We shall now illustrate the connection by using the expectation value procedure to establish a mathematically precise form of the uncertainty relation. We consider the example of two conjugate quantities, the position x and the momentum p.

The average value of the position coordinate x is its expectation $\langle x \rangle = \int \psi^* x \psi \, dV$. The usual measure of the extent to which individual measurements fluctuate about this average is the mean square deviation

$$\langle (\Delta x)^2 \rangle = \langle (x - \langle x \rangle)^2 \rangle = \langle x^2 \rangle - \langle x \rangle^2 \tag{10.66}$$

If we choose coordinates so that $\langle x \rangle = 0$, the root-mean-square deviation or average uncertainty in x is

$$\Delta x = \sqrt{\langle x^2 \rangle} \tag{10.67a}$$

For the conjugate momentum p we have the average uncertainty

$$\Delta p = \sqrt{\langle p^2 \rangle} \tag{10.67b}$$

Now consider the quantity

$$I = \int D \, dV \geq 0, \qquad D = \left| x \frac{\psi}{\langle x^2 \rangle} + \lambda \frac{d\psi}{dx} \right|^2 \tag{10.68}$$

where λ is an arbitrary real parameter at our disposal. The integral I in (10.68) is over all space, and it is essentially non-negative because the integrand D is also non-negative, being the square of an absolute value. Writing out the expression for I, we have

$$
\begin{aligned}
I = {} & \frac{1}{\langle x^2 \rangle^2} \int \psi^* x^2 \psi \, dV + \frac{\lambda}{\langle x^2 \rangle} \int \left(\frac{d\psi^*}{dx} x\psi + \psi^* x \frac{d\psi}{dx} \right) dV \\
& + \lambda^2 \int \frac{d\psi^*}{dx} \frac{d\psi}{dx} \, dV \\
= {} & \frac{1}{\langle x^2 \rangle} + \frac{\lambda}{\langle x^2 \rangle} \int \left[\frac{d}{dx} (\psi^* x\psi) - \psi^*\psi \right] dV \\
& + \lambda^2 \int \left[\frac{d}{dx} \left(\psi^* \frac{d\psi}{dx} \right) - \psi^* \frac{d^2\psi}{dx^2} \right] dV
\end{aligned}
\tag{10.69}
$$

For integrals like

$$J = \int \frac{d}{dx} (\psi^* x \psi) \, dV = \psi^* x \psi \Big]_{x=-\infty}^{x=+\infty}$$

we recall that for a bound state wave function, one of the necessary physical conditions is that $\psi \to 0$ as x or r goes to infinity. Therefore the integral J equals zero. A slight modification in the argument is needed when ψ refers to a free particle, but we can still conclude that $J = 0$ and $\int \psi^* \psi \, dV = 1$. Thus

$$I = \frac{1 - \lambda}{\langle x^2 \rangle} - \lambda^2 \int \psi^* \frac{d^2 \psi}{dx^2} \, dV \tag{10.70}$$

To evaluate the last term of (10.70) we note that by (10.6), $\partial^2/\partial x^2 \to -p^2/\hbar^2$, so that the last term is just proportional to $\langle p^2 \rangle = (\Delta p)^2$. Hence finally

$$I = \frac{1 - \lambda}{(\Delta x)^2} + \frac{\lambda^2 (\Delta p)^2}{\hbar^2} \geq 0 \tag{10.71}$$

We may regard (10.71) as a quadratic equation in λ. The condition that any quadratic expression $(az^2 + bz + c)$ be never negative is that its discriminant $b^2 - 4ac$ is never negative. In this case the discriminant condition becomes

$$\frac{1}{(\Delta x)^4} - \frac{4}{\hbar^2} \frac{(\Delta p)^2}{(\Delta x)^2} \geq 0$$

$$(\Delta p)^2 (\Delta x)^2 \geq \frac{\hbar^2}{4} \tag{10.72}$$

$$\Delta p \, \Delta x \geq \frac{\hbar}{2}$$

The last line of (10.72) has exactly the form of the uncertainty relation (9.59), but is somewhat more precise. The uncertainties Δp and Δx have the meanings of root-mean-square deviations, and the numerical constant multiplying $\hbar$ turns out to be $\geq \frac{1}{2}$. Using the ideas of expectation values, we can carry through similar arguments for all pairs of conjugate quantities subject to the uncertainty relation.

10.8. Stationary states and radiation

Since Eq. (10.15) is time-independent, we say that the wave functions ψ describe *stationary states* of the system. By means of (10.14b) it is possible to associate a time dependence with each stationary state,

$$\Psi(x,y,z,t) = \psi(x,y,z)e^{-iWt/\hbar} \tag{10.73}$$

The time dependence is a simple harmonic variation, $e^{-i\omega t} = \cos \omega t - i \sin \omega t$ where $\hbar\omega = W$. It is still physically reasonable to speak of a stationary state, for the density distribution $| \Psi(x,y,z,t) |^2 = | \psi(x,y,z) |^2$ is independent of the time t. This perfect constancy with time can also be seen with the aid of the uncertainty principle, $\Delta W \, \Delta t \gtrsim \hbar/2$. In this case the energy W is a precisely known eigenvalue, so that $\Delta W = 0$ and $\Delta t = \infty$. An infinite uncertainty in t means that there is no way of measuring time by means of this state, or hence that it is absolutely constant with time.

The Schroedinger equation (10.28) implies that all the energy levels of the hydrogen atom correspond to stationary states. This disagrees with the observed fact that all excited states pass rapidly to the ground state by emitting photons of appropriate energies. The Eq. (10.28) is incomplete because it does not include the effects of radiation. To do this in complete detail is beyond the scope of our present discussion, but we may mention some of the important features. The possibility of radiation means that an excited state is no longer perfectly stationary but tends to decay with time according to the law

$$\frac{dN}{dt} = - \frac{1}{\tau} N \tag{10.74}$$

where N is the number of atoms in an excited state at any time t, and τ is the mean lifetime of that state. The solution of (10.74) is

$$N/N_0 = e^{-t/\tau} \tag{10.75}$$

which says that the fraction of atoms that are excited decays exponentially with time t. In order to obtain such an exponential time dependence for the density distribution $| \Psi(x,y,z,t) |^2$, it is necessary to assume that the excited energy W is not a real number but has a small negative imaginary part. Hence to account for radiative decay we may write

$$W \rightarrow W - i\Gamma/2 \tag{10.76}$$

so that now

$$| \Psi(x,y,z,t) |^2 = | \psi(x,y,z) |^2 e^{-\Gamma t/\hbar} \tag{10.77}$$

Comparison with (10.75) indicates that the mean life τ satisfies

$$\Gamma\tau = \hbar \tag{10.78}$$

This is just in the form of an uncertainty relation; it implies that just as the time is no longer infinitely uncertain, so the energy of the level is no longer infinitely certain. A spectral line is hence not infinitely sharp, even when observed in a perfect spectrometer, but has a natural width as illustrated in Fig. 10.7. The width of the peak at half its maximum

height is called the half width and on a
frequency scale is just equal to $\Gamma/\hbar$. In
the lowest excited states of hydrogen $\Gamma/\hbar$
is on the order of $10^8/\text{sec}$.

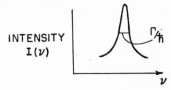

Fig. 10.7. Natural width of a
spectral line.

Thus without actually correcting Eq.
(10.28) to take account of radiation, we
have been able to describe some properties of the solution of this corrected equa-
tion. This account may be made quantitative by estimating τ. We
shall indicate how this estimate is made in the simplest approximation, although the calculation can in principle be refined to any
desired degree. Consider first the radiation from a classical electron
oscillator, which we take for convenience to be oscillating only in the
x-direction. The instantaneous rate at which it radiates energy is

$$dU/dt = (\tfrac{2}{3})e^2 a^2/c^3 \qquad (10.79)$$

where a is the acceleration. Now $a = d^2x/dt^2$ where $x = x_0 \cos \omega t$ and
x_0 is the amplitude, ω the frequency of oscillation. The average rate of
energy radiation is

$$\overline{dU/dt} = (\tfrac{2}{3})(e^2\omega^4 x_0^2/c^3) \,\overline{\cos^2 \omega t} = (\tfrac{1}{3})e^2\omega^4 x_0^2/c^3 \qquad (10.80)$$

since the average value of $\cos^2 \omega t$ per cycle is $\tfrac{1}{2}$.

The quantum mechanical treatment differs from the classical in one
important detail: in quantum mechanics we must distinguish between
positive and negative frequencies. In

$$x = x_0 \cos \omega t = (x_0/2)e^{i\omega t} + (x_0/2)e^{-i\omega t}$$

the term with $e^{i\omega t}$ corresponds to photon emission, the one with $e^{-i\omega t}$
to photon absorption. We are only concerned with one of these processes,
for which the amplitude is $x_0' = x_0/2$. Thus

$$x_0 \text{ (classical)} = 2(x_0/2) = 2x_0' \text{ (quantum)} \qquad (10.81)$$

In quantum mechanics it is natural to take something like the expectation value of x in place of the amplitude x_0'. Since the radiation occurs
in a transition between the states ψ_{nlm} and $\psi_{n'l'm'}$ we take a sort of transition expectation value,

$$\langle n'l'm'|\, x\, |nlm \rangle = \int \psi^*_{n'l'm'} x\, \psi_{nlm}\, dV \qquad (10.82)$$

In this notation the previously discussed expectation values for a single
state are $\langle q \rangle = \langle nlm|\, q\, |nlm \rangle$. On substitution of (10.82), (10.81) in
(10.80) the quantum mechanical radiation formula takes the form

$$\frac{d\overline{U}}{dt} = \frac{4}{3} \frac{e^2 \omega_{nn'}^4}{c^3} | \langle n'l'm' | x | nlm \rangle |^2 \tag{10.83}$$

where $\omega_{nn'} = (W_n - W_{n'})/\hbar$. Since all the radiation occurs in photons of energy $\hbar\omega_{nn'}$, we can write $d\overline{U}/dt = \hbar\omega_{nn'}/\tau$, where τ is the mean lifetime (10.74) for emission of one photon. Then

$$\frac{1}{\tau} = \frac{4}{3} \frac{e^2}{\hbar c} \frac{\omega_{nn'}^3}{c^2} | \langle n'l'm' | x | nlm \rangle |^2 \tag{10.84}$$

Equation (10.84) gives the quantum mechanical estimate for the rate at which an atomic system goes between states with quantum numbers nlm and $n'l'm'$ by emission of radiation. It assumes the model of an oscillating electric dipole that moves only in the x-direction. The radiation is accordingly plane polarized in this direction. To obtain the total electric dipole radiation rate, we must allow for oscillation in the y- and z-directions as well. Thus we have for the final radiation formula

$$\frac{1}{\tau} = \frac{4}{3} \alpha \frac{\omega_{nn'}^3}{c^2} (| \langle x \rangle |^2 + | \langle y \rangle |^2 + | \langle z \rangle |)^2 \tag{10.85}$$

The quantities in angle brackets, defined as in (10.82), are the *matrix elements*, so called because of their historical association with a method originated by Heisenberg (1925).

In Eqs. (10.83)–(10.85) we include absolute value signs around the squared matrix elements. This is to insure that $d\overline{U}/dt$ and $1/\tau$ are real quantities—as they must be physically—regardless of the character of ψ.

Other types of matrix elements besides those for an electric dipole will cause radiative transitions. They are called magnetic dipole, magnetic and electric quadrupole, octopole, 2^4, 2^5, $\cdots$, 2^n-pole matrix elements. In the atomic case they lead to values of τ that are several factors of 10 larger than for the electric dipole (10.85). Since the intensity of radiation is proportional to $1/\tau$, the intense spectrum lines will all correspond to electric dipole transitions.

Frequently an initial state nlm can undergo radiative transition to several different final states $n'l'm'$, $n''l''m''$, $\cdots$, etc. Each such transition proceeds independently of all the others with its characteristic half life τ', τ'', $\cdots$. The chief factor affecting τ is the energy of the transition, which enters (10.85) to the third power. The total rate (intensity) of decay of the initial state is

$$1/\tau = 1/\tau' + 1/\tau'' + \cdots \tag{10.86}$$

and the fractional rate (intensity) in any transition is

$$\frac{1/\tau'}{1/\tau' + 1/\tau'' + \cdots} \tag{10.87}$$

When several possible decay processes can occur simultaneously in this way, they are said to be in *competition*.

10.9. Selection rules

One of the satisfactory features of wave mechanics is its ability to interpret the observed selection rules for atomic spectra. The empirically observed rule is $\Delta l = \pm 1$, which must apply to the electric dipole radiation (10.85), which is the most intense. To see an example of these selection rules, consider the matrix element $\langle n'l'm' | \, x \, | nlm \rangle$. With the expression (10.29) for x, the integral over the coordinate φ becomes

$$\int_0^{2\pi} e^{-im'\varphi} \cos\varphi \, e^{im\varphi} \, d\varphi = \tfrac{1}{2} \int_0^{2\pi} (e^{i(m-m'+1)\varphi} + e^{i(m-m'-1)\varphi}) \, d\varphi \qquad (10.88)$$

This integral vanishes unless

$$m' - m = \Delta m = \pm 1 \qquad (10.89)$$

We have therefore a selection rule on m for allowed transitions. The matrix element of y gives the same rule, and for z we have simply

$$\int_0^{2\pi} e^{-im'\varphi} e^{im\varphi} \, d\varphi, \qquad \Delta m = 0 \qquad (10.90)$$

The complete selection rule on m for electric dipole transitions is therefore

$$\Delta m = 0, \pm 1 \qquad (10.91)$$

Similar integrals over the coordinate θ will lead to the selection rule on l. As these integrals are rather involved, we shall present here only a physical argument. The quantity Δm in (10.91) actually represents the z-component of the angular momentum that is carried away by the photon in the transition. The equation $m' - m = \Delta m$ simply states the conservation of the angular momentum z-component among the initial and final atomic states and the emitted photon. According to (10.54) $\Delta m = 0, \pm 1$ corresponds to a total angular momentum $\Delta l = 1$, which the photon carries off. This Δl is a vector quantity, which is added to (or subtracted from) the vector l of the initial state to yield the vector l' of the final state. The quantum mechanical rule (10.55) of vector addition with $\Delta l = 1$ are that

$$l' = l, l \pm 1 \qquad (10.92)$$

as illustrated in Figure 10.5. Actually, not all these potential combinations occur in practice. There is one further quantum number and associated selection rule that eliminates the possibility $l' = l$ from

(10.92). This quantum number is the *parity* of the wave function, discussed in section 10.5.

Consider the matrix element $\langle x \rangle$. This is a physical quantity, and its value cannot depend upon the mathematical coordinate system used to evaluate the integral involved. In particular, $\langle x \rangle$ must not change when we put $x, y, z \to -x, -y, -z$:

$$\langle x \rangle = \int \psi_{n'l'm'}^*(x,y,z)x\psi_{nlm}(x,y,z) \ dV \tag{10.93a}$$

$$= \int \psi_{n'l'm'}^*(-x,-y,-z)(-x)\psi_{nlm}(-x,-y,-z) \ dV. \tag{10.93b}$$

By use of (10.61), Eq. (10.93b) becomes

$$\langle x \rangle = (-1)^{l'+l+1} \int \psi_{n'l'm'}^*(x,y,z)x\psi_{nlm}(x,y,z) \ dV \tag{10.93c}$$

Equations (10.93c) and (10.93a) are automatically identical if $l' = l \pm 1$; but if $l' = l$, they imply $\langle x \rangle = -\langle x \rangle$, which can be true only if

$$\langle x \rangle = 0 \tag{10.94}$$

The same argument holds for $\langle y \rangle$ and $\langle z \rangle$, so that the parity selection rule (10.94) in combination with (10.92) leads to the final form

$$l' - l = \Delta l = \pm 1 \tag{10.95}$$

in full agreement with the observed (10.45).

Explicit calculation shows that there are no other selection rules for electric dipole emission than (10.91), (10.95). These rules are specific to electric dipole emission; other multipoles have their own selection rules.

REFERENCES

D. Bohm, *Quantum Theory*, Prentice-Hall, New York (1951).

W. Pauli, *Handbuch der Physik*, Vol. 24 (1), Springer, Berlin (1933).

L. Pauling and E. B. Wilson, *Introduction to Quantum Mechanics*, McGraw-Hill, New York (1935).

V. Rojansky, *Introductory Quantum Mechanics*, Prentice-Hall, New York (1938).

E. Schroedinger, *Wave Mechanics*, Blackie, London (1928).

E. T. Whittaker and G. N. Watson, *Modern Analysis*, Macmillan, New York (1947).

SUMMARY

This chapter presents some of the mathematical apparatus necessary to determine in complete detail the motion of de Broglie waves and wave packets. The nonrelativistic equation of motion in wave mechanics follows from the classical equation of particle motion by a prescription: in the Hamiltonian equation representing conservation of energy, $p^2/2m_0 + V = W$, make the replacement $p_x \rightarrow -i\hbar \, \partial/\partial x$, etc. and apply the whole equation as an operator on a wave function $\psi(x, y, z)$. This is the time-independent Schroedinger equation; we obtain the time-dependent form by also substituting $W \rightarrow i\hbar \, \partial/\partial t$. The wave function ψ completely describes the motion of a mechanical system in wave mechanics: it contains all the physical information that we can have about the system.

The particle in a rectangular box provides an example of the solution of the Schroedinger equation. The wave function ψ must satisfy physical boundary condition at the edges of the box. These conditions determine not only the form of ψ but also the eigenvalues of the energy W. The eigenvalues depend on three integral quantum numbers, corresponding to the three spatial dimensions. *Degeneracies* frequently occur in which wave functions of different geometrical configuration have identical energy eigenvalues. These degeneracies are generally removed by small perturbations. For the rectangular box a dent in the side represents a perturbation; the phenomenon of degenerate eigenvalues and perturbations is a general effect not limited to the particular case of the rectangular box.

The Schroedinger equation is applied to the bound states of the hydrogen atom. By assuming a ψ that vanishes as $r \rightarrow \infty$, we obtain the eigenvalues $W = -\frac{1}{2}m_0 c^2 (\alpha Z)^2/n^2$, as in the simplified Bohr treatment of the previous chapter. Three independent quantum numbers n, l, and m characterize each eigenfunction corresponding to W. In a pure Coulomb field W depends only on n and is hence degenerate with respect to l and m; the degree of the degeneracy (number of geometrically different wave functions with the same energy) is n^2. When the atom has a core of inner electrons, the degeneracy with respect to l is removed: the $(2l + 1)$-fold degeneracy with respect to m vanishes only in an external magnetic field, as discussed in Chapter 11.

In quantum mechanics the angular momentum L is quantized in two respects: its projection along an arbitrary axis (conventionally taken as the z-axis) is $m\hbar$, where m is an integer limited by $-l \leq m \leq l$, and l is an integer specifying the magnitude of the angular momentum. The absolute magnitude of L is not $l\hbar$, but $\sqrt{l(l + 1)}\hbar$, so that the vector L never lies entirely along the z-axis. There are $(2l + 1)$ possible projections along the z-axis. The addition of two angular momenta l and l' leads to a quantized angular momentum l'', where $|l - l'| \leq l'' \leq l + l'$. The corresponding z-components add algebraically: $m'' = m + m'$.

An important physical parameter of atomic systems is the parity. This is the eigenvalue of ψ on the reflection of the coordinate system and can have the values $P = \pm 1$. This is the first example of a physical quantity that is essentially quantum mechanical in character, since ψ does not exist for classical systems.

The physical interpretation of the wave function is that $|\psi(x, y, z)|^2$ represents the probability of finding a particle per unit volume at the point x, y, z. For free particles we normalize $|\psi|^2$ to one particle in a standard unit of volume; for a bound state we normalize the wave function so that the integral of $|\psi|^2$ over all space is unity, corresponding to one particle in the bound state.

The interpretation of $|\psi|^2$ as a probability density leads to the idea of the *expectation value* of any quantity q: $\langle q \rangle = \int \psi^* q \psi \, dV$. If in the integral q is not a differential operator, the integral is $\int q |\psi|^2 \, dV$, the usual expression for a statistical average. The physical interpretation is that $\langle q \rangle$ represents the expected average of a large number of measurements on the system of the quantity q, but that we can never predict exactly what will be the result of any particular measurement of q. Exceptions to this rule occur when q is quantized and yields an identical *eigenvalue* for each measurement. For example, the eigenvalue of L_z is $m\hbar$. The idea of the expectation value can be applied to give a more precise form of the uncertainty relation: $\Delta p \, \Delta x \geq \hbar/2$, where Δp and Δx are root-mean-square values. The same relation can be obtained for all pairs of conjugate variables.

The wave functions of the Schroedinger equation describe stationary states of the system: the configuration does not vary with time. Such stationary states are in general an approximation except for the ground state of an atom. All other states can decay by emission of radiation to lower energy states. This decay occurs at an average rate $1/\tau = \Gamma/\hbar$, where τ is the mean lifetime of the state and Γ is the corresponding uncertainty or half-width of the energy level that is dictated by the uncertainty principle. By applying a sort of expectation value argument to the classical radiation formula, we are able to estimate $1/\tau$ in terms of an integral over the wave functions ψ of the stationary states involved in the transition. A closer examination of this integral reveals the selection rules $\Delta m = 0, \pm 1$ and $\Delta l = \pm 1$, in agreement with experiment. This explanation of selection rules is possible only with the fully developed form of wave mechanics discussed in this chapter and is one of the indications that this wave mechanics is essentially correct for atomic problems.

ILLUSTRATIVE PROBLEMS

1. Show in what sense Newton's law $F = ma = \partial p/\partial t$ is satisfied in wave mechanics.

Solution. In wave mechanics we must always deal with a wave function ψ, so that we cannot simply write $F = \partial p/\partial t$. An equation of this form does hold between expectation values, however. For simplicity we state the proof for motion in the x-direction only, although the procedure is also applicable to three-dimensional motion.

The force is $F = -\partial V/\partial x$, where V is the potential function in the Schroedinger equation. For any state Ψ of the system the expectation value of the momentum in the x-direction is, using (10.6),

$$\langle p \rangle = \int \Psi^* p \Psi \, dx = -i\hbar \int \Psi^* \frac{\partial \Psi}{\partial x} \, dx$$

The time derivative of this quantity is

$$\partial \langle p \rangle / \partial t = -i\hbar \int \left(\frac{\partial \Psi^*}{\partial t} \frac{\partial \Psi}{\partial x} + \Psi^* \frac{\partial^2 \Psi}{\partial x \, \partial t} \right) dx$$

Substituting the time-dependent Schroedinger equation (10.13), we have

$$\frac{\partial \langle p \rangle}{\partial t} = \frac{-\hbar^2}{2m_0} \int \left(\frac{\partial^2 \Psi^*}{\partial x^2} \frac{\partial \Psi}{\partial x} - \Psi^* \frac{\partial^3 \Psi}{\partial x^3} \right) dx$$

$$+ \int \left[V\Psi^* \frac{\partial \Psi}{\partial x} - \Psi^* \frac{\partial}{\partial x} (V\Psi) \right] dx$$

$$= \frac{-\hbar^2}{2m_0} \int \frac{\partial}{\partial x} \left(\frac{\partial \Psi^*}{\partial x} \frac{\partial \Psi}{\partial x} - \Psi^* \frac{\partial^2 \Psi}{\partial x^2} \right) dx - \int \Psi^* \frac{\partial V}{\partial x} \Psi \, dx$$

The first integral is just

$$\frac{-\hbar^2}{2m_0} \left(\frac{\partial \Psi^*}{\partial x} \frac{\partial \Psi}{\partial x} - \Psi^* \frac{\partial^2 \Psi}{\partial x^2} \right)_{x=-\infty}^{x=+\infty} = 0$$

since the physical conditions on the wave function are that $\Psi \to 0$ as x approaches the end of its range, taken here as $x \to \pm \infty$. Thus we have

$$\partial \langle p \rangle / \partial t = - \int \Psi^* (\partial V/\partial x) \Psi \, dx = \langle F \rangle$$

Thus in wave mechanics Newton's law is exactly satisfied by the expectation values of p and F. This illustrates the relation between quan-turn and classical mechanics: the expectation values in quantum mechanics play the role of classical variables. For macroscopic bodies the fluctuations from the expectation values are imperceptible, so that classical mechanics is a valid approximation.

2. Find the energy eigenvalues and wave functions of the one-dimensional harmonic oscillator in wave mechanics.

Solution. For an oscillator centered at the origin the potential is $V = \frac{1}{2}kx^2$, and the Schroedinger equation (10.15) becomes

$$d^2\psi/dx^2 + 2m/\hbar^2(W - \tfrac{1}{2}\,m\omega_0^2x^2)\psi = 0$$

where $\omega_0 = \sqrt{k/m}$ is the classical frequency of the oscillator. If we put $y = (m\omega_0/\hbar)^{1/2}x$, $\alpha = 2W/\hbar\omega_0$, this becomes

$$\frac{d^2\psi}{dy^2} + (\alpha - y^2)\psi = 0$$

The wave function ψ must satisfy physical restrictions as $y \to \pm\infty$ and $y \to 0$. As $y \to \pm\infty$, the term in y^2 becomes very much larger than the term in α, so the equation is approximately $d^2\psi/dy^2 - y^2\psi = 0$. This suggests a solution of the form $\psi \approx e^{y^2}$ or $\psi \approx e^{-y^2}$. The first choice $\to\infty$ as $y \to \pm\infty$, and is therefore not acceptable as a physical wave function. Taking the second choice, we write $\psi = e^{-1/2(y^2)}H(y)$ and substitute in the equation above, obtaining

$$d^2H/dy^2 - 2y\,dH/dy + (\alpha - 1)H = 0$$

For H we try a power series solution of the form

$$H(y) = a_ny^n + a_{n-1}y^{n-1} + \cdots + a_1y + a_0.$$

We take the highest power of y to be y^n, so that $a_n \neq 0$. The series stops with a_0 because the next terms would be powers of $1/y$, which would make ψ an unacceptable wave function (i.e., we could not interpret $|\psi|^2$ as a finite probability) as $y \to 0$. Substituting in the equation, we have

$$a_n(\alpha - 2n - 1)y^n + a_{n-1}(\alpha - 2n + 1)y^{n-1}$$

$$+ [a_nn(n - 1) + a_{n-2}(\alpha - 2n + 3)]y^{n-2}$$

$$+ [a_{n-1}(n - 1)(n - 2) + a_{n-3}(\alpha - 2n + 5)]y^{n-3} + \cdots$$

$$+ [6a_3 + a_1(\alpha - 3)]y + [2a_2 + a_0(\alpha - 1)] = 0$$

The coefficient of each power of y must be zero for this expression to be generally satisfied. For the first term $a_n \neq 0$, so we must have $\alpha = 2n + 1$; for the second term $\alpha - 2n + 1 = 2$, so we must have $a_{n-1} = 0$. The successive terms relate a_n, a_{n-2}, a_{n-4}, $\cdots$ and a_{n-1},

a_{n-3}, a_{n-5}, $\cdots$; hence $a_{n-1} = a_{n-3} = a_{n-5} = \cdots = 0$. The series for H therefore contains only even or odd powers of y, according as n is even or odd.

The eigenvalues of the energy are

$$W_n = \hbar\omega_0\alpha/2 = (n + \tfrac{1}{2})\hbar\omega_0$$

$$n = 0, 1, 2, \cdots$$

The energy levels of the harmonic oscillator in quantum mechanics are equally spaced with a spacing $\hbar\omega_0 = h\nu_0$, where ν_0 is the classical oscillator frequency. Even in its ground state with $n = 0$, the quantum mechanical oscillator has energy $\tfrac{1}{2}\hbar\omega_0$, which is known as the "zero-point energy." Thus in quantum mechanics the oscillator is never entirely at rest. The zero-point energy can never be extracted from the oscillator and transferred to any outside system; it can generally be neglected in considering the interaction of the oscillator with external systems.

PROBLEMS

1. An electron is confined in a rectangular box of sides D_x, D_y, and D_z. For a state with quantum numbers n_x, n_y, n_z, find the pressure exerted on the three faces of the box. This pressure is defined as $A_s P_s = -\partial/\partial s(W_{n_x,n_y,n_z})$, where A_s is the area of the face and s is the axis perpendicular to this face.

Show that this pressure is in general different on different faces of the box, in distinction to the classical case. Under what circumstances are the pressures equal in all three directions? What are the pressures if the box is a cube 1 cm on a side and the electron is an $n_x = n_y = n_z = 1$ state?

2. Find the simplest wave mechanical solution for a particle in a spherical box of radius R. The procedure may be outlined as follows:

(a) Write the Schroedinger equation in coordinates appropriate to the spherical box.

(b) Separate out the θ- and φ-dependent parts in the same way as for the hydrogen atom. Write the remaining radial equation.

(c) Reduce the radial differential equation to a simpler form by putting $R(r) = (1/r)u(r)$ and finding the equation for u.

(d) To obtain the simplest form of this reduced equation, put $l = 0$. The corresponding solutions are called s-waves in accordance with the spectroscopic notation. The radial equation is now in a simple standard form.

(e) The solution u of the radial equation is subject to two conditions, similar to those for the square box: $u = 0$ for $r = 0$ and $r = R$. Find the energy values in terms of the radial quantum number,

$$W_n = (\pi^2 \hbar^2 / 2m_0 R^2)n^2.$$

Since $l = m = 0$ for these levels, they should be written W_{n00}.

(f) Find the normalized wave functions that represent one particle contained in the box $\int |\psi|^2 dV = 1$. Remember that $\psi = u/r$ and that $dV = r^2 dr \sin\theta\, d\theta\, d\varphi$.

(g) Use the results of (f) to argue that the lowest permissible value of n is 1 and not 0.

3. Using the experience gained in problems 1 and 2, determine the pressure necessary to keep an electron inside a nucleus of radius 5×10^{-13} cm. Assume the electron to be in the lowest s-state.

What does the result of this calculation suggest about the physical likelihood that electrons are contained inside the nucleus? Is the neglect of relativistic effects justified? (Note that a relativistic treatment would lead to qualitatively the same results.)

This problem is an elementary example of a technique that is quite useful in solving original problems in physics. If a new physical problem arises that one is not at first able to solve directly, he may first try a few practice problems. These exercises have the properties that: (a) their solutions are readily obtainable; (b) they have some physical features in common with the given problem. From the experience gained on the practice problems it is frequently possible to pass to a solution of the given problem. The chief inventiveness required is to find suitable practice problems. In this simple example the physical problem was to find the pressure of an electron in a nucleus, and problems 1 and 2 served as practice exercises.

4. For an S state the probability of finding the electron at a distance r or less from the nucleus in the hydrogen atom is proportional to

$$P(r) = 4\pi \int_0^r R^2 r^2 \, dr = 4\pi r_n^3 \int_0^{y=r/r_n} Q^2(y) y^2 \, dy$$

Using this equation and the information in problem 5, determine

(a) The ratio of the probabilities of finding the electron at a distance from the nucleus smaller and a distance larger than the Bohr radius in the normal $1S$ state.

(b) The ratio of the probabilities of finding the electron inside and outside of the spherical node for the $2S$ state. Note that the electron is mostly "outside" the Bohr orbits, especially for the higher values of n.

5. The radial dependence of the hydrogen wave function is determined by the quantum numbers n and l, and is of the form $R_{nl}(r) = Q_{nl}(y_n)e^{-y_n}$ where $y_n = r/r_n$ and $r_n = na_0$ is the radius of the nth Bohr orbit. Then $Q_{nl}(y_n)$ is a polynomial in y_n of degree $(n - 1)$ and has the following values:

n	l	$Q_{nl}(y)$
1	0	-1
2	0	$2(y - 2)$
2	1	$-6y$
3	0	$-3(y^2 - 6y + 6)$
3	1	$24y(y - 4)$
3	2	$-120y^2$

The general equation for $Q_{nl}(y)$ is

$$Q_{nl}(y) = y^l \frac{d^{2l+1}}{dy^{2l+1}} \left[L_{n+l}(y) \right]$$

where L_{n+l} is a Laguerre polynomial, defined by

$$L_k(y) = e^y d^k(y^k e^{-y})/dy^k.$$

Using these equations and a_0 as a unit, draw to scale the positions of the spherical nodes of the $2S$, $3S$, and $3P$ states.

6. Using the data of problem 5, compute the expectation value of the electrostatic potential energy $V_c = -e^2/r$ for a hydrogen atom in the state ψ_{100}. Since $T + V = W$, we can obtain directly the expectation value of the kinetic energy T. How does the ratio $\langle T \rangle / \langle V \rangle$ compare with that computed on a classical model?

7. The term $l(l + 1)/x^2$ in (10.39) can be regarded as a sort of "centrifugal potential" V_l associated with the angular momentum. Compute the expectation values of V_l, V_c, and the radial kinetic energy T for the state ψ_{210} and show that their total is W_2. Use this argument to show that the lowest energy level of a particle in a spherical box must be an s-state, as assumed in problem 2.

8. The Legendre polynomials are defined by

$$P_l = \frac{1}{2^l l!} \frac{d^l}{dx^l} [(x^2 - 1)^l]$$

and have the following values:

$P_0 = 1;$ $P_3 = \frac{1}{2}(5x^3 - 3x)$

$P_1 = x;$ $P_4 = (35 x^4 - 30x^2 + 3)/8$

$P_2 = \frac{1}{2}(3x^2 - 1);$

The "associated" Legendre polynomials are $P_l{}^m(x) = (1 - x^2)^{m/2} d^m/dx^m P_l(x)$.

Show that

(a) When $l = m$ there is no conical node.

(b) When $l = m + 1$ the conical node degenerates into a plane node in the equatorial plane.

(c) When $l = m + 2$ the conical node is a double cone.

(d) When $l = m + 3$ the nodal surfaces are a double cone and an equatorial plane.

(e) Compute the angles of the cone representing the conical node of the wave function of the $3D$ state with $m = 0$.

(f) Compute these angles for the conical nodes of the wave functions representing the $4F$ states with $m = 0$, and $m = 1$.

9. Sketch the wave functions representing the 4 types of $4F$ states.

10. Using the information in problems 5 and 8, compute the half-width of the $2P$ state of hydrogen. Note that (10.85) should be calculated for a single fixed value of m in the initial state, and summed over all degenerate final states with different m'. In this case the final $1S$ state must have $m' = 0$ only.

Chapter 11

ELECTRON SPIN AND MULTIPLET SPECTRA

The preceding chapters have discussed the quantized energy levels of electrons in atoms. The wave mechanical treatment in Chapter 10 is adequate to explain the gross structure of the energy levels and may be summarized by the formula $T = R/n'^2$. Actually, atomic spectra are not so simple as we have considered them up to this point. We must inquire what refinements in the atomic model are necessary to explain some of the more complex details of atomic spectra.

A close inspection of what we have previously called a single "line" of an alkali spectrum (excluding hydrogen) reveals that each line is a doublet, consisting of a narrow pair (or double pair) of lines. A well-known example is the yellow sodium line, which appears as a doublet even in a spectroscope of medium resolving power.

Another spectral phenomenon that we have not accounted for is the anomalous Zeeman effect. The wave mechanical treatment of the Zeeman effect, according to the models of the previous chapters, leads to just the classical result that in a magnetic field each line splits into three equally spaced lines with a frequency difference ν_L (4.9). Actually, most spectral lines (and in particular those of the alkalis) display an anomalous Zeeman effect, splitting in a magnetic field into more than three lines with unequal spacings.

The existence of these unexplained effects does not force us to abandon all the wave mechanical explanation that has proved so successful. Rather, we must find some way of improving our picture of the atom in order to explain these relatively fine details without disturbing the gross structure already established. It will turn out that only one improvement is necessary to explain both these spectral effects; namely, the assumption of electron spin.

The present chapter describes the experimental background and the applications for the idea of electron spin.

11.1. The Stern-Gerlach experiment on hydrogen

We have described the Stern-Gerlach measurement in section 3.7. A beam of neutral particles with permanent magnetic dipole moments passes the length of an inhomogeneous magnetic field. The symmetry of the field defines an axis (z) perpendicular to the path of the beam. The deflection of a particle after passing through the field is proportional to μ_z, the projection of its magnetic moment along the z-axis. The magnetic moment of an electron circulating in an orbit is a vector $\mathbf{u}$ proportional to the angular momentum vector L. According to the definitions of the g factor and Bohr magneton in (9.49), (9.50), we can write

$$\mathbf{u} = g_L \mu_0 L / \hbar \tag{11.1}$$

or for the z-component

$$\mu_z = g_L \mu_0 L_z / \hbar \tag{11.2}$$

where $g_L = 1$, $\mu_0 = e\hbar/2m_0c$. The discussion of section 10.4 tells us that orbital angular momentum is always quantized. By (10.52) the projection of L along the z-axis is $L_z = m\hbar$, where m takes on every integral value running from $-l$ to $+l$, and l is a positive integer (or zero) specifying the quantized magnitude of the angular momentum.

The z-component of the magnetic moment associated with the orbital angular momentum of an electron is therefore

$$\mu_z = g_L \mu_0 m, \qquad\qquad -l \leq m \leq l \tag{11.3}$$

The quantized μ_z can assume just $(2l + 1)$ different values so that the incident beam in a Stern-Gerlach apparatus splits into $(2l + 1)$ separate components on traversing the inhomogeneous magnetic field. The qualitative observation of this splitting into discrete components is the most direct evidence of space quantization. Quantitatively, the observed splitting is not in exact accord with the following features of (11.3): the beam should split into an odd number of equally spaced components, since l is an integer and $(2l + 1)$ is always an odd number. Also, since one possible value of m is zero, we expect one of the beam components to be undeviated.

Now consider a Stern-Gerlach experiment using neutral hydrogen atoms. This should give information relating to a single electron, since neutral hydrogen with $Z = 1$ contains just one electron. To produce atomic hydrogen we use instead of the conventional oven an electric discharge tube. The tube contains hydrogen at a pressure of about 10^{-4} atmosphere maintained by differential pumping; the main constituent of the high voltage discharge is a current of electrons, which decomposes hydrogen molecules into neutral atoms by collision. In the middle of the discharge tube is an aperture for the hydrogen atoms to escape and enter the initial slit system of the Stern-Gerlach apparatus. The effective temperature of the atoms is that of the discharge in the tube; this is hard to estimate exactly, but in a typical case may be around 400°C.

The method of detection as well as of production also requires modification for hydrogen atoms. The usual method with metallic atoms is simply to let them deposit on a cold glass plate. For hydrogen, the plate carries a thin film of some compound that will react chemically with atomic hydrogen and change color in the process. A suitable substance is MoO_3, which is white but becomes dark blue on reduction to lower oxides by atomic hydrogen. It does not respond to molecular hydrogen, so the presence of molecules in the beam causes no essential difficulty. This experiment was performed in 1927 by Phipps and Taylor and by Wrede.

This experiment shows that in an inhomogeneous field a beam of hydrogen splits into two components, with equal and opposite deflections from the original undeviated beam, as suggested in Fig. 11.1. The magnitude of the deflection indicates that

$$g_s m_s = \pm 1 \qquad (11.4)$$

for the two components. The same proves to be true of other atoms (Na, K, etc.) with one optical electron, which is presumed to be solely responsible for the magnetic deflection. We have used the subscript s to distinguish (11.4) from (11.3), for it is clear that the magnetic moment here is different from that associated with orbital angular momentum. The Stern-Gerlach pattern resembles that for an orbital momentum, with the important difference that the central (undeviated) component is missing.

Not only is this pattern of unexpected form, but our previous considerations would have led us to predict that there would be no pattern at all. The normal or ground state of the hydrogen atom is the $1S$ state, which has $l = 0$. Hence $m = 0$ only, corresponding to a single, undeviated beam even in the magnetic field.

We must ascribe the observed splitting to some heretofore neglected magnetic moment associated with the electron. It could not be associated with the single proton that forms the nucleus of ordinary hydrogen, for any magnetic moment associated with the proton should be of order of magnitude $e\hbar/2Mc$, where M is the mass of the proton. This proton moment is smaller than the observed moment μ_0 for hydrogen by a factor of order $m/M \approx 10^{-3}$. Thus any proton moment would be much too small to explain the observed effect. Since the ordinary hydrogen atom contains nothing but a proton and an electron, the effect must reside in a single electron.

Up to this point our only source of electronic magnetic moments has

Fig. 11.1. Pattern in the Stern-Gerlach experiment with hydrogen: (a) without field; (b) with field.

been orbital motion; the magnetic moment $\mathbf{u}_L$ is directly proportional to the angular momentum $\mathbf{L}$. If the electron has some magnetic moment in addition to $\mathbf{u}_L$, it is natural to look for some other angular momentum that the electron might have. The locus of this additional angular momentum is readily apparent when we consider the analogy between the classical picture of the atom and the solar system. The electron moving in an orbit about the nucleus resembles a planet circling the sun. The planet has orbital angular momentum from this circling motion, but at the same time it is rotating about its own axis. We could also ascribe to the classical electron a rotation about its own axis, or spin. Since the electron is a charged particle, this spin angular momentum $\mathbf{s}$ should also have a certain magnetic moment $\mathbf{u}_s$ associated with it. Consideration of any simple mechanical model indicates that $\mathbf{u}_s$ is directly proportional to $\mathbf{s}$, or

$$\mathbf{u}_s = G_s \mathbf{s} \tag{11.5}$$

in analogy with (4.4). In the classical picture of the electron as a "solid" particle, the gyromagnetic ratio G_s depends on the specific model of the electron. Since quantum mechanics describes the electron only by a wave function ψ and does not permit a detailed mechanical model in the classical sense, we must expect to determine G_s only by comparison with experiment.

In quantum mechanics all angular momenta must be quantized. This rule applies also to the electron spin $\mathbf{s}$. The prescription for quantization of any angular momentum $\mathbf{J}$ is a natural generalization of (10.49) and (10.52)

$$\begin{aligned} \mathbf{J}^2 &= j(j+1)\hbar^2 \\ J_z &= m_j\hbar, \quad -j \leq m_j \leq j \end{aligned} \tag{11.6}$$

Here $\mathbf{J}^2$ is the square of the absolute magnitude of the vector $\mathbf{J}$, and J_z is its projection along some axis, conventionally taken as the z-axis. The pure numbers j and m_j are not necessarily integers, but all the possible values of m_j must differ by integers. That is, $m_j = j, j-1, j-2, \cdots, -(j-2), -(j-1), -j$, a sequence formed by integral steps. This requirement limits j (and hence m_j) to have integral or half-integral values. We have already explored the possibilities of integral j in discussing the quantization of orbital angular momentum, but the half-integral values are something new.

What value of this quantum number shall we assign to the electron spin? We have seen above that the Stern-Gerlach pattern in hydrogen must be entirely caused by the magnetic moment associated with the electron spin, and that this spin has no $m = 0$ component. Thus the electron spin must have a half-integral value; it is immediately tempting to try the simplest (smallest) value, $\frac{1}{2}$.

We assume that the electron spin s satisfies

$$s^2 = s(s + 1)\hbar^2, \qquad s = \tfrac{1}{2}$$
$$s_z = m_s\hbar, \qquad m_s = \pm\tfrac{1}{2} \tag{11.7}$$

Equation (11.7) leads to a Stern-Gerlach pattern of two components with equal and opposite displacements from the undeviated beam. This is indeed what we observe for hydrogen, confirming the assignment $s = \frac{1}{2}$. In analogy with (9.48) we write the gyromagnetic ratio for spin in terms of the Bohr magneton and a g factor for spin,

$$G_s = g_s\mu_0 \tag{11.8a}$$

From (11.4) and (11.7) we see that

$$g_s = 2 \tag{11.8b}$$

Thus the gyromagnetic ratio for the spin is twice that for orbital motion (9.50). This need not occasion any surprise, since we had no *a priori* reason to expect them to be the same.

11.2. Doublets in alkali spectra

As mentioned in the introduction, the spectral "lines" of the alkali atoms reveal themselves on closer inspection to be narrowly spaced pairs or double pairs of lines. These doublets or *fine structure* find a natural interpretation in terms of electron spin. Indeed, the fine structure was historically the first phenomenon to be explained in terms of a two-valued quantum number, $m_s = \pm\frac{1}{2}$, although the physical interpretation as an intrinsic electron spin did not come until later. We first review the experimental facts relating to alkali doublets.

If we examine the spectrum of an alkali atom like sodium or potassium with a spectroscope of fairly good resolving power, we find that each line of the sharp and principal series is in reality a rather narrowly spaced pair of lines, called a *doublet*. For all other series there is in addition a faint "satellite" line attached to each doublet. Although each of these groups really contains three lines, their customary name is *compound doublets*. We should emphasize that none of the present discussion applies to the hydrogen spectrum, which is a special case in this regard.

The compound structure of the alkali spectra reveals quite simple laws when we express the doublet separations in wave numbers or frequency differences:

1. For the principal series, $1S - nP$, all lines are doublets, and the doublet separation decreases regularly with increasing n.

2. For the sharp series, $2P - nS$, all lines are doublets with a constant wave number difference, regardless of n.

3. For the diffuse series, $2P - nD$, all the lines are compound doublets. There are three lines, two quite close together and a third more widely separated from this pair. The "doublet separation" in this case is the wave number difference between the separated line and the farther member of the pair: this separation remains constant for all n and equals that of the sharp series. The spacing of the narrow pair decreases regularly with the increasing n.

4. For the fundamental series, $3D - nF$, the multiplet structure has the same character as for the diffuse series, that of compound doublets. The major separation is constant for all n, and is equal to the narrow spacing of the $2P - 3D$ doublet; the narrow separation again decreases with n.

The combination principle (6.15) states that all spectral lines may be expressed as differences between term values or energy levels. We must ascribe these doublets to a splitting of the energy levels. The exact manner in which the term values split is easily deducible from the experimental facts. Since the separation of the $2P - nS$ lines does not vary with n, this simple doublet must be due to splitting of the common $2P$ term into two terms. The S terms apparently do not split. The variable separation of the $1S - nP$ lines must be due to variable splitting of the P terms; that is, all P terms are doublets and all S terms are singlets. The compound doublets of the $2P - nD$ series comprise a fixed doublet due to the $2P$ splitting and a variable doublet due to splitting of the nD terms.

Since both the P and D levels are doublets, we might expect their various combinations to result in four components for each of the $2P - nD$ lines; actually, however, only three components appear in each compound doublet. The nonoccurrence of one of the possible combinations points to the existence of a selection rule between the components of the doublet levels.

The structure of the $3D - nF$ lines is the same as for $2P - nD$ lines, and the same conclusions are to be drawn: the F levels are also doublets, and the same type of selection rule operates between the doublet components as in the $2P - nD$ case. The same conclusions will hold for all higher terms, such as G, H, etc. We can therefore draw without ambiguity the energy level diagram (Fig. 11.2) and the corresponding transitions; the transition forbidden by the selection rule appears as a dotted line. To denote the fact that each level is split into two components, it is conventional to insert the number 2 as an upper left-hand index in the term notation; that is, the superscript in 3^2P, 4^2F, 6^2D indicates that these terms are all doublets. Note that although we have seen

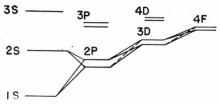

Fig. 11.2. Doublet spectrum lines; dotted transitions are forbidden.

them to be single, the S terms are also designated as ^2S (and not ^1S) for the alkali atoms. This notation simply indicates that they belong to a system of terms which are all doublets, with the sole exception of the S terms. This notation will create no confusion in practice, because we shall see presently that the S terms are always single for any atom, no matter what its spectral system. The notation 5^2D is read, "five doublet D."

It is also possible to have a system composed entirely of single levels, which are designated by ^1S, ^1P, ^1D, $\cdots$ and read "singlet S" etc. If the levels (with the exception of S) are all triple, we have a triplet system, denoted by ^3S, ^3P, ^3D, $\cdots$; quadruplet, quintuplet, etc., systems have corresponding designations. These different multiplet systems are all observed among the spectra of atoms in various rows of the periodic table.

In our previous discussion it appeared that each spectral energy level corresponded to a different set of quantum numbers. It is natural to try to extend this principle to the present case. For this purpose we have available a new quantum number represented by the electron spin. The alkali spectra result from a single optical electron, for which the spin is always $s = \frac{1}{2}$; this quantum number in itself would not cause any doubling of the energy levels. Now consider the vector addition of the spin and orbital angular momenta of the electron,

$$L + S = J \qquad (11.9)$$

Here J is the total angular momentum of the electron. The addition rule (10.55a) for quantized angular momenta tells us that the quantum numbers corresponding to (11.9) satisfy the relation

$$l + s \geq j \geq |l - s| \qquad (11.10)$$

Since $s = \frac{1}{2}$, this means that

$$j = l \pm \tfrac{1}{2} \qquad (11.11)$$

Since j is always a positive number, the $\pm$ sign in (11.11) holds for every value of l except $l = 0$, in which case only the $+$ sign applies, and $j = \frac{1}{2}$.

This total angular momentum j is exactly the quantum number we need to interpret the doublet energy levels: for each value of l there are two values of j, one for each doublet level. And for s terms there is only one value of j, so that they all remain single in spite of being members of a doublet system. The selection rule necessary to assure that only three out of the four possible transitions occur between two doublet levels is clearly

$$\Delta j = 0, \pm 1 \qquad (11.12)$$

This is quite similar to the selection rule (10.45), $\Delta l = \pm 1$.

In distinguishing the various states, we attach the j value to the term symbol as a lower right-hand index. Thus the terms of the alkali spectra are $n^2 S_{1/2}$, $n^2 P_{1/2}$, $n^2 P_{3/2}$, $n^2 D_{3/2}$, etc. The notation $4^2 D_{3/2}$ reads "four doublet D-three-halves" and implies a state with $n = 4$, $l = 2$, $j = \frac{3}{2}$.

The hydrogen fine structure shows some exceptional degeneracies in comparison with the fine structure of the alkali atoms. The degeneracy is no longer so extensive as in the simple theory without fine structure where all levels of a given n had the same energy, regardless of l. When fine structure is taken into account, pairs of hydrogen levels with the same n, j are equal, regardless of l. In the alkali atoms the presence of the core removes the degeneracy by making the energies depend also on l.

11.3. Two-electron spectra

Before examining the role of the electron magnetic moment in the anomalous Zeeman effect, let us consider the spectra of atoms with more than one optical electron. Normal He and the alkaline earths Be, Mg, Ca, Sr, Ba, and Ra have two optical electrons each, and all show spectra of the same general form. If we neglect the multiplet structure of the lines this spectrum appears simply to resemble the superposition of two alkali spectra, similar to what is observed in a discharge containing Na and K. The energy level diagram is made up of two diagrams, each of the same type as for the alkalis, with a set of S, P, D, F terms. Within each diagram the same combinations occur as for the alkalis, but there are no transitions from levels of one diagram to levels of the other diagram. For a time it was actually thought that the two parts of the spectrum were due to two kinds of atoms, and it was customary to speak of the *ortho-* and *para-*helium spectrum. Another possible elementary explanation would have been to assign one spectrum to one optical electron, the other to the second optical electron.

Actually, no such simple explanation is possible. This is because of the different multiplet structures of the two sets of lines and term schemes. All lines of one spectrum are strictly single lines, and therefore the terms composing this spectrum are singlets. The lines of the other spectrum are triplets or compound triplets. The multiplicity rules are similar to those for alkali atoms; the principal and sharp series are simple triplets, the principal with variable spacing and the sharp with constant spacing of the lines in the triplets. All other series are compound triplets, which consist of six lines. This must mean that the term system consists of triplets; the S terms are again single, but are nevertheless called triplet S terms because they belong to a triplet system. The two term systems of the two-electron atoms are therefore the singlet and the triplet system with the notations ^1S, ^1P, ^1D, $\cdots$ and ^3S, ^3P, ^3D, $\cdots$.

To assign quantum numbers to these triplets, we recall that the doublet levels of the alkali atoms are distinguished by different values of the quantum number j for total angular momentum. For the doublets $j = l \pm \frac{1}{2}$, and the most obvious extension to the present case is

$$j = l, l \pm 1 \quad \text{(triplet)}$$
$$j = l \quad \quad \text{(singlet)}$$

$$(11.13)$$

for the two types of terms in two-electron spectra. This assignment makes the structure of the compound triplets consistent with the selection rule (11.12). In order to obtain simple triplets for $S - P$ transitions, we must assign $j = 1$ only for the S levels of the triplet system. The j values are again appended as subscripts to the term notation: $^1S_0$, $^1P_1$, $^1D_2$, etc; $^3S_1$; $^3P_0$, $^3P_1$, $^3P_2$; $^3D_1$, $^3D_2$, $^3D_3$; etc.

For the lines of the singlet system, we have $j = l$; that is, the electron spin does not play a role, meaning that it is effectively zero. It is unlikely that the electron has a spin in some atoms and not in others. A much more satisfactory assumption is that the singlets correspond to states where the spins of the two optical electrons are in opposite directions and cancel each other. This assumption automatically explains the origin of the triplet terms. They correspond to states where the two electron spins are parallel and add up to a total spin of 1 in units of $\hbar$. Indeed, all j values of the triplet states can be understood as the magnitude of the vector sum of the l vector and a unit vector, as shown in Fig. 11.3 for the $3D$ state.

This interpretation implies that the various energy levels do not refer to either electron individually. They refer to the assembly of both electrons, taken as a whole. The entire system of optical electrons possesses a set of energy levels, and it is these levels that determine the radiation of the atom. It is in the nature of wave mechanics and the principle of indeterminacy that the two optical electrons in the atom cannot be distinguished; one can take the place of the other, without altering the description of the atomic properties. In a multielectron system it makes no sense to speak of the wave function of one specific electron,

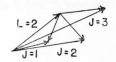

Fig. 11.3. The three j values for a ^3D state.

when several electrons are more or less equivalent. We can consider only the wave function of the combined system. Consequently the quantum numbers n, j, s do not refer to any particular electron, but are numbers characterizing the whole assembly of optical electrons; or we may say that they are the quantum numbers of the atom and not of any electron.

To emphasize this important distinction, the quantum numbers of the atom are designated by capital letters L, J, S, M, M_J, M_S. Here L is the orbital angular momentum of all electrons, M its component in the z(field) direction, and S the total spin of all electrons (which should not be confused with the S term notation); J is the total angular momentum of the complete system, M_J is its component along the field direction, and M_S bears the corresponding relation to S. All the statements valid for the quantities represented by small letters are valid for the corresponding quantities represented by capital letters. Specifically, the selection rules for the emission of radiation are

$$\Delta J \quad = 0, \pm 1 \qquad (\text{no } 0 \leftrightarrow 0) \qquad (11.14a)$$

$$\Delta M_J = 0, \pm 1 \qquad\qquad\qquad (11.14b)$$

$$\Delta L \quad = \pm 1 \qquad\qquad\qquad (11.14c)$$

$$\Delta M \quad = 0, \pm 1 \qquad\qquad\qquad (11.14d)$$

In (11.14c), the possibility $\Delta L = 0$ cannot be definitely excluded because for many electron spectra the parity of the system is in general not definitely related to the total L. For the lowest energy states, however, it usually happens to be true that $P = (-1)^L$. Therefore (11.14c) holds for combinations of the lowest terms, which are the simplest and most instructive to analyze. We may see the reason for the special rule no $0 \leftrightarrow 0$ in (11.14a) by returning to the original discussion of the radiation selection rule in section 10.9. There we observed that the photon always carries off one unit of angular momentum from the atom in a radiative transition. Thus if J and J' are the total atomic angular momenta before and after the transition, we have

$$J' = J + l \qquad\qquad\qquad (11.15)$$

where l is a unit vector. According to the rule (10.55a), the quantum numbers J' and J satisfy

$$J + 1 \geq J' \geq |J - 1| \qquad\qquad\qquad (11.16)$$

Thus if $J = 0$, $J' = 1$ only; and if $J = \frac{1}{2}$, $J' = \frac{1}{2}, \frac{3}{2}$. These are the only exceptions to $\Delta J = J' - J = 0, \pm 1$. In particular, J' and J cannot both be zero, because of the vector properties of the photon.

The states of the alkaline earth spectra have quantum numbers and designations as follows:

	L	S	J
Singlet system	L	S	J
n^1S_0	0	0	0
n^1P_1	1	0	1
n^1D_2	2	0	2
general	L	0	L
Triplet system	L	S	J
n^3S_1	0	1	1
n^3P_0	1	1	0
n^3P_1	1	1	1
n^3P_2	1	1	2
n^3D_1	2	1	1
n^3D_2	2	1	2
n^3D_3	2	1	3
etc.			

It is evident that the highest multiplicity of the terms in a given term system is determined by the value of S for this system. The value of the left upper index is $(2S + 1)$. Hence the notations, singlet, doublet, triplet, quartet, ... indicate the value of S for the system: $0, \frac{1}{2}, 1, \frac{3}{2}, \ldots$.

The number of components in a multiplet does not always equal $(2S + 1)$, however. The minimum value of J is $|L - S|$, which must be a positive number. The total number of J values (multiplet components) is therefore determined by the smaller of the two numbers L and S. Only when $L \geq S$ is the number of components $(2S + 1)$; when $S \geq L$, the number of components is $(2L + 1)$. This accounts for the fact that all S terms with $L = 0$ are single, regardless of the multiplet with which they are classed. The multiplets are classed according to $(2S + 1)$, regardless of the exact number of components.

In the alkaline earths and in He the term 1^1S_0 is the lowest energy level. It corresponds to the normal state of the atom and determines the ionization potential. The absorption spectrum consists only of the singlet series $1^1S_0 - n^1P$, since no other levels can combine with 1^1S_0. The other lines of the singlet system originate in the same way as in the alkalis. But to create the lines in the triplet system it is necessary first to ionize the atom. In the normal atom the electron spins are antiparallel, so that one electron must first be removed from the atom, later to rejoin the atom with its spin parallel to the spin of the electron which was not removed. In doing this it gives out the radiations of the triplet system, pursuing successive jumps between these triplet levels until it has reached the lowest triplet state, which is the 1^3S_1 level. The latter has a higher energy than the normal state, but the electron does not jump from the 1^3S_1 to the 1^1S_0 level because transitions from the triplet to the singlet states are not permitted. This general rule of the non-existence of transitions between levels of different multiplicity constitutes the selection rule

$$\Delta S = 0 \qquad (11.14e)$$

which states that ordinarily in a transition no electron can reverse its spin. As a corollary, also

$$\Delta M_s = 0 \qquad (11.14f)$$

Thus the electron is *trapped* in the lowest triplet state, and one might expect that after continuing a discharge for a long time all atoms might finally end up in the triplet state. Actually this does not happen. The atom can make the prohibited transition to its normal state. This transition does not occur spontaneously, as do all the other transitions, but becomes possible during the impact of two atoms. Impacts of atoms which give rise to prohibited transitions are called *collisions of the second kind*. (A collision of the first kind is the opposite process, in which an atom gains excitation energy by the collision, rather than losing it. In the Franck-Hertz experiment, section 7.3, the atoms make collisions of the first kind with electrons.) Thus an atom in the lowest triplet state remains stable until it is hit by another atom. Depending on temperature and pressure of the gas it may remain in this state for what in optical radiation phenomena is a relatively long time, perhaps as long as some 10^{-3} sec. Such levels are called *metastable* states. The impacts of the second kind may be due mainly to atoms of a different chemical nature, explaining the fact that additions of a small amount of another gas can modify the radiation of a gas discharge. De-excitation of metastable states can also occur, of course, in collisions of gas atoms with the walls of the container.

The fact that the quantum numbers of the energy levels, which determine the radiation of an atom, refer to the whole atom and not to the individual electrons does not imply that no such quantum numbers exist for the electrons. If an alkaline earth atom is ionized, so that it possesses only one optical electron, its spectrum is analogous to that of an alkali. The remaining electron has definite quantum numbers, l_1, s_1, j_1. When the removed electron rejoins the atom, it brings with it a definite angular momentum and a definite spin, given by l_2, s_2. The problem arises of how to add the momenta together to determine L, S, and J of the combination and to retain conservation of the angular momentum.

11.4. Vector model and complex spectra

To classify the spectra of complex atoms with three or more optical electrons, it is convenient to extend the *vector model* already used in connection with two-electron spectra. The ith electron in a complex atom has associated with it two angular momentum vectors, its spin s_i and orbital angular momentum l_i. All the vectors for the optical electrons must combine to give the total angular momentum J of the atom. The way in which they do this constitutes the coupling scheme of the atom.

In quantum mechanics we can picture an angular momentum vector as continuously precessing about its fixed J_z component (Fig. 11.4). This is just a visual way of representing the quantum mechanical fact that if we specify J_z exactly, we cannot say anything at all about J_x and J_y individually. In much the same way we picture vector addition as in Fig. 11.5, with the two component vectors j_1 and j_2 precessing about their sum J. In the vector model the speed of this precession measures the strength of the interaction between the motions producing j_1 and j_2.

Now consider the combination of a large number of vectors as in a complex atom. The general principle for building up this combination is as follows: the angular momenta with the strongest coupling forces between them combine first to form resultant vectors about which they precess; these resultant vectors, which are more weakly coupled to each other, then combine to form the final resultant. We can see which coupling forces are usually strongest by returning to the two-electron case.

The spectroscopic facts for two optical electrons demonstrate clearly that the spins of two electrons must have a strong interaction. The spin of one electron strongly affects the spin of the other; they can be only parallel or antiparallel, and to switch from one position to the other, it is necessary first to remove one electron from the atom and later to bring it back in reversed position. We say that we have strong

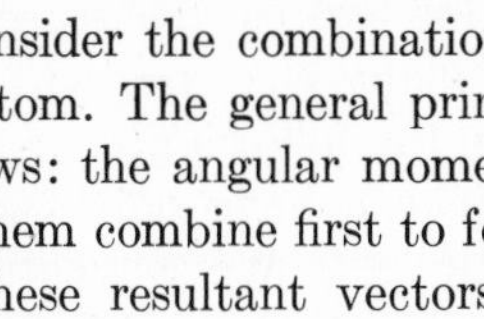

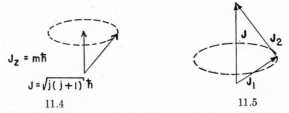

$$J_z = m\hbar$$
$$J = \sqrt{j(j+1)}\,\hbar$$

11.4 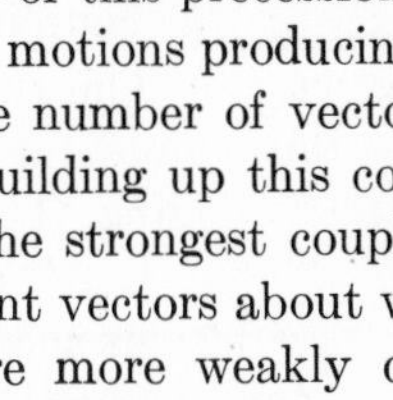   11.5

Fig. 11.4. Precession of an angular momentum vector about its *z*-axis projection.

Fig. 11.5. Precession of two angular momentum vectors about their sum.

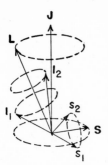

Fig. 11.6. In the vector model, the speed ω of precession of two angular momenta about their resultant is proportional to the strength of the coupling between the momenta. The strength of this coupling is expressed by E, the interaction energy between the momenta and the angular frequency $\omega = E/\hbar$. Thus in building up the total momentum J in L-S coupling, the precession of l_1, l_2 about L and s_1, s_2 about S is more rapid than that of L and S about J.

s coupling. Similarly, the orbital motions of two electrons are strongly coupled, since their wave functions overlap. As a result the two l vectors precess about each other, and the two s vectors do likewise, forming L and S; and only the latter again couple to form J. This type of interaction is called L-S *coupling* or Russell-Saunders coupling, after the discoverers of the principle. It is illustrated in Fig. 11.6.

In a few atoms there is a tendency away from L-S coupling to socalled *j-j coupling*. In this case the l_1 and s_1 first combine to make j_1, while l_2 and s_2 combine to form j_2. Then j_1 and j_2 couple to form the resultant J. This type of coupling is relatively rare in atoms, and we shall discuss first the rules for constructing many-electron configurations in L-S coupling. Chapter 12 discusses some further aspects of *j-j* coupling.

The rules derived for two electrons are generally valid for systems of many electrons with L-S coupling. These rules are the following:

1. All electron spins can have only two orientations according as $m_s = \pm\frac{1}{2}$. We conventionally call these orientations "up" and "down." It follows that when the number N of optical electrons is even—as for elements in the second, fourth, sixth, and last columns of the periodic system—the total spin S takes integral values, $J = 0, 1, 2, \cdots, \frac{1}{2}N$. For elements with an odd number of optical electrons the total spin S has half-odd values, $S = \frac{1}{2}, \frac{3}{2}, \frac{5}{2}, \cdots, \frac{1}{2}N$.

2. Now **L** is the vector sum of all l vectors, and L and all the l quantum numbers are always positive integers or zero. For example, the sum of $l = 3$ and $l' = 4$ can have by (10.55a) the values 7, 6, 5, 4, 3, 2, 1 but not 0, as seen from a vector diagram. If we know the quantum numbers l, l' and L, we can compute the angle between the vectors l and l', which we denote by (l, l'). Since in quantum mechanics $L^2 = l(l + 1)\hbar^2$, the trigonometric law of cosines reads

$$L(L + 1) = l(l + 1) + l'(l' + 1) - 2\sqrt{l(l + 1)l'(l' + 1)} \cos (l,l')$$

or hence

$$\cos (l, l') = \frac{l(l + 1) + l'(l' + 1) - L(L + 1)}{2\sqrt{l(l + 1)} \sqrt{l'(l' + 1)}} \tag{11.17}$$

3. The total angular momentum J of the atom is the vector resultant of L and S. The quantum number J is always positive and is a "half" or a "whole" number, depending on whether S is half or whole. For a given L and S these correspond to several values of J; that is, all the values obtained by counting in integral steps from $|L - S|$ to $L + S$. The number of possible J values or hence multiplet components is $(2S + 1)$ or $(2L + 1)$, whichever is smaller. The angle between the S and L vectors is deduced by the same method as above:

$$\cos (S, L) = \frac{S(S + 1) + L(L + 1) - J(J + 1)}{2\sqrt{L(L + 1)}\ \sqrt{S(S + 1)}} \quad (11.17a)$$

In L-S coupling the spacing of the various levels with different J values in a given ^{2s+1}L multiplet depends directly on the angle between S and L. The energy difference of the multiplet levels arises from the interaction of the magnetic dipole moments associated with the vectors L and S. This interaction energy is proportional to the scalar product of these vectors,

$$E_J = \lambda L \cdot S$$

$$= -\lambda\sqrt{L(L + 1)}\sqrt{S(S + 1)}\ \cos (S, L) \quad (11.18)$$

$$= (\lambda/2)[J(J + 1) - S(S + 1) - L(L + 1)]$$

where λ is a constant for a given multiplet. We can eliminate the unknown constant λ by taking the energy differences between successive levels:

$$E_J - E_{J-1} = \Delta E_J = \lambda J$$
$$\Delta E_J : \Delta E_{J'} = J/J' \quad (11.19)$$

Relation (11.19) is useful only for $S > \frac{1}{2}$, where it is known as the Landé interval rule. For example, in a ^3D multiplet, the spacings between the $J = 1, 2,$ and 3 levels are in the ratio of 3 to 2.

This interval rule is useful for identifying the J values of a multiplet, and for determining the larger of the two quantum numbers L, S (the smaller follows simply by counting the number of terms in the multiplet). The rule (11.19) is valid only for l-s coupling; it is therefore useful even where the observations fail to agree with it, for such failure implies in turn a deviation from pure L-S coupling in the atom.

We should emphasize that there is nothing mysterious about these effective forces between different vectors in the atom; the coupling forces are all electromagnetic in character. They arise in the electric and magnetic interactions among different motions of the electrons. For example, consider the spin-orbit (l-s) coupling of a single electron.

In the classical picture the electron circulates about the nucleus in an orbit with angular momentum l. The electron sees the nucleus as moving in a circle, which creates a magnetic induction B at the position of the electron. Then B is parallel to l. The interaction energy of B with the magnetic moment $\mathbf{\mu}_s$ associated with the electron spin is

$$\Delta E = -\mu_s B \cos{(\mu_s, B)} \qquad (11.18a)$$

$$= A \sqrt{s(s+1)} \sqrt{l(l+1)} \cos{(s, l)}$$

where A is a constant and s, l are parallel to $\mathbf{\mu}_s$, B. The generalization of this formula for S and L of several electrons leads to (11.18) and the Landé interval rule (11.19).

11.5. The Zeeman effect

When atomic radiation takes place in an external magnetic field, all the lines of the original spectrum are split into several components. This is the Zeeman effect, the classical interpretation of which we have given in Chapter 4. In the classical theory each spectral line splits into first three components of frequency ν_0, $\nu_0 \pm eB/4\pi mc$, where ν_0 is the original frequency, B is the applied magnetic induction, and e/m is the "specific charge" of the electron. Although a few spectral lines do happen to show this classical or "normal" Zeeman effect, most of them do not, and have instead anomalous Zeeman effects, in which there are more than three components of each spectral line, and these components do not have equal spacings.

For atoms with L-S coupling the rules of the preceding section are sufficient to predict the complex phenomena of the anomalous Zeeman effect, with the addition of two more rules.

4. In a magnetic field the J vector, representing the total angular momentum, orients itself in such a way that the component of J along the field is quantized according to M_J. Then M_J is an integer when J is integer, and is half-integral when J is half-integral, and M_J takes all values from J to $-J$, causing each original level to split into $2J + 1$ levels in the magnetic field.

5. The magnetic moment associated with the orbital momentum is $\mu_L = g_L \mu_0 \sqrt{L(L+1)}$, where L is the quantum number of the total L vector, $g_L = 1$, and μ_0 is the Bohr magneton $e\hbar/2mc$. The magnetic moment associated with the spin is $\mu_S = g_S \mu_0 \sqrt{S(S+1)}$, where S is the spin quantum number and $g_S = 2$.

The direction of the magnetic moment vectors $\mathbf{\mu}_L$ and $\mathbf{\mu}_S$ are along the L and S vectors, respectively. Actually, $\mathbf{\mu}_L$ and $\mathbf{\mu}_S$ are directed oppositely to L and S because the charge on the electron is intrinsically negative. Since this is only a matter of a sign convention, we may neglect it and for convenience consider μ_L and μ_S co-incident with L and S. It is clear that the resulting magnetic moment $\mu = \mu_L + \mu_S$ will not point along the J vector, because of the difference in the g factors. The resulting moment μ will precess with the atom about the J direction, as illustrated in the schematic vector diagram Fig. 11.7. The effective magnetic moment μ_J is given by the component of the total moment μ along J. Since the effective μ_J is parallel to J, we can express it in terms of an appropriate g factor:

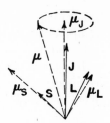

Fig. 11.7. Resultant magnetic moment in the vector model for L-S coupling. The total moment μ precesses with L and S about J, so that the net effective moment is μ_J in the direction of J.

$$\mu_J = \mu_0 g_J \sqrt{J(J+1)} \qquad (11.20)$$

where the magnitude of the vector J is $\hbar\sqrt{J(J+1)}$, as in (11.6)

We can readily compute the factor g_J from the wave mechanical laws of vector addition. Diagram 11.7 gives

$$\mu_J = \mu_L \cos(L,J) + \mu_S \cos(S,J) \qquad (11.21)$$

where for the cosines we have

$$\cos(L,J) = \frac{L(L+1) + J(J+1) - S(S+1)}{2\sqrt{L(L+1)}\sqrt{J(J+1)}}$$

$$\cos(S,J) = \frac{S(S+1) + J(J+1) - L(L+1)}{2\sqrt{S(S+1)}\sqrt{J(J+1)}} \qquad (11.22)$$

Introducing these expressions along with the magnitudes of the moments μ_L and μ_S into Eqs. (11.21) and (11.20), we have

$$g_J = \frac{\mu_J}{\mu_0\sqrt{J(J+1)}} = 1 + \frac{S(S+1) + J(J+1) - L(L+1)}{2J(J+1)} \qquad (11.23)$$

This equation along with $\mu_J = \mu_0 g_J J$ gives the magnetic moment of an atom in the quantum state characterized by the quantum numbers L, J, S.

This g factor performs the same function as when it was first introduced in Chapter 4 to describe the magnetic moment of the electron; that is, it specifies the relation between the angular momentum of a given configuration and its effective magnetic moment.

If the total angular momentum is J, the effective magnetic moment, oriented along J, is $\mu_J = \mu_0 g_J J$. Equation (11.23) for g_J was arrived at empirically from observations of the anomalous Zeeman effect by Landé several years before the vector model and the electron spin were recognized. The agreement of Eq. (11.23) with experiment verifies the procedure given and represents the best proof of existence for the electron spin and its associated magnetic moment.

In a magnetic induction B the J or $\mathbf{\mu}_J$ vector orients itself so that the component of J along B is $\hbar M_J$. The angle between the magnetic moment and the field direction is therefore γ, where

$$\cos \gamma = M_J / \sqrt{J(J+1)} \tag{11.24}$$

This equation gives the possible orientations for space quantization. The potential energy of a magnetic dipole moment in a field is

$$-\mu_J B \cos \gamma = V \tag{11.25}$$

This represents a change of the energy level in a magnetic field. Each level is split into $2J + 1$ components, characterized by different M_J values, with an energy difference from the original, unsplit level of

$$\Delta E = \mu_0 B g_J M_J \tag{11.26}$$

obtained by introducing (11.23) and (11.24) into (11.25). The minus sign in (11.25) is canceled by taking account of the heretofore neglected negative charge of the electron.

With the splitting of the level known from (11.24), it is a simple matter to compute the pattern of the anomalous Zeeman effect for a transition from a level L_1, S_1, J_1, to a level L_2, S_2, J_2. Each level has its own g factor, g_1 and g_2. Of course we need only those transitions that satisfy the selection rules for L, S, J. To obtain the Zeeman pattern, we have simply to apply the frequency condition $\Delta E = h\nu$ and take into account the selection rule for M_J,

$$\Delta M_J = 0, \pm 1 \tag{11.27}$$

Transitions in which M_J is not altered are π components of the Zeeman pattern. They are polarized parallel to the magnetic field in transverse observation. All other transitions are σ components, polarized normal to the field in transverse observation, and circularly polarized in longitudinal observation (π components do not appear in longitudinal observation of the Zeeman effect).

If E_1 and E_2 are the energies of the unsplit levels, and $\nu = (E_1 - E_2)/h$, the frequency of the unsplit spectrum line, we have as general expressions for the split levels

$$E_1' = E_1 + \mu_0 g_1 B M_{J_1}, \qquad E_2' = E_2 + \mu_0 g_2 B M_{J_2} \tag{11.28}$$

Hence the frequencies of the transitions are

$$\nu = \frac{E_1' - E_2'}{h} = \nu_0 + \frac{\mu_0 B}{h}\left(g_1 M_{J_1} - g_2 M_{J_2}\right)$$

(11.29)

$$= \nu_0 + \Delta\nu$$

$$\Delta\nu = \nu_L \times \begin{cases} M_J(g_1 - g_2) & \text{if } \Delta M_J = 0 & (\pi) \\ M_J(g_1 - g_2) \pm g_2 & \text{if } \Delta M_J = \pm 1 & (\sigma) \end{cases}$$

(11.30)

where in (11.30) we take $M_J = M_{J_1}$, and $\nu_L = eB/4\pi mc$ is the Larmor frequency. This equation shows that in general the line splits into a considerable number of components, with various displacements from the original line. These spacings are of the same order of magnitude as the Larmor frequency ν_L.

The normal Zeeman effect appears as a special case of the above equations, namely, when $S = 0$. In this case $J = L$ and $g_1 = g_2 = 1$ by (11.23). Then (11.30) reduces to

$$\Delta\nu = \nu_L \times \begin{cases} 0 & (\pi) \\ \pm 1 & (\sigma) \end{cases}$$

(11.31)

Note that (11.31) gives rise to a much simpler spectral pattern than (11.30) because the dependence on M_J drops out. Equation (11.31) is that of the normal Zeeman effect. It appears only for lines that are

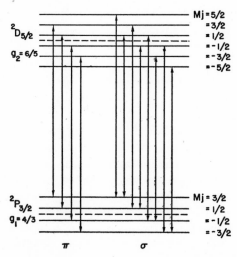

Fig. 11.8. Construction of lines in the Zeeman pattern of a $^2P_{3/2} - {}^2D_{5/2}$ transition. The dotted lines are the levels in the absence of a magnetic field.

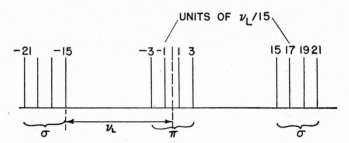

Fig. 11.9. Frequency plot of the Zeeman components of Fig. 11.8. The dotted line in the center of the diagram represents the original spectrum line in the absence of a magnetic field. The scale factor ν_L is shown.

members of a genuine singlet series. Since singlet lines are relatively rare, most observed Zeeman effects are anomalous.

As an example of the anomalous Zeeman effect we calculate the pattern for the transitions corresponding to one of the multiplet lines of the diffuse series of an alkali, namely $^2P_{3/2} - {}^2D_{5/2}$. We have $L_1 = 1$, $S_1 = \frac{1}{2}$, $J_1 = \frac{3}{2}$, $g_1 = \frac{4}{3}$, and $L_2 = 2$, $S_2 = \frac{1}{2}$, $J_2 = \frac{5}{2}$, $g_2 = \frac{6}{5}$. For the first state M_J assumes the values $\pm\frac{3}{2}$, $\pm\frac{1}{2}$. The π lines have therefore the frequency shifts

$$\Delta\nu = (\pm\tfrac{1}{2}, \pm\tfrac{3}{2})\nu_L(\tfrac{4}{3} - \tfrac{6}{5}) = \pm\tfrac{1}{15}\nu_L, \pm\tfrac{1}{5}\nu_L$$

while the σ transitions involve the frequency shifts

$$\nu = \nu_L \times \begin{cases} \pm(\tfrac{1}{15} \pm\tfrac{6}{5}) = \pm\tfrac{19}{15}, \pm\tfrac{17}{15} \\ \pm(\tfrac{1}{5} \pm\tfrac{6}{5}) = \pm\tfrac{7}{5}, \pm 1 \end{cases}$$

The term level diagram with the transitions and the appearance of the pattern are illustrated in Figs. (11.8) and (11.9).

11.6. Theory of the electron spin

In our discussion we have introduced the electron spin merely as a supplement to wave mechanics. Actually, the electron spin can be incorporated into the theory of wave mechanics, as was shown by Dirac. The detailed theory of electron spin is beyond the scope of this text, although the procedure is a logical extension of Schroedinger's equation from the nonrelativistic case in which $p^2/2m = E$ for a free particle to the relativistic case where $E^2 = p^2c^2 + m_0^2c^4$. In the solution of this problem there is a certain analogy with optics. In optics the wave character of light is adequately described by a single wave function, but this representation is not sufficient to describe its polarization. To specify this parameter, it is necessary to introduce four quantities

E_x, E_y, H_x, and H_y, of which all satisfy the wave equation and may be called wave functions. These electric and magnetic field components are not independent, but are related by Maxwell's equations.

The electron spin appears as the counterpart of polarization of light; the electron wave is "polarized," either right or left circularly according to the spin direction ($m_s = \pm\frac{1}{2}$). If we neglect this polarization, we can specify the electron by a single wave function; but to include the spin in our description again requires the introduction of four different wave functions that are not independent but related by Dirac's equations. These equations show that the electron magnetic moment is naturally related to its spin.

SUMMARY

The concept of intrinsic electron spin and an associated magnetic moment succeeds in explaining several otherwise anomalous phenomena: the Stern-Gerlach experiment on hydrogen, the existence of multiplets in atomic spectra, and the anomalous Zeeman effect.

The Stern-Gerlach measurement on neutral hydrogen atoms shows them to have a magnetic moment of approximately one Bohr magneton, $\mu_0 = e\hbar/2mc$. This magnetic moment must reside in the electron, since any proton effects would be about 1000 times smaller. It must reside in a single electron, because neutral hydrogen contains just one electron. On the other hand, normal hydrogen is in an S state with $l = 0$ and hence has no magnetic moment due to orbital motion of the electron. We must therefore associate the observed moment with an intrinsic *spin* of the electron. The splitting of the hydrogen beam into just two components, with no central undeviated component, indicates that the quantum number of this spin angular momentum must be $s = \frac{1}{2}$. The total magnitude of the spin vector is $\hbar\sqrt{s(s + 1)} = \sqrt{\frac{3}{4}}\hbar$, and its z-components are $\hbar m_s$, with $m_s = \pm\frac{1}{2}$. This accounts for the splitting of the beams into two components in the Stern-Gerlach experiment. The associated magnetic moment component along the z-axis is $\mu_z = \mu_0 g_s m_s$; the measurements imply that $g_S = 2$, in contrast to $g_L = 1$ for orbital angular momentum.

The spin s and orbital angular momentum l combine by the laws of vector addition to give the total angular momentum j of the electron. This j is also a quantum mechanical vector, having absolute magnitude $\hbar\sqrt{j(j + 1)}$ and z-component $\hbar m_j$, where m_j runs from $-j$ to $+ j$ in integral steps. According to the quantum mechanical rules of vector addition, $j = l \pm \frac{1}{2} > 0$. The fact that there are two values of j for each value of l (except $l = 0$, when $j = \frac{1}{2}$ only) accounts for the doublet spectra of the alkali metals with one optical electron. Spin-orbit interaction (cf p. 277) causes a small splitting of the levels with the same l and different j. From the alkali doublet spectra the selection rule $\Delta j = 0, \pm 1$ is found. The notation for doublet lines is $^2S_{1/2}$, $^2P_{1/2}$, $^2P_{3/2}$, $\cdots$, etc., with the value of j a lower right-hand subscript.

This same vector model carries over readily to more complex spectra arising from more than one optical electron. The spectra here depend on the quantum numbers of the optical electron system as a whole, rather than on the quantum numbers of individual electrons. In the most common form of coupling between optical electrons (L-S or Russell-Saunders), we may suppose that all the spins combine to give a total spin $S = s_1 + s_2 + \cdots$. The individual spin vectors s_1 precess relatively rapidly about the resultant S. Likewise, the individual l precess rapidly about their resultant $L = l_1 + l_2 + \cdots$. Finally L and S precess rather more slowly about the total resultant angular momentum for the whole system, $J = L + S$. For sufficiently large L there are $(2S + 1)$ different values of J associated with each L, where S is the quantum number of S. Thus each level splits into $(2S + 1)$ levels, constituting a system of $(2S + 1)$-plets. The term designations are $^{2S+1}(L)_J$. The selection rules are $\Delta J = 0, \pm 1$, and $\Delta S = 0$. If there are n optical electrons, the possible values of S are $n/2$, $n/2 - 1$, $\cdots$, ($\frac{1}{2}$ or 0). Thus the totality of term values for the atom may contain a number of sets of different multiplicity, which do not combine because of the selection rule $\Delta S = 0$. Two optical electrons as in He, for example, give rise to singlet and triplet term systems.

In L-S coupling the spacing of levels in a multiplet follow the Landé interval rule. If the energies or term values of the different levels in a multiplet are E_J, and the spacings are $\Delta E_J = E_J - E_{J-1}$, then $\Delta E_J : \Delta E_{J'} = J : J'$. The accuracy with which this rule is followed gives a measure of the validity of L-S coupling.

Because the g factors are different for S and L, the total magnetic moment of any atom in L-S coupling is not generally parallel to J. The magnetic moment $\mathbf{u}$ precesses with L and S about J, so that only its component $\mathbf{u}_J$ parallel to J is effective. We can define a g factor for this effective moment,

$$g_J = \frac{\mathbf{u}_J}{J} \frac{\hbar}{\mu_0} = 1 + \frac{S(S + 1) + J(J + 1) - L(L + 1)}{2J(J + 1)}$$

In a magnetic induction B the displacement of an energy level is $\Delta E = \mu_0 B g_J M_J$, where $\hbar M_J$ is the component of J along B. Since the g_J factor is in general different for the two levels of a transition, a single line splits into a very complex pattern in a magnetic field. The spacings of the pattern are of the order of the Larmor frequency $\nu_L = eB/4\pi mc$ but are not uniform. This is the anomalous Zeeman effect; the normal Zeeman effect with three equally spaced components occurs only for singlet lines with $S = 0$. The quantitative agreement of the anomalous Zeeman effect with calculated g_J factors is the best quantitative evidence that the electron spin exists and has $g_s = 2$.

The detailed theory of electron spin is beyond the mathematical scope of this text. The electron spin appears naturally in the relativistic theory of Dirac, where the electron is described by not one but four related wave functions ψ, which specify the different states of electron polarization or spin.

REFERENCES

W. Gerlach and O. Stern, *Z. Physik*, **9**, 349, 353 (1922).

V. Rojansky, *Introductory Quantum Mechanics*, Prentice-Hall, New York (1938).

H. N. Russell and F. A. Saunders, *Astrophys. J.*, **61**, 38 (1925).

G. E. Uhlenbeck and S. Goudsmit, *Nature*, **117**, 264 (1926).

H. E. White, *Introduction to Atomic Spectra*, McGraw-Hill, New York (1934).

ILLUSTRATIVE PROBLEMS

1. How many components has the multiplet ^5P? What are their designations?

Solution. The multiplet ^5P is a term in a quintet system. The number of components is $(2L + 1)$ or $(2S + 1)$, whichever is smaller. In this case $L = 1$, so $2L + 1 = 3$ is smaller than $2S + 1 = 5$. There are accordingly three components. The values of J are given by $L + S \geq J \geq |L - S|$, or $1 + 2 = 3 \geq J \geq |2 - 1| = 1$. Thus $J = 1, 2, 3$, and the term designations are $^5P_1$, $^5P_2$, $^5P_3$.

2. In atoms with several optical electrons a somewhat less usual type of coupling than L-S (Russell-Saunders) is j-j coupling. In this scheme the spin s_i of each electron adds to the orbital angular momentum l_i of the same electron to form the total angular momentum j_i for that electron. The several j_i then combine vectorially to form the total J of the system. Find the g_J factor from the vector model for two electrons in j-j coupling.

Solution. Let the electrons have momenta j_1 and j_2 with g factors

g_1 and g_2. They couple to give total spin J. The total magnetic moment component along J is

$$\mu_J = \mu_1 \cos (j_1, J) + \mu_2 \cos (j_2, J)$$

$$= \mu_0 g_1 \sqrt{j_1(j_1 + 1)} \left[\frac{j_1(j_1 + 1) - j_2(j_2 + 1) + J(J + 1)}{2\sqrt{j_1(j_1 + 1)} \sqrt{J(J + 1)}} \right]$$

$$+ \mu_0 g_2 \sqrt{j_2(j_2 + 1)} \left[\frac{j_2(j_2 + 1) - j_1(j_1 + 1) + J(J + 1)}{2\sqrt{j_2(j_2 + 1)} \sqrt{J(J + 1)}} \right]$$

$$= \mu_0 g_J \sqrt{J(J + 1)}$$

Thus

$$g_J = \frac{1}{2} (g_1 - g_2) \left[\frac{j_1(j_1 + 1) - j_2(j_2 + 1)}{J(J + 1)} \right] + \frac{1}{2} (g_1 + g_2)$$

Note that if $j_1 = j_2$, g_J is just the average of g_1 and g_2, regardless of J.

3. Show that wave mechanics gives the correct polarizations in the normal Zeeman effect: polarized parallel to B (π) for $\Delta m = 0$, opposite circular polarizations (σ) about the axis of B for $\Delta m = \pm 1$.

Solution. The normal Zeeman effect occurs when the spin vanishes, so that it should be appropriate to use the wave mechanics of a spinless electron, as presented in Chapter 10. The electric dipole radiation rate (10.85) is proportional to the sum of the squared matrix elements

$$1/\tau \sim | \langle x \rangle |^2 + | \langle y \rangle |^2 + | \langle z \rangle |^2$$

$$= \tfrac{1}{2} | \langle x + iy \rangle |^2 + \tfrac{1}{2} | \langle x - iy \rangle |^2 + | \langle z \rangle |^2$$

The polarization of the emitted light is that of the matrix element: for $| \langle z \rangle |^2$ the light is polarized along the z-axis, which is the direction of B; for the matrix elements $\langle x \pm iy \rangle$ the light is right or left circularly polarized about the axis of B.

We obtain the selection rules for $\langle m' \mid x \pm iy \mid m \rangle$ from a formula like (10.88), in which the integral over the coordinate becomes

$$\langle m' \mid x \pm iy \mid m \rangle \sim \int_0^{2\pi} e^{-im'\varphi} e^{\pm i\varphi} e^{im\varphi} \, d\varphi$$

This integral vanishes (and with it the matrix element) unless $m' - m = \Delta m = +1$ for $\langle x + iy \rangle$, $\Delta m = -1$ for $\langle x - iy \rangle$. Thus the two directions of circular polarization are associated with different values of Δm, one with $\Delta m = +1$, the other with $\Delta m = -1$. Polarization in the z-direction is associated with $\Delta m = 0$, as in (10.90).

PROBLEMS

1. (a) What are the quantum numbers L, J, S of a ${}^4P_{3/2}$ term?

(b) Show in a diagram the relative orientations of the L, J, and S vectors for this state.

(c) How many components has the multiplet to which the ${}^4P_{3/2}$ term belongs?

(d) Into how many components will the ${}^4P_{3/2}$ level split under the influence of a magnetic field?

2. (a) What are the quantum numbers L, S, J of a ${}^3D_3$ term? of a ${}^4F_{3/2}$ term?

(b) Into how many components will the levels ${}^3D_3$ and ${}^4F_{3/2}$ split under the influence of a magnetic field?

(c) Give the notations of all terms of the multiplets to which the terms ${}^3D_3$ and ${}^4F_{3/2}$ belong.

3. Draw to scale the multiplets ${}^4F$, ${}^3P$, ${}^6G$.

4. Give the L and S values of multiplets with the relative spacings 4, 3, 2, 1; 7, 5, 3; 9, 7, 5, 3.

5. The ground state of sulfur is ${}^3P_2$. In a Stern-Gerlach experiment on sulfur, into how many components would the beam split? Sketch their positions relative to the original undeviated beam. What magnetic moment will the experiment measure for these atoms?

6. In the illustrative example 2, how are the factors g_1 and g_2 obtained? Give a general expression for such a g factor in terms of the electron l for the two cases $j = l + \frac{1}{2}$ and $j = l - \frac{1}{2}$.

7. In the coupling of a spin S and an orbital angular momentum L, suppose that the respective g factors have arbitrary values g_S and g_L, not necessarily equal to 2 and 1, respectively. Obtain a formula for g_J.

8. In an atom with two optical electrons, suppose that one electron occupies a p and one electron a d orbit. What terms of the system as a whole will they produce in Russell-Saunders coupling?

9. The line $2P - 4D$ of rubidium is a compound doublet with lines of the following wavelengths and wave numbers:

$$\lambda = 7759.5 \text{ A} \qquad k = 12{,}883.9 \times 10^2 \text{ m}^{-1}$$

$$= 7757.9 \text{ A} \qquad = 12{,}886.6 \times 10^2 \text{ m}^{-1}$$

$$= 7619.2 \text{ A} \qquad = 13{,}121.2 \times 10^2 \text{ m}^{-1}$$

(a) Noting that the doublet separation of terms decreases with increasing n, determine to what transitions these lines correspond.

(b) Compute the Zeeman effect of the three lines in an induction of 1 weber/m^2, and illustrate the results in diagrams, showing all three lines on the wave number and the wavelength scale.

(c) For what induction B will the Zeeman patterns overlap (Paschen-Back effect, Chapter 12)?

10. In the spectrum of cesium lines are found corresponding to

$$4F - nG, \qquad n = 5, 6, 7, \cdots$$

(a) How many fine structure components will these lines have and what are their notations?

(b) Into how many components will each fine structure line split in a magnetic field?

Chapter 12

THE PERIODIC TABLE, EXCLUSION PRINCIPLE, AND OTHER TOPICS

With the addition of intrinsic spin to the electron, we have completed the basis of our present wave mechanical understanding of atomic structure. In this chapter we discuss some further ramifications and applications of these ideas.

Our first approach to the atom in the opening chapters was from a chemical point of view. No picture of the atom, however elaborate, can be considered accurate and significant unless it provides some insight into chemical questions. As a single example of chemical application, we consider how the periodic table of chemical elements is related to the structure of the corresponding atoms. This example leads directly to establishment of the *exclusion principle*, which is of great importance throughout the theory and application of wave mechanics.

Some additional details of atomic spectra are also discussed, including statistical weights, *j-j* coupling, and the Paschen-Back effect in strong magnetic fields.

12.1. The build-up of the periodic system

The analysis of optical atomic spectra permits us to assign quantum numbers to the ground state or normal term of each atom. Among other features, the normal term has in L-S coupling the quantum numbers S, L, and J. These represent respectively the total spin, orbital angular momentum, and total angular momentum of the optical electrons. From a knowledge of S, L, and J for a single atom we get no indication in general of just how many optical electrons are involved. In going from one atom to the next higher one in the periodic table, however, we must add one electron to the outside, and it is safe to assume that this is an optical electron. Thus by comparing the ground states of neighboring atoms, we can obtain some information about their optical electrons. Continuing this comparison step by step through the periodic system, we can build up a comprehensive knowledge of the optical electron structure of all atoms.

The simplest ground state configuration is $^1S_0$. This configuration has no spin or angular momentum of any sort, for $S = L = J = 0$. In fact, this state is the same as would be formed by no electrons at all.

It therefore seems reasonable to assume that atoms with these normal terms have no optical electrons. All their electrons are somehow contained in inner shells that do not contribute to the ordinary optical spectrum. This assumption leads to a great simplification in constructing the electronic configurations of the atoms; for it means that whenever an $^1S_0$ term appears, we can set the number of optical electrons $n_0 = 0$ and start counting over again. And it is particularly easy to tell the l and j values of the optical electron for the atom just above an $^1S_0$ term. In this case $l = L$, $j = J$. Throughout all this analysis we tacitly assume that the addition of one more optical electron does not disturb the quantum numbers of those already present.

To start the analysis, we look for a set of atoms with similar $^1S_0$ states. We may reasonably expect the periodic table of chemical elements to provide such a set. The chemical as well as the optical properties of atoms derive from their outermost electrons; we therefore anticipate that elements with similar chemical properties, forming one row of the periodic table in Fig. 1.1, should have similar optical ground states. A prominent set of this sort is the noble gases, He, Ne, A, Kn, Xe, and Rn. All these atoms have $^1S_0$ normal states. Thus they have no optical electrons, but contain all their electrons in closed shells. Extending the idea of closed shells a little farther, we remark that they also have no electrons to spare for chemical interactions, and hence are especially inert. Other evidence that the noble gases consist of closed electron shells is discussed in section 7.2.

The atoms following the noble gases, Li, Na, K, Rb, Cs, (Fr), have normal states $^2S_{1/2}$. This implies that the single optical electron outside the closed noble gas shell is in each case an "s-electron"; that is, it has $l = 0$. When we add another electron to form the elements in the second row of the periodic table, it produces in every case another $^1S_0$ ground state. The normal terms of Be, Mg, Ca, Sr, Ba, and Ra are all $^1S_0$. This means that the second electron is also an s-electron in each case. The first electron has $l_1 = 0$, and the total orbital momentum of the two electrons is $L = 0$, so by vector addition in quantum mechanics, $l_2 = L - l_1 = 0$.

Thus we see that the first two rows of the periodic table in Fig. 1.1 correspond to addition of s-electrons to closed shell cores. Furthermore, the addition of just two s-electrons forms a new closed shell, signalized by a $^1S_0$ ground state. We therefore conclude that two s-electrons form a closed shell, or perhaps better "subshell." The elements Be, Mg, etc., are not so inert chemically as the noble gases; it therefore seems appropriate to speak of them as "closed subshells" reserving the title "closed shells" for the more distinctive noble gases.

Consider next the remaining elements in the second column of the periodic table, Fig. 1.1. These are B, C, N, O, F, (Ne), with normal terms $^2P_{1/2}$, $^3P_0$, $^4S_{3/2}$, $^3P_2$, $^2P_{3/2}$, $(^1S_0)$, respectively. For two successive atoms in this series, let the orbital momenta be L and L', and let the orbital momentum of the added electron be l. Then by the rules of vector addition $|L - L'| \leq l \leq L + L'$. In particular if $L(L')$ is zero (S term), then $L'(L) = l$. This rule shows that the electrons added in going from Be to B, C to N, N to O, and F to Ne must be p-electrons. The electrons added in going from B to C and from O to F are not so certain. In these cases $0 \leq l \leq 2$, and the added electron can be s, p, or d. It seems most likely, however, that we are here filling up a subshell with electrons all of one kind, namely, p-electrons. Certainly the facts are all consistent with this assumption. The shell is closed at Ne after the addition of six p-electrons. The same argument holds for the other periods of six elements in Fig. 1.1.

With these examples as guides, it becomes easy to guess how to account for the remaining periods of the table. We have catalogued all the periods of two (s-electrons) and of six (p-electrons). The next subshells should be those of d-electrons. The next longest periods are the groups Sc-Zn, Y-Cd, and La-Hg, each comprising ten elements. For example, Sc has a ground state $^2D_{3/2}$, while the preceding element Ca has $^1S_0$. Therefore the first electron in this subshell is a d-electron. Other D-S neighbors in the group support this conclusion, and the presence of D-F and F-F neighbors does not contradict it. There are a few slight irregularities, but in general we cannot doubt that these periods represent the filling of subshells of d-electrons. Exactly ten electrons complete a d-subshell, and the closed subshell elements Zn, Cd, and Hg all have normal terms $^1S_0$.

There is one more possible complete subshell in the periodic table, represented by the rare earths, which comprise fourteen elements. This must be at least an f-subshell. The ground states are not all certain, but variations of neighboring ground states like $^2D_{3/2}$-$^3H_4$ are present. These neighbors require at least $l = 3$ (f-electron) for the added electron. We therefore associate the rare earths with an f-subshell, which is filled with fourteen electrons. Thorium begins a second f-subshell that extends into the transuranic elements but is not complete.

We have now accounted for the entire periodic table of chemical elements in terms of the building up of subshells of electrons. The number of optical electrons in a subshell bears a distinct correlation with the chemical valence of the element. It is therefore natural to ascribe the valence properties to the optical electrons. Here we have a direct interpretation of a chemical phenomenon, valence, in terms of the physical picture of atomic structure as consisting of shells and subshells of electrons.

12.2. The exclusion principle

One of the most striking features of the atomic shells is that they contain definite small numbers of electrons. The s, p, d, f shells are complete with 2, 6, 10, and 14 electrons, respectively. This immediately points to some sort of exclusion principle for the electrons. Apparently the p-shell, for example, has just six vacancies for electrons; when these are all filled, all further electrons are excluded from the shell. The repeated filling of p-shells in the periodic table simply indicates that there are several different p-shells. The exclusion principle must apply to the individual positions in a shell, so that no two electrons can occupy the same position. Otherwise there could be more electrons than positions in the shell, and the total number of electrons would become indefinite.

Let us inquire more precisely what we mean by the words "vacancy" or "position" in a shell. We have observed that in quantum mechanics, the only quantities describing an electron that are absolutely certain with no indeterminacy are its quantum numbers. We cannot specify the position or momentum of an electron precisely; but its principal quantum number n, orbital angular momentum number l, and magnetic quantum number m (l_z component) assume only precise, integer values. To these three quantum numbers we can add a fourth, $m_s = \pm\frac{1}{2}$, the z-component of the electron spin, which has just two values. The number of electrons in a shell is a definite integer with no uncertainty, just like the electron quantum numbers. We therefore look to see if there is a closer connection.

The values of m for an electron are subject to the condition $-l \leq m \leq l$, where m and l are integers. Hence there are $(2l + 1)$ different possible values of m for a given l. For each value of m, an electron can have two values of m_s. The total number of different combinations of m and m_s for fixed values of n and l is therefore $2(2l + 1)$. This number takes the values 2, 6, 10, 14, $\cdots$ for s, p, d, f, $\cdots$ electrons with $l = 0$, 1, 2, 3, $\cdots$. But these are just the numbers of the shell structure. We may therefore say that a shell consists of electrons with the same n, l quantum numbers but different m, m_s quantum numbers. The various s, p, d, f subshells correspond to different values of l. It is a natural generalization to assume that the different subshells with the same l, like B-Ne and Al-A, correspond to different values of n.

We can construct this picture of the subshells entirely from a single principle; namely, that in building up the electronic structure of an atom, we assign to no two electrons exactly the same four quantum numbers n, l, m, and m_s. This is the *exclusion principle* for electrons.

Although we have developed it here indirectly from atomic ground states, it holds quite generally:

$$\text{in any system containing several electrons, no two} \atop \text{electrons can have all quantum numbers identical} \qquad (12.1)$$

By looking at the order of the subshells for different l values in atoms, we can infer the corresponding values of the principal quantum number n. Equation (10.42d) states that $l \leq n - 1$. The first subshell is an s-shell, comprising H and He; after this comes another s-shell (Li, Be), followed by a p-shell (B-Ne); next comes another s-shell. This pattern indicates that H, He have $n = 1, l = 0$; Li-Ne have $n = 2, l = 0, 1$, where the $l = 0$ occurs for Li, Be. For succeeding subshells the value of n increases in regular order. Thus we specify subshells by both n and l: 1s, 2s, 2p, 3s, etc. The general order for the filling of the subshells throughout the periodic table is the following:

$$\text{the subshells fill in order of increasing } N = (n + l), \atop \text{and for constant } N \text{ the subshells of lowest } n \text{ fill first} \qquad (12.2)$$

This rule has a number of minor exceptions but gives a good general picture of the building up of the periodic table of elements. It is represented as a diagram in Fig. 12.1.

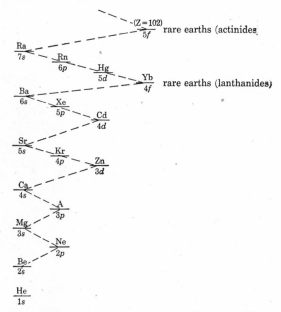

Fig. 12.1. Filling up of orbits in the periodic table. The elements listed mark the closing of the respective subshells. The diagram is schematic only and not supposed to represent actual level spacings.

In this discussion the principal quantum number n has the value $n = 1$ for the lightest elements, and goes up to $n \approx 6$ or 7 for the optical electrons of the heaviest elements. This choice of n means that we refer each electron orbit to the nucleus of charge $+Ze$. It is an obvious choice to make when discussing the build-up of the periodic table element by element. On the other hand, when considering optical spectra we frequently find it convenient to refer the orbits of the optical electrons to the *core* a nucleus plus closed electron shells. When referred to this rather artificial basis, each optical electron starts with $n = 1$ in its ground state. Although this point of view was useful for the optical spectra of Chapter 7, in the present chapter we shall adhere entirely to the other notation, specifying the levels by counting $n = 1, 2, 3, \cdots$ from the innermost orbits.

We can express the exclusion principle more mathematically by saying that the wave function for all the electrons in a system must be totally antisymmetric in the exchange of any two electrons. Suppose that the wave function for all the n electrons of a system is

$$\psi(x_1y_1z_1s_1; \quad x_2y_2z_2s_2; \quad \cdots \quad x_ny_nz_ns_n) \tag{12.3}$$

where the coordinate s_k represents the spin of the kth electron. The wave function is totally antisymmetric if

$$\psi(x_2y_2z_2s_2; \quad x_1y_1z_1s_1; \quad \cdots \quad x_ny_nz_ns_n) =$$
$$- \psi(x_1y_1z_1s_1; \quad x_2y_2z_2s_2; \quad \cdots \quad x_ny_nz_ns_n) \tag{12.4}$$

and likewise for the exchange of any pair (i, k) of electrons. To see that (12.4) is equivalent to (12.1), we may argue as follows: according to quantum mechanics, the only features of electrons 1 and 2 that can be measured with certainty are contained in their quantum numbers $(n_1l_1m_1m_{s_1})$ and $(n_2l_2m_2m_{s_2})$. Now if these two sets of quantum numbers were identical, electrons 1 and 2 would be indistinguishable, or hence

$$\psi(x_2y_2z_2s_2; \quad x_1y_1z_1s_1; \quad \cdots \quad x_ny_nz_ns_n)$$
$$= \psi(x_1y_1z_1s_1; \quad x_2y_2z_2s_2; \quad \cdots \quad x_ny_nz_ns_n) \tag{12.5}$$

But (12.4) and (12.5) together imply that $\psi = 0$. That is, if we try to give two electrons identical quantum numbers in an antisymmetric wave function, the wave function vanishes. This is just the property we want in order to satisfy the exclusion principle automatically. Thus (12.4) is the mathematical equivalent of (12.1).

Thus electrons somehow have a highly individualistic behavior. It is possible to prove by abstract arguments that electrons must behave this way if they are to have intrinsic spin $\frac{1}{2}$ and at the same time satisfy the requirements of the special theory of relativity.

12.3. X-ray spectra

With this picture of the build-up of the periodic table, and the exclusion principle that is postulated to explain it, we can give a complete interpretation of the X-ray spectra discussed in Chapter 6. It is necessary only to identify the K, L, M, $\cdots$ shells observed in X-rays with the electron shells defined by $n = 1, 2, 3, \cdots$. These two notations for the shell are interchangeable, and we shall generally use the X-ray notation.

The K shell has $n = 1$ and contains two s-electrons with $l = 0$. There are no subshells in the K shell. Next comes the L shell with $n = 2$. This shell can have both s- and p-electrons: there are two $2s$-electrons, and six $2p$-electrons. The X-ray absorption edges and emission spectra indicate the existence of definite subshells L_I, L_II and L_III in the L shell, and we inquire how to associate these subshells with different quantum numbers of the electrons. It is natural to assume that the two s-electrons form one subshell; but how do the six p-electrons form *two* other subshells? We must search for more quantum numbers, and they are not hard to find. In the discussion of the previous chapter on doublets in the spectrum of a single optical electron, we saw that the energy levels depend not only on n and l, but to some extent also on $j = l \pm \frac{1}{2}$, the quantum number of the vector sum of l and s. The dependence on j is rather slight compared with the dependence on l and n, but it is sufficient to account for the relatively narrow doublet splitting. In a similar fashion, the energy difference of the L_II and L_III energy levels is relatively small compared with the separation between the K and L groups. Thus we attribute the three L subshells in X-ray spectra to $s_{1/2}$-, $p_{1/2}$-, and $p_{3/2}$-electrons, where the lower right-hand subscript conventionally gives the value of j. For s-electrons, $l = 0$ and $j = +\frac{1}{2}$ only, so that the K shell does not split into subshells on the introduction of the quantum number j.

The X-ray M shell corresponds in this scheme to $n = 3$, and contains s-, p-, and d-electrons. If we classify these further according to their j-values, they form five subshells with $s_{1/2}$-, $p_{1/2}$-, $p_{3/2}$-, $d_{3/2}$-, and $d_{5/2}$-electrons. Observations on the X-ray spectra do indeed show the existence of subshells M_I, M_II, M_III, M_IV and M_V. This further evidence confirms our assumption that we should associate subshells with different values of j.

To determine how the electrons divide between $j = l + \frac{1}{2}$ and $j = l - \frac{1}{2}$ subshells, we can use the exclusion principle. It is first necessary to rearrange the electron quantum numbers somewhat. In addition to n each electron has the quantum numbers l, s, j, m, m_s, and m_j. These quantum numbers refer to various angular momenta and their components along the z-axis. The spin quantum number is $s = \frac{1}{2}$ for all electrons, so this quantum number plays no role in the exclusion considerations. The remaining five quantum numbers are not all independent; in fact, only three of them are independent. We can be sure of this because it is possible to deduce the exclusion principle from the periodic table by using only l, m, and m_s in addition to n. Now by (10.55b), $m_j = m + m_s$, so that we could just as well have used the quantum numbers l, m_s, and m_j to label the electrons. For each value of l, there are just two values of m_s; but there are likewise just two values of $j = l \pm \frac{1}{2}$ in general. Therefore we anticipate that an equally good labeling scheme can be constructed with l, j, and m_j. This scheme is the most appropriate for consideration of the X-ray levels; it is completely equivalent to the l, m, m_s scheme, and the choice of which to use is dictated solely by convenience. For each value of l, j there are $(2j + 1)$ values of m_j, which has the range $-j \leq m_j \leq j$. Hence by the exclusion principle there can be two electrons in an atom with the same values of n, l, and $j = \frac{1}{2}$; four electrons if $j = \frac{3}{2}$, six if $j = \frac{5}{2}$, etc. In particular, the six electrons in a p-subshell divide into two in the $p_{1/2}$-subshell, four in the $p_{3/2}$-subshell; in a d-subshell there are four $d_{3/2}$-electrons and six $d_{5/2}$-electrons, making the previously observed total of ten. These relations can be extended to shells with higher n.

In order to complete the identification of X-ray spectra and the subshells built up by means of the exclusion principle, we have only to assign the quantum numbers $s_{1/2}$, $p_{1/2}$, $p_{3/2}$, $\cdots$ to the appropriate subshells I, II, III, $\cdots$ in X-ray notation. This we accomplish by applying the selection rules (10.45) and (11.12), which govern the most intense (electric dipole) atomic transitions, in the X-ray as well as optical regions. The observed selection rules in emission spectra of X-rays are (6.17). From the existence of K-L_{II}, K-L_{III} transitions and the absence of K-L_I transitions, we infer that L_I subshells consist of s-electrons. To determine which of the L_{II}, L_{III} subshells is $p_{1/2}$ and $p_{3/2}$, we consider the combinations with M_{IV} and M_V which are $d_{3/2}$ and $d_{5/2}$ subshells in this scheme. The $p_{1/2}$-subshell can combine only with the $d_{3/2}$-subshell because of the selection rules (10.45) and (11.12); the $p_{3/2}$-subshell, on the contrary, can combine with both $d_{3/2}$ and $d_{5/2}$. The observations are that the II subshell combines only with IV, while III combines with IV and V. This identifies the II, III, IV, V subshells as $p_{1/2}$, $p_{3/2}$, $d_{3/2}$, $d_{5/2}$, respectively. This analysis extends in the same way to higher subshells. A schematic diagram of the allowed transitions between energy levels in the first three shells and subshells is given in Fig. 12.2.

This level diagram for X-ray spectra possesses great similarity to the term diagram for the single optical electron of the alkali spectra. In the alkali spectra there also exists only one level for $n = 1$ ($1^2S_{1/2}$) corre-

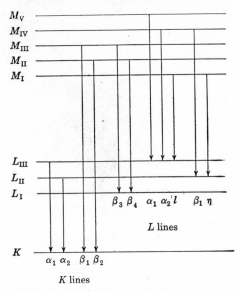

Fig. 12.2. Allowed transitions in the K- and L-lines of X-ray emission spectra. The energy differences are not to scale. The subscripts $\alpha, \beta, \cdots$ are standard X-ray notation.

sponding to the single K level. For $n = 2$ there are three optical levels $(2^2S_{1/2},\ 2^2P_{1/2},\ 2^2P_{3/2})$, which correspond to the three L levels in the X-ray diagram; and the five $n = 3$ levels $(3^2S_{1/2},\ 3^2P_{1/2},\ 3^2P_{3/2},\ 3^2D_{3/2},\ 3^2D_{5/2})$ are analogous to the five M levels, and so forth. The selection rules for transitions between the levels are the same for the optical and X-ray cases. The origin of this analogy can be understood as follows: X-rays lines are produced when an electron jumps from a higher shell into an empty space or "hole" in a lower shell. This process leaves a hole in the higher shell that is filled by an electron from a still higher shell, and so on. This is equivalent to saying that the hole jumps upward from one shell to the next, emitting X-rays in the process. Thus we conclude that a single hole in a closed shell behaves much like a single electron outside a closed shell: the energy levels of the atom have quantum numbers characteristic of the hole, and radiation of the atom can be described in terms of transitions of the hole, following the same selection rules as for a single electron. The equivalence of the level diagrams for electrons and holes arises from the fact that a closed shell has $L = S = J = 0$; the removal of an electron from this shell leaves a state with the same L, S, J quantum numbers as the single removed electron, according to the laws of vector addition. The equivalence of electrons and holes is a useful concept in dealing with states involving several electrons; in the next section, for example, we see that for electrons in a single shell of capacity N it is never necessary to consider more than $\frac{1}{2}N$ electrons or holes.

The striking difference between single electron optical spectra and X-ray spectra occurs in absorption. The production of X-ray spectra depends on the creation of a hole in a closed shell, which can occur only by removing one electron entirely from the atom. This is why the X-ray absorption edges are simple and are at shorter wavelengths than the corresponding emission lines (Chapter 6). The observed differences between X-ray absorption edges and emission lines provide graphic evidence for the exclusion principle.

12.4. Equivalent electrons in complex atoms

For atoms with more than one optical or valence electron, the exclusion principle places strong restrictions on the configurations that are possible as a shell is being filled. To discuss these restrictions, we define "equivalent electrons" as those having identical n and l quantum numbers, that is, occupying the same subshell. In Chapter 11 we obtained the S, L, and J values for systems of several optical electrons by adding the s and l vectors of individual electrons in accord with the vector model. This addition tacitly assumed that each electron could have any arbitrary m and m_s values; in particular, two electrons could simultaneously have identical m and m_s. According to the exclusion principle, this is possible only for nonequivalent electrons. The build-up of the periodic table, however, suggests that the several electrons in a complex spectrum are most likely to be equivalent. We must therefore take account of the exclusion principle in constructing states of S, L, and J.

The effect of the exclusion principle is always to eliminate certain states that would require two electrons with identical m and m_s values. It thus reduces the total number of possible configurations. As the simplest example, consider two s electrons. Here $l_1 = l_2 = 0$, so that $L = 0$, and an S state can result. The spins are $s_1 = s_2 = \frac{1}{2}$, so that the total spin can be $S = 0$ or $S = 1$, if the electrons are not equivalent (have different quantum numbers n). If the electrons are equivalent, we must have $m_{s_1} \neq m_{s_2}$; or hence

$$m_{s_1} = -m_{s_2} \tag{12.6}$$

since each quantum number has only the values $m_s = \pm\frac{1}{2}$. Now by (10.55b), the z-projection of the total spin is

$$M_S = m_{s_1} + m_{s_2} = 0 \tag{12.7}$$

because of (12.6). This is compatible only with a total spin $S = 0$; for
if the spin could be $S = 1$, it would be necessary to have $M_s = 0, \pm1$,
in contradiction with (12.7). Thus in the simplest case of two s-elec-
trons, the exclusion principle for equivalent electrons eliminates one of
the two states available to nonequivalent electrons.

For equivalent p and d electrons, the calculations become more complicated but proceed along the same lines of counting up the various
possible sets of m and m_s values consistent with the exclusion principle.
The results are given in Fig. 12.3. The notation d^3 means "three equivalent d electrons," etc. For no electrons, p^0 and d^0, the configuration is
that of the core, $^1S_0$. The J values are not given in Fig. 12.3; they follow
by vector addition of L and S with no restrictions, since we have entirely
satisfied the exclusion principle in obtaining the allowed values of L
and S.

The tables in Fig. 12.3 have a simple symmetry: the configurations
obtained from n equivalent electrons are identical with those obtained
from $(N - n)$ equivalent electrons, where N is the total number in a
completed shell. We can readily understand this by noting that for
vectors addition and subtraction are in fact identical operations. Since
the p^6 and d^{10} configuration form closed shells, they must have $^1S_0$
configurations, just like p^0 and d^0. Now in the vector model the addition of a single p-electron to $^1S_0$ (p^0) is mathematically the same as subtraction of a single p-electron from $^1S_0(p^6)$, with a similar argument for
the d-shell. The exclusion principle does not alter this general equality

p^0	^1S			
p^1		^2P		
p^2	$^1S,D$		^3P	
p^3		$^2P,D$		^4S
p^4	$^1S,D$		^3P	
p^5		^2P		
p^6	^1S			

d^0	^1S			
d^1		^2D		
d^2	$^1S,D,G$		$^3P,F$	
d^3		$^2D,P,D,F,G,H$		$^4P,F$
d^4	$^1S,D,G,S,D,F,G,I$		$^3P,F,P,D,F,G,H$ ^5D	
d^5		$^2D,P,D,F,G,H,S,D,F,G,I$	$^4P,F,D,G$	^6S
d^6	$^1S,D,G,S,D,F,G,I$		$^3P,F,P,D,F,G,H$ ^5D	
d^7		$^2D,P,D,F,G,H$		$^4P,F$
d^8	$^1S,D,G$		$^3P,F$	
d^9		^2D		
d^{10}	^1S			

Fig. 12.3. Values of S and L for equivalent p- and d-electrons.
Repeated values of L in a single line correspond to different configurations that happen to give the same total angular momentum.

of addition and subtraction in the vector model. Continuing this argument step by step we see that addition of n electrons to $^1S_0(l^0)$ is the same as subtracting n electrons from $^1S_0(l^N)$. Therefore the configurations of n electrons in a single subshell must be identical with those obtained from n "holes" or hence $(N - n)$ electrons in the same subshell.

We may use the results of Fig. 12.3 for a closer analysis of the way in which the periodic table is built up. In particular, we can discuss some of the irregularities. The $2p$- and $3p$-shells fill up in a regular fashion. If we include the p^0 and p^6 configurations, these shells comprise the elements Be-Ne and Mg-A. The order of the ground states for p^0, p_1, $\cdots$, p^6 is $^1S_0$, $^2P_{1/2}$, $^3P_0$, $^4S_{3/2}$, $^3P_2$, $^2P_{3/2}$, $^1S_0$. We can describe all these ground states by three simple rules:

   (1) The spin S assumes its maximum value.
   (2) The orbital quantum number L assumes the maximum
       value consistent with (1).   (12.8)
   (3) The total angular momentum has $J = L - S$ for
       $n < N/2$, $J = L + S$ for $n > N/2$.

The second rule is redundant for the p-shell but will not be for the d-shell.

Now consider the first d-subshell. After the $3p$-subshell closes at A, the electrons can go into the $3d$-subshell to fill up the $(n = 3)$-shell. Actually, however, they first fill the $4s$-shell first in K and Ca. Then the $3d$-subshell fills, closing at Zn. The succession of ground states in the elements Ca-Zn (starting with d^0 at Ca) is $^1S_0$, $^2D_{3/2}$, $^3F_2$, $^4F_{3/2}$, $^7S_3$, $^6S_{5/2}$, $^5D_4$, $^4F_{9/2}$, $^3F_4$, $^2S_{1/2}$, $^1S_0$. Comparing this succession with Fig. 12.3, we find agreement with the rules (12.5) up till chromium. This element should have the configuration $(4s^2 3d^4)^5 D_{5/2}$, but actually shows a ground state of $^7S_3$. The very high multiplicity of 7 immediately indicates that at least six electrons are involved; since two $4s$-electrons must form a closed shell by the exclusion principle, the only reasonable assumption is that the configuration is $(4s 3d^5)^7 S_3$. The five d-electrons should form a $^6S_{5/2}$ state according to (12.8), and the single s-electron adds to make a $^7S_2$ or $^7S_3$ state. This is the first case of a slight aberration in the filling of the subshells.

The next element after Cr is Mn with a normal state of $^6S_{5/2}$ from which we conclude that the $4s$-subshell is again filled, and the ground state represents a $3d^5$ configuration. The d-subshell fills regularly until Cu, which should be $(4s^2 3d^9)^2 D_{5/2}$ but is $^2S_{1/2}$ instead. This indicates that the configuration is really $(4s 3d^{10})^2 S_{1/2}$ with the $3d$-subshell completely closed.

From Ga to Kr the $4p$-subshell fills regularly, followed by the $5s$-subshell. The $4d$-subshell then fills in the elements Sr-Cd, with even more irregularities than in the $3d$-subshell. Proceeding in the same way as above, we can specify the most likely ground state configurations for each of these elements. Extending this process throughout the table, we arrive at the assignment of ground state configurations in Fig. 12.4.

We can associate the valences and chemical properties of elements with these ground state configurations, at least in a qualitative way. The subshells that fill in the most regular fashion are the s- and p-subshells, and the corresponding elements have the least variety in their valences. The elements with a single s-electron outside a closed shell have always the valence $+1$, corresponding to loss of that electron: H, Li, Na, K, Rb, Cs, (Fr). In addition, Cu, Ag, and Au have a single $1s$ electron outside a closed d-subshell. These elements have $+1$ as one of their prominent valence states, although they have other valences as well. It is noteworthy that these elements with $(d^{10}s)$ configurations are the three best conductors of electricity.

The elements with two s-electrons have closed 2-subshells; but these subshells do not seem to be closed very tightly, since the elements are chemically active, with valence $+2$. The elements with two s-electrons outside a tightly closed p-subshell are Be, Mg, Ca, Sr, Ba, and Ra. In addition, Zn, Cd, and Hg have two s-electrons outside of closed d-subshells; these elements have $+2$ as their most prominent valence state.

Each p-subshell fills outside of a previously completed but not very tightly closed s-subshell. Thus these elements can generally have two or three valences: a positive valence n corresponding to loss of all the p-electrons; a positive valence $(n + 2)$ corresponding to loss of both p- and s-electrons; a negative valence $(6 - n)$ corresponding to acquisition of enough electrons to complete the p-subshell. Thus in the second major division of Fig. 1.1, the valences of successive elements in the p-subshell are $+1$, $+3$; $+2$, $+4$; $+3$, $+5$, -3; $+4$, $+6$, -2; $+5$, $+7$, -1; and 0. The zero valence is for the noble gases that correspond to closing of the p-subshell. This appears to be the most tightly closed of all subshells, since the noble gases are chemically inactive. The element He is an exception, having the only s-subshell that is tightly closed.

For the higher subshells the valences become more complicated and irregular, especially since the d- and f-subshells fill after some higher subshells are complete. This reversal in the filling order is associated with a number of anomalous chemical effects. For instance, it seems to lead to a high prevalence of colored ions in solution. The first d-shell contains the ferromagnetic elements Fe, Co, and Ni with configuration $(4s^2 3d^{6,\,7,\,8})$. The question arises why the other d-subshells do not also contain ferromagnetic elements. Inspection shows that the configurations $(s^2 d^{6,\,7,\,8})$ do not occur in the higher d-subshells; instead we find $(5s4d^{7,8},\,4d^{10})$, $(6s5d^7,\,5d^{9,\,10})$. We can thus associate the presence or absence of ferromagnetism with the irregularities in d-subshell filling.

FIG. 12.4. FILLING OF ATOMIC SHELLS AND SUBSHELLS. THE LAST COLUMN GIVES THE OBSERVED OPTICAL GROUND STATE.*

SHELL	K $n=1$	L $n=2$		M $n=3$			N $n=4$				O $n=5$				P $n=6$		Q $n=7$	Normal state
SUBSHELL	$l=0$	$l=0$	$l=1$	$l=0$	$l=1$	$l=2$	$l=0$	$l=1$	$l=2$	$l=3$	$l=0$	$l=1$	$l=2$	$l=3$	$l=0$	$l=1$	$l=0$	
1 H	$1s$																	$^2S_{1/2}$
2 He	$1s^2$																	$^1S_0$
3 Li	$1s^2$	$2s$																$^2S_{1/2}$
4 Be	"	$2s^2$																$^1S_0$
5 B	$1s^2$	$2s^2$	$2p$															$^2P_{1/2}$
6 C	"	"	$2p^2$															$^3P_0$
7 N	"	"	$2p^3$															$^4S_{3/2}$
8 O	"	"	$2p^4$															$^3P_2$
9 F	"	"	$2p^5$															$^2P_{3/2}$
10 Ne	"	"	$2p^6$															$^1S_0$
11 Na	$1s^2$	$2s^2$	$2p^6$	$3s$														$^2S_{1/2}$
12 Mg	"	"	"	$3s^2$														$^1S_0$
13 Al	$1s^2$	$2s^2$	$2p^6$	$3s^2$	$3p$													$^2P_{1/2}$
14 Si	"	"	"	"	$3p^2$													$^3P_0$
15 P	"	"	"	"	$3p^3$													$^4S_{3/2}$
16 S	"	"	"	"	$3p^4$													$^3P_2$
17 Cl	"	"	"	"	$3p^5$													$^2P_{3/2}$
18 A	"	"	"	"	$3p^6$													$^1S_0$
19 K	$1s^2$	$2s^2$	$2p^6$	$3s^2$	$3p^6$		$4s$											$^2S_{1/2}$
20 Ca	"	"	"	"	"		$4s^2$											$^1S_0$

	$1s$	$2s$	$2p$	$3s$	$3p$	$3d$	$4s$	$4p$	$4d$	$5s$	Term
21 Sc	$1s^2$	$2s^2$	$2p^6$	$3s^2$	$3p^6$	$3d$	$4s^2$				$^2D_{3/2}$
22 Ti	"	"	"	"	"	$3d^2$	$4s^2$				$^3F_2$
23 V	"	"	"	"	"	$3d^3$	$4s^2$				$^4F_{3/2}$
24 Cr	"	"	"	"	"	$3d^5$	$4s$				$^7S_3$
25 Mn	"	"	"	"	"	$3d^5$	$4s^2$				$^6S_{5/2}$
26 Fe	"	"	"	"	"	$3d^6$	$4s^2$				$^5D_4$
27 Co	"	"	"	"	"	$3d^7$	$4s^2$				$^4F_{9/2}$
28 Ni	"	"	"	"	"	$3d^8$	$4s^2$				$^3F_4$
29 Cu	"	"	"	"	"	$3d^{10}$	$4s$				$^2S_{1/2}$
30 Zn	"	"	"	"	"	$3d^{10}$	$4s^2$				$^1S_0$
31 Ga	$1s^2$	$2s^2$	$2p^6$	$3s^2$	$3p^6$	$3d^{10}$	$4s^2$	$4p$			$^2P_{1/2}$
32 Ge	"	"	"	"	"	"	"	$4p^2$			$^3P_0$
33 As	"	"	"	"	"	"	"	$4p^3$			$^4S_{3/2}$
34 Se	"	"	"	"	"	"	"	$4p^4$			$^3P_2$
35 Br	"	"	"	"	"	"	"	$4p^5$			$^2P_{3/2}$
36 Kr	"	"	"	"	"	"	"	$4p^6$			$^1S_0$
37 Rb	$1s^2$	$2s^2$	$2p^6$	$3s^2$	$3p^6$	$3d^{10}$	$4s^2$	$4p^6$		$5s$	$^2S_{1/2}$
38 Sr	"	"	"	"	"	"	"	"		$5s^2$	$^1S_0$
39 Y	$1s^2$	$2s^2$	$2p^6$	$3s^2$	$3p^6$	$3d^{10}$	$4s^2$	$4p^6$	$4d$	$5s^2$	$^2D_{3/2}$
40 Zr	"	"	"	"	"	"	"	"	$4d^2$	$5s^2$	$^3F_2$
41 Nb	"	"	"	"	"	"	"	"	$4d^4$	$5s$	$^6D_{1/2}$
42 Mo	"	"	"	"	"	"	"	"	$4d^5$	$5s$	$^7S_3$
43 Tc	"	"	"	"	"	"	"	"	$4d^5$	$5s^2$	$^6S_{5/2}$
44 Ru	"	"	"	"	"	"	"	"	$4d^7$	$5s$	$^5F_5$
45 Rh	"	"	"	"	"	"	"	"	$4d^8$	$5s$	$^4F_{9/2}$
46 Pd	"	"	"	"	"	"	"	"	$4d^{10}$		$^1S_0$
47 Ag	"	"	"	"	"	"	"	"	$4d^{10}$	$5s$	$^2S_{1/2}$
48 Cd	"	"	"	"	"	"	"	"	$4d^{10}$	$5s^2$	$^1S_0$

* Based on data in NBS Circular 467.

FIG. 12.4. (*Con't.*) FILLING OF ATOMIC SHELLS AND SUBSHELLS. THE LAST COLUMN GIVES THE OBSERVED OPTICAL GROUND STATE.

SHELL	K $n=1$	L $n=2$		M $n=3$			N $n=4$				O $n=5$				P $n=6$			Q $n=7$	Normal state
SUBSHELL	$l=0$	$l=0$	$l=1$	$l=0$	$l=1$	$l=2$	$l=0$	$l=1$	$l=2$	$l=3$	$l=0$	$l=1$	$l=2$	$l=3$	$l=0$	$l=1$	$l=2$	$l=0$	
49 In	$1s^2$	$2s^2$	$2p^6$	$3s^2$	$3p^6$	$3d^{10}$	$4s^2$	$4p^6$	$4d^{10}$		$5s^2$	$5p$							$^2P_{1/2}$
50 Sn	"	"	"	"	"	"	"	"	"		"	$5p^2$							$^3P_0$
51 Sb	"	"	"	"	"	"	"	"	"		"	$5p^3$							$^4S_{3/2}$
52 Te	"	"	"	"	"	"	"	"	"		"	$5p^4$							$^3P_2$
53 I	"	"	"	"	"	"	"	"	"		"	$5p^5$							$^2P_{3/2}$
54 Xe	"	"	"	"	"	"	"	"	"		"	$5p^6$							$^1S_0$
55 Cs	$1s^2$	$2s^2$	$2p^6$	$3s^2$	$3p^6$	$3d^{10}$	$4s^2$	$4p^6$	$4d^{10}$		$5s^2$	$5p^6$			$6s$				$^2S_{1/2}$
56 Ba	"	"	"	"	"	"	"	"	"		"	"			$6s^2$				$^1S_0$
57 La	$1s^2$	$2s^2$	$2p^6$	$3s^2$	$3p^6$	$3d^{10}$	$4s^2$	$4p^6$	$4d^{10}$		$5s^2$	$5p^6$	$5d$		$6s^2$				$^2D_{3/2}$
58 Ce	"	"	"	"	"	"	"	"	"		"	"			$6s^2$				
59 Pr	"	"	"	"	"	"	"	"	"	$4f^3$	"	"			"				$^4I_{9/2}$
60 Nd	"	"	"	"	"	"	"	"	"	$4f^4$	"	"			"				$^5I_4$
61 Pm	"	"	"	"	"	"	"	"	"		"	"			"				
62 Sm	"	"	"	"	"	"	"	"	"	$4f^6$	"	"			"				$^7F_0$
63 Eu	"	"	"	"	"	"	"	"	"	$4f^7$	"	"			"				$^8S_{7/2}$
64 Gd	"	"	"	"	"	"	"	"	"	$4f^7$	"	"	$5d$		"				$^9D_2$
65 Tb	"	"	"	"	"	"	"	"	"		"	"			"				
66 Dy	"	"	"	"	"	"	"	"	"		"	"			"				
67 Ho	"	"	"	"	"	"	"	"	"		"	"			"				
68 Er	"	"	"	"	"	"	"	"	"		"	"			"				
69 Tm	"	"	"	"	"	"	"	"	"	$4f^{13}$	"	"			$6s^2$				$^2F_{7/2}$
70 Yb	"	"	"	"	"	"	"	"	"	$4f^{14}$	"	"			$6s^2$				$^1S_0$

Z	Elem	1s	2s	2p	3s	3p	3d	4s	4p	4d	4f	5s	5p	5d	5f	6s	6p	6d	7s	Term
71	Lu	$1s^2$	$2s^2$	$2p^6$	$3s^2$	$3p^6$	$3d^{10}$	$4s^2$	$4p^6$	$4d^{10}$	$4f^{14}$	$5s^2$	$5p^6$	$5d$		$6s^2$				$^2D_{3/2}$
72	Hf	"	"	"	"	"	"	"	"	"	"	"	"	$5d^2$		$6s^2$				$^3F_2$
73	Ta	"	"	"	"	"	"	"	"	"	"	"	"	$5d^3$		$6s^2$				$^4F_{3/2}$
74	W	"	"	"	"	"	"	"	"	"	"	"	"	$5d^4$		$6s^2$				$^5D_0$
75	Re	"	"	"	"	"	"	"	"	"	"	"	"	$5d^5$		$6s^2$				$^6S_{5/2}$
76	Os	"	"	"	"	"	"	"	"	"	"	"	"	$5d^6$		$6s$				$^5D_4$
77	Ir	"	"	"	"	"	"	"	"	"	"	"	"	$5d^7$						$^4F_{3/2}$
78	Pt	"	"	"	"	"	"	"	"	"	"	"	"	$5d^9$						$^3D_3$
79	Au	"	"	"	"	"	"	"	"	"	"	"	"	$5d^{10}$		$6s$				$^2S_{1/2}$
80	Hg	"	"	"	"	"	"	"	"	"	"	"	"	$5d^{10}$		$6s^2$				$^1S_0$
81	Tl	$1s^2$	$2s^2$	$2p^6$	$3s^2$	$3p^6$	$3d^{10}$	$4s^2$	$4p^6$	$4d^{10}$	$4f^{14}$	$5s^2$	$5p^6$	$5d^{10}$		$6s^2$	$6p$			$^2P_{1/2}$
82	Pb	"	"	"	"	"	"	"	"	"	"	"	"	"		"	$6p^2$			$^3P_0$
83	Bi	"	"	"	"	"	"	"	"	"	"	"	"	"		"	$6p^3$			$^4S_{3/2}$
84	Po	"	"	"	"	"	"	"	"	"	"	"	"	"		"	"			
85	At	"	"	"	"	"	"	"	"	"	"	"	"	"		"	"			
86	Rn	"	"	"	"	"	"	"	"	"	"	"	"	"		"	$6p^6$			$^1S_0$
87	Fr	$1s^2$	$2s^2$	$2p^6$	$3s^2$	$3p^6$	$3d^{10}$	$4s^2$	$4p^6$	$4d^{10}$	$4f^{14}$	$5s^2$	$5p^6$	$5d^{10}$		$6s^2$	$6p^6$		$(7s)$	
88	Ra	"	"	"	"	"	"	"	"	"	"	"	"	"		"	"		$7s^2$	$^1S_0$
89	Ac	$1s^2$	$2s^2$	$2p^6$	$3s^2$	$3p^6$	$3d^{10}$	$4s^2$	$4p^6$	$4d^{10}$	$4f^{14}$	$5s^2$	$5p^6$	$5d^{10}$		$6s^2$	$6p^6$	$6d$	$7s^2$	
90	Th	"	"	"	"	"	"	"	"	"	"	"	"	"		"	"	$6d^2$	$7s^2$	$^3F_2$
91	Pa	"	"	"	"	"	"	"	"	"	"	"	"	"		"	"		$7s^2$	
92	U	"	"	"	"	"	"	"	"	"	"	"	"	"	$5f^3$	"	"	$6d$	$7s^2$	$^5L_6$

* Based on data from NBS Circular 467.

12.5. Statistical weights and intensities

According to the exclusion principle, the number of electrons of total angular momentum j that can occupy any state of a system is $(2j + 1)$, since this is the number of possible m_j values. If all the states of the system are filled, and we compile statistics about the electrons, we should count each state containing j-electrons $(2j + 1)$ times. This factor is therefore called the *statistical weight* associated with a state of total angular momentum j. In a similar way we can associate statistical weights $(2l + 1)$ and $2s + 1 = 2$ with the orbital and spin angular momenta of a single electron. Since l, s, and j are not all independent but satisfy the relation $|l - s| \le j \le l + s$, we expect a relation among the corresponding statistical weights. This relation is

$$(2s + 1)(2l + 1) = \sum_{j=|l-s|}^{j=l+s} (2j + 1) \tag{12.9}$$

Equation (12.9) assures us that the total statistical weight associated with a given choice of the independent vectors l and s is a constant, regardless of how it is computed. On the left-hand side of (12.9) we compute it by considering l and s as independent; on the right-hand side we combine l and s in all possible ways to form j and then add the statistical weights of j. We can easily check (12.9) for the case of one electron where $s = \frac{1}{2}$ and $j = l \pm \frac{1}{2}$. For $j = l + \frac{1}{2}$, $2j + 1 = 2l + 2$; and for $j = l - \frac{1}{2}$, $2j + 1 = 2l$. Then $\sum(2j + 1) = 2l + 2 + 2l = 2(2l + 1) = (2s + 1)(2l + 1)$, as in (12.9).

The basic feature of the statistical weight factor is that it represents a sum over all m_j in a case where the property under consideration does not depend on m_j. In the example used above, the property under consideration is the state (i.e., energy eigenvalue) of individual electrons. The same argument applies to the states or energy eigenvalues of many-electron systems. If several optical electrons in an atom combine to form a state of total angular momentum J, its statistical weight is $(2J + 1)$. In L-S coupling, relation (12.9) holds among L, S, and J. An alternative statement is that the statistical weight factor represents the degree of degeneracy of the energy levels. In the absence of external fields the energy levels do not depend on M_J, so that a level of spin J is $(2J + 1)$-fold degenerate. Summing over all individual states in this degeneracy produces the statistical factor $(2J + 1)$.

Another property of atomic systems that does not depend on M_J is the probability for radiative transitions of the electrons. Suppose that an atom is in a multiplet state with quantum numbers J, M_J. It can emit a photon and go to another multiplet state having quantum numbers J', $M_{J'}$. The selection rules allow $J' = J$, $J \pm 1$ and $M_{J'} = M_J$,

$M_J \pm 1$. The total transition probability from the initial state will involve the sum of squared matrix elements like those in (10.85) over all possible values of J' and M_J'. It turns out that this sum is independent of M_J. Thus if we sum over all M_J also, we have the result that the total transition probability to all possible final states is proportional to $(2J + 1)$, the statistical weight of the initial state. The matrix elements (10.85) are certainly symmetric between the initial and the final states, which is equivalent to the statement that all quantum mechanical processes are *reversible*. Hence by the above argument in reverse the total transition probability to a single final state J' from all possible initial states of a multiplet is proportional to $(2J' + 1)$, the statistical weight of the final state.

In quantum mechanics the intensity of electric dipole radiation is proportional not only to the matrix element squared but also to $\omega_{nn'}{}^4 \sim \nu^4$, where ν is the frequency of the emitted photon. Thus the relative intensities of the different lines in a multiplet will be slightly affected by their different frequencies; these frequency differences are relatively small ($\Delta\nu \ll \nu$), however. Hence we can neglect this dependence and in first approximation compute the relative intensities of multiplet lines on the basis of the statistical weight factors alone. We have then the rule for transitions between two multiplet states denoted by i (initial) and f (final):

> the sum of intensities of all transitions arriving at a state of quantum number J_f in the final multiplet is proportional to the statistical weight $(2J_f + 1)$; the sum of intensities of all transitions from a state of quantum number J_i in the initial multiplet is proportional to the statistical weight $(2J_i + 1)$ $\qquad$ (12.10)

These so-called "sum rules" are not in general sufficient to determine the relative intensities of lines within a multiplet. They are useful in analysis of spectral measurements, however, where they help in identifying the various members of a given multiplet. In cases of special simplicity, the sum rules alone will specify the relative intensities of transitions. For example, consider the transitions from ^2D to ^2P states. Here $J_i = \frac{3}{2}, \frac{5}{2}$, and $J_f = \frac{1}{2}, \frac{3}{2}$. Call the intensities of the $\frac{5}{2} \to \frac{3}{2}$, $\frac{3}{2} \to \frac{3}{2}$, and $\frac{3}{2} \to \frac{1}{2}$ transitions A, B, and C, respectively. The sum rules state that

$$(A + B)/C = (2 \times \tfrac{3}{2} + 1)/(2 \times \tfrac{1}{2} + 1) = 2,$$

$$A/(B + C) = (2 \times \tfrac{5}{2} + 1)/(2 \times \tfrac{3}{2} + 1) = \tfrac{3}{2}.$$

From this we have $A:B:C = 9:1:5$. These intensities are representative of all doublet transitions: the two lines with $\Delta J = 1$ are the strongest, and that with $\Delta J = 0$ is much weaker. In an instrument of only moderate resolution and sensitivity, this weak "satellite" line would be masked by the nearer strong line, and the observation would reveal only two lines of apparent relative intensity $(9 + 1)/5 = 2:1$. This is why the notation doublet, triplet, $\cdots$ has remained for these multiplets, even though they ultimately appear to consist of more than two, three, $\cdots$ lines. Only two, three, $\cdots$ lines of the multiplet are relatively intense, and the rest appear as satellites.

12.6. j-j coupling in complex spectra

Some points in the previous sections suggest that the quantum number j of the individual electron has some validity in complex atoms. The X-ray subshells show a definite dependence upon this quantum number. The inversion of the ground state from $J = L - S$ in subshells that are less than half filled to $J = L + S$ in subshells that are more than half filled can be traced to interaction between the l and s vectors of each individual electron. It is just this interaction that gives rise to the validity of j as a quantum number. Accordingly, we review briefly here the features of j-j coupling in complex spectra. This type of coupling is less prevalent than L-S coupling but is by no means unknown.

The j-j scheme follows whenever the strongest coupling forces among the optical electrons are those between l_i and s_i, the orbital and spin vectors of the same (ith) electron. This occurs when the force binding the electrons to the nucleus is stronger than the forces acting between

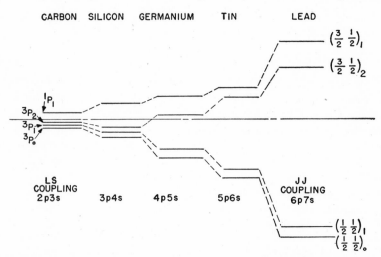

Fig. 12.5. Progression from L-S to j-j coupling. (From H. E. White, *Introduction to Atomic Spectra*, New York, McGraw-Hill, 1934).

the electrons themselves; i.e., when the effective nuclear charge Z_{eff} is large. Thus optical j-j coupling is most favored for heavy elements; and for a given atom the significance of j as a quantum number is greatest for the inner shells, as indicated by X-ray data. The vector model picture is that for each electron l_i and s_i precess rapidly about their resultant j_i. The j_i then add to make a total resultant J, about which they precess more slowly. For several electrons in j-j coupling the notation is not so convenient as in L-S coupling; we must specify each individual j value as well as the total $J : (j_1 j_2 \cdots j_n)_J$.

We illustrate j-j coupling with atoms having two optical electrons, where the j-j and L-S notations are equally simple. Consider, for example, the first excited states of the elements that have two p-electrons in their ground states: C, Si, Ge, Sn, Pb. This first excited state consists of one s-electron and one p-electron. In L-S coupling they can form states ${}^3P_{0, 1, 2}$ and ${}^1P_1$; in j-j coupling they can form states $(\frac{1}{2}, \frac{1}{2})_{0, 1}$ and $(\frac{1}{2}, \frac{3}{2})_{1, 2}$. The total selection of J values is the same in each case, but they are differently distributed. In L-S coupling the triplet levels have relative spacings in accord with the interval rule (11.19), and the singlet level is separated from them by a much wider interval. In j-j coupling the pattern comprises two narrow doublets separated by a relatively wide interval. The progression from good L-S coupling in C to relatively good j-j coupling in Pb is illustrated in Fig. 12.5. The intermediate elements show an intermediate coupling that is neither pure L-S nor pure j-j.

The selection rules for radiation are independent of the coupling scheme. For j-j coupling they remain as in (11.14):

$$\Delta J = 0, \pm 1 \qquad \text{(0 to 0 excluded)}$$
$$\Delta M = 0, \pm 1 \tag{12.11}$$

For the individual j's we add the selection rules

$$\Delta j_i = 0, \pm 1$$
$$\Delta m_{j_i} = 0, \pm 1 \tag{12.12}$$
$$\Delta j_k = \Delta m_{j_k} = 0 \qquad \text{for } k \neq i$$

That is, only one electron at most changes its quantum numbers in a strict j-j transition. The relative intensities of transitions between members of j-j multiplets also satisfy the sum rules (12.10). The detailed intensity relations of the various transitions turn out to be different for j-j and for L-S coupling, however. The intensity relations provide another means of distinguishing experimentally between j-j and L-S coupling.

Various forms of intermediate coupling are possible. If more than two optical electrons are present, the so-called J-j coupling may obtain. In an excited state, one electron may carry all or most of the excitation energy; it therefore couples rather loosely to the other electrons and its l and s vectors combine to form its total angular momentum j. The remaining electrons, however, have little or no excitation energy and form a resultant J' by L-S coupling. The vectors J' and j then combine to form the total resultant angular momentum J of the atom. This situation is referred to as J-j coupling and is observed, for example, in the excited states of the inert gases, neon, argon, krypton, and xenon.

Any form of j-j coupling leads to an anomalous Zeeman pattern in a magnetic field. The observed lines follow by the selection rules given above; in particular, $\Delta M_J = \pm 1$ corresponds to emitted light that is polarized circularly about the axis of B, and $\Delta M_J = 0$ to light linearly polarized in the direction of the field. We compute the separations of the allowed lines in the Zeeman pattern as in the examples given for L-S coupling, except that the g factors depend entirely on the type of coupling assumed. For pure j-j coupling, a derivation similar to that for L-S coupling yields (illustrative problem 2, Chapter 11)

$$ g_J = \frac{1}{2}\left\{ (g_1 + g_2) + (g_1 - g_2)\frac{[j_1(j_1 + 1) - j_2(j_2 + 1)]}{J(J + 1)} \right\} \quad (12.13) $$

where g_1 and g_2 are the respective g factors appropriate to the angular momenta j_1 and j_2 which combine to make up the total angular momentum J. This form applies whether the momentum j_1 is that of a single electron (in which case $j_1 = l_1 \pm \frac{1}{2}$) or whether j_1 is the resultant of several electrons in L-S coupling, as appears in the case of J-j coupling. In this latter case g_1 is given by (11.23).

12.7. Coupling in strong external fields

We have seen that in an external magnetic field each component in a multiplet spectral line splits into a separate Zeeman pattern, the total width of which is directly proportional to B. The spread of the Zeeman patterns is usually much smaller than the separation between the lines of the multiplet. However, it is possible to produce strong magnetic fields in which the spread of the Zeeman patterns is so large that the patterns from a single multiplet would overlap. In this case a new phenomenon occurs: the combined Zeeman pattern of the lines of a multiplet gradually approaches, in a strong magnetic field, the pattern corresponding to the normal Zeeman effect of a singlet line. For instance, the doublet of the principal series of an alkali splits up into ten lines in a weak magnetic field. As the field strength is increased, the ten lines gradually "bunch" together into three groups and finally unite into three single lines with equal separations and polarization corresponding to a normal Zeeman effect. This phenomenon is called the Paschen-Back effect. It arises from the circumstance that a strong magnetic field is able to overcome the interaction forces responsible for spin-orbit coupling.

We can interpret this transition simply in terms of the vector model. In a weak field, the energy of the magnetic interaction between the spin and orbital motions of the electrons (symbolized by vectors S and L) is much greater than the energy of interaction between either of these motions (vectors) and the magnetic induction B. Thus we can consider the L and S vectors as precessing rapidly about their resultant J, which in turn precesses more slowly about B, giving rise to the anomalous Zeeman effect discussed in Chapter 11.

As we increase the strength of B, its interaction energy with S and with L increases proportionately until it greatly exceeds the interaction between S and L. Then the S and L vectors precess rapidly and independently about the direction of B. We say that the action of the strong external field has uncoupled the spin and orbital motions. Now the energy term of a given configuration depends on the two separate quantum numbers M and M_S, since S and L represent independent motions:

$$E' = E + \mu_0 g_L BM + \mu_0 g_S BM_S = E + \mu_0 B(M + 2M_S) \quad (12.14)$$

Here the g factors have their usual values, $g_L = 1$, $g_S = 2$. Of course the value of $(M + M_S)$ in the strong field equals the M_J value of the corresponding weak-field configuration. The selection rules for transitions in this case are

$$\Delta M_S = 0 \quad\quad\quad\quad\quad (12.15)$$

corresponding to the selection rule (11.14), $\Delta S = 0$, and

$$\Delta M = 0, \pm 1 \quad\quad\quad\quad\quad (12.16)$$

with the usual rule $\Delta L = \pm 1$. That is, since uncoupling of L and S has destroyed the vector J, the selection rules are just those appropriate to L and S independently.

From these selection rules it is clear why the Paschen-Back effect shows a "normal" Zeeman pattern. Since neither S nor M_S can change during a transition, the atom behaves as if it had no electron spin but only an L vector, at least as far as the transition frequencies are concerned. But this is exactly the case that corresponds to the normal Zeeman effect as in (11.31).

Actually, the approach to a normal Zeeman pattern for strong fields is not quite perfect; even though the L and S vectors precess independently about B, there is still a certain average interaction energy between them, which has the form

$$\Delta E = -\lambda M M_s \tag{12.17}$$

Here λ is the same constant as appears in (11.18), expressing the strength of interaction forces between the magnetic moments associated with L and S. The additional ΔE is small relative to E', but from its form we see that the observed line shift will depend on M_s when $M = \pm 1$, but will be independent of M_s when $M = 0$. Thus the central (π) line of the strong field pattern will be a single line, but the two side lines (σ) will split into $(2S + 1)$ equally spaced lines, where $(2S + 1)$ is the number of different possible values for M_s and is hence the multiplicity of the original multiplet in the absence of a magnetic field. The splitting of the σ lines is much narrower than the total spread of the total strong-field pattern, however, so that to first order it is still proper to describe it simply as a "normal" pattern.

Between the weak-field (Zeeman) and the strong-field (Paschen-Beck) regions is a transition region where the coupling between B and L or B and S is of the same order of magnitude as that between L and S. This corresponds to the case where the spread of the Zeeman pattern would about equal the multiplet spacing. The line structure in the transition region is quite complicated.

The Paschen-Back effect also occurs for j-j coupling. If we apply a strong field B to an atom containing two optical electrons in j-j coupling, the interactions between j_1 and B and between j_2 and B become stronger than between j_1 and j_2. Accordingly these vectors become uncoupled and precess independently about B. The energy of a level now depends on m_{j_1} and m_{j_2} separately:

$$E' = E + \mu_0 g_1 B m_{j_1} + u_0 g_2 B m_{j_2} \tag{12.18}$$

In this case g_1 and g_2 do not have simple integral values, and the transition may be either $\Delta m_{j_1} = 0, \pm 1$ or $\Delta m_{j_2} = 0, \pm 1$. Therefore in j-j coupling even the Paschen-Back pattern shows no general regularities. There is an additional term similar to (12.17), representing residual j-j coupling:

$$\Delta E' = -\lambda' m_{j_1} m_{j_2} \tag{12.19}$$

Here λ' is not generally equal to the λ of (12.17).

With an even stronger magnetic induction we could in principle produce the *complete* Paschen-Back effect. That is, all the l and s vectors of the individual electrons become uncoupled and precess independently about B. There is no longer L-S or j-j coupling, because none of the vectors J, L, S, j_1, or j_2 has constant magnitude in this strong field. The selection rules are that $\Delta s = 0$ for all electrons, and $\Delta l = \Delta m = 0$ for all electrons but one, which has $\Delta l = \pm 1$, $\Delta m = 0, \pm 1$ with the usual rules about polarization. This is once again a situation that leads to a normal Zeeman pattern: i.e., where the transition involves a change of l and m only, not of j and m_j. There are now many small correction terms corresponding to the interaction of each pair of s vectors, l vectors, and l-s pairs. Because of these small terms, each of the three main lines (σ-π-σ) of the "normal" pattern splits into a number of components; moreover, the spacings between these components vary according to whether j-j or L-S or some intermediate coupling ordinarily exists.

SUMMARY

Comparison of the ground states of successive elements in the periodic table allows the assignment of individual quantum numbers to the successive electrons. The ground states configurations $^1S_0$ represent closed shells or subshells of electrons. The optical electrons of an atom or ion generally are only those outside of closed subshells. These electrons are also responsible for chemical valence. To judge from valence properties, the most tightly closed subshells occur for the noble gases He, Ne, A, Kn, Xe and Rn. For the first two rows of the periodic table in Fig. 1.1 the optical electrons are filling s-subshells; in the next six rows they are filling p-subshells; for the two long periods they are filling d-subshells; and for the rare earths they fill an f-subshell.

From the buildup of the periodic table, the s-, p-, d-, f-subshells appear to be filled by 2, 6, 10, and 14 electrons, respectively. This is just the number of possible different m and m_s values for electrons with a given value of l. The spin projection can have two values, $m_s = \pm\frac{1}{2}$; and $-l \le m \le l$, so that m can assume $(2l + 1)$ different values. The total number of different values is $2(2l + 1) = 2, 6, 10, 14$, for $l = 0$, 1, 2, 3, $\cdots$. This rule for filling of subshells directly implies an *exclusion principle*: no two electrons in an atomic system can have all quantum numbers the same. The repetition of p-subshells, etc., corresponds to different values of the principal quantum number n. The electron in an atom has four independent quantum numbers, to which the exclusion principle applies; they are $nlmm_s$ or $nljm_j$.

The build-up of the periodic table and the exclusion principle make it clear that the $K, L, M, \cdots$ shells discussed in X-ray spectra correspond to shells formed by electrons with principal quantum number $n = 1, 2, 3, \cdots$. The subshells I, II, III, IV, V, $\cdots$ correspond to $s_{1/2}$, $p_{1/2}$, $p_{3/2}$, $d_{3/2}$, $d_{5/2}$, $\cdots$ electrons, where the subscript is the value of j. The selection rules for X-rays are the same as for optical spectra: $\Delta l = \pm 1$, $\Delta j = 0, \pm 1$. The exclusion principle explains why X-ray absorption edges are at higher frequencies than the corresponding emission lines. The K emission lines, for example, represent electron jumps from the L shell to an unfilled position previously excited in the K shell. On X-ray absorption, the L shell is normally filled, however, and the K electron must jump to a higher energy level, corresponding practically to ionization of the atom.

Electrons with the same n and l values in an atom are *equivalent*. Because of the exclusion principle equivalent electrons cannot attain all the total L and S values that the vector model would allow. Taking these limitations into account, we can give simple rules for the L, S, and J values of atomic ground states: S has its maximum value, L the maximum consistent with S, and $J = L - S$ if the shell is less than half filled, $J = L + S$ if the shell is more than half filled. This difference is caused by a tendency towards j-j coupling.

Many phenomena, such as the probability of a radiative transition, do not depend on the value of M_J. Thus when we sum over all possible M_J values, a *statistical weight* factor of $(2J + 1)$ appears. Statistical weight factors occur in all quantum mechanical transitions. They lead to intensity sum rules for lines in a multiplet: the sum of all intensities arriving at a state of total angular momentum J_f is proportional to $(2J_f + 1)$; the sum of intensities leaving a state J_i is proportional to $(2J_i + 1)$. These rules do not completely determine the multiplet intensities except in special cases, but are useful as conditions that any supposed multiplet must follow.

Although L-S coupling is predominant in atoms, there is some tendency to j-j coupling, which increases for heavier atoms. The selection rules for optical transitions are $\Delta J = 0, \pm 1$ (no $0 \leftrightarrow 0$), $\Delta M_J = 0, \pm 1$, where J, M_J are the quantum numbers of the whole atom. The same rules apply to one electron, while the rest have $\Delta j = \Delta m_j = 0$.

A very strong magnetic induction $\boldsymbol{B}$ produces the Paschen-Back effect, in which the $\boldsymbol{L}$ and $\boldsymbol{S}$ vectors are decoupled from each other and precess independently about $\boldsymbol{B}$. Spectroscopically, the Zeeman patterns become so broad that they overlap the multiplet splitting. As the field strength increases, the spectral pattern tends to approach the normal Zeeman pattern. This is true for L-S coupling but not for j-j, although it would be true in the extreme case where all the $\boldsymbol{l}$ and $\boldsymbol{s}$ vectors of individual electrons are decoupled and precess independently about $\boldsymbol{B}$.

REFERENCES

G. Herzberg, *Atomic Spectra and Atomic Structure*, Dover (1945).

A. Sommerfeld, *Atomic Structure and Spectral Lines*, Methuen, London (1923).

H. E. White, *Introduction to Atomic Spectra*, McGraw-Hill, New York (1934).

ILLUSTRATIVE PROBLEMS

1. Show that an atom with $J = 0$ cannot have any magnetic moment, regardless of the individual values of L and S.

Solution. We may use a geometric or an algebraic argument. Geometrically, the vector model tells us that in quantum mechanics the only measurable component of the magnetic moment $\boldsymbol{\mu}$ is its projection along the direction of J. The component of $\boldsymbol{\mu}$ perpendicular to J precesses about J and averages to zero. Now when $J = 0$, there is no vector J and therefore no component of $\boldsymbol{\mu}$ parallel to J; hence there is no measurable component of $\boldsymbol{\mu}$. Algebraically, we can suppose the total $J = 0$ to be composed of the vector sum of j_1 and j_2, with associated g factors. In order to make $J = 0$, the rules of vector addition require that $j_1 = j_2 = j$.

Then the measurable magnetic moment is, using (12.13)

$$\mu = \mu_0 J g_J = \frac{\mu_0}{2}\left[(g_1 + g_2)J + (g_1 - g_2)(j_1 - j_2)\frac{(j_1 + j_2 + 1)}{(J + 1)} \right] = 0$$

since $J = j_1 - j_2 = 0$.

The conclusion that $J = 0$ implies no magnetic moment is perfectly general and rigorous, applying to all quantum mechanical systems.

2. Prove Eq. (12.9) for integer l and s.

Solution. We use the mathematical formula for the sum over all the integers from 1 to n, $S(n) = \sum_1^n x = n(n + 1)/2$. The sum over all even integers from 2 to $2n$ is $E(n) = \sum_2^{2n} x = 2S(n) = n(n + 1)$. The sum over all odd integers from 1 to $2n + 1$ is $O(n) = S(2n + 1) - E(n) = (n + 1)^2$. In terms of the quantity O we have.

$$\sum(2j + 1) = O(l + s) - O(|l - s| - 1)$$
$$= (l + s + 1)^2 - (l - s)^2$$
$$= 4ls + 2l + 2s + 1 = (2l + 1)(2s + 1)$$

3. Show that the number and variety of total J values for two electrons is the same in L-S and in j-j coupling. From this result we can extrapolate to the general conclusion that the distribution of J values for any number of electrons is independent of the coupling scheme L-S, j-j or intermediate. This conclusion remains valid when the exclusion principle is taken into account.

Solution. Consider two electrons of orbital angular momenta l_1 and l_2; neglect the exclusion principle. In L-S coupling, the total L value can run from $|l_1 - l_2| = l$ to $l_1 + l_2 = l'$. For the singlet term $S = 0$ and

$J = L$, so that j runs from l to l'. For the triplet terms $S = 1$, and the L and S vectors can have three relative orientations in a quantum mechanical vector diagram: approximately "parallel," "perpendicular," and "antiparallel." Then j runs from $l + 1$ to $l' + 1$ when they are "parallel," from l to l' when "perpendicular," from $|l - 1|$ to $l' - 1$ when "antiparallel." Thus the assortment of j values in L-S coupling is the following: $|l - 1|$ and $l' + 1$ occur once, l and l' occur 3 times; and each value from $l + 1$ to $l' - 1$ occurs 4 times.

In j-j coupling we first form j_1 and j_2. When $j_1 = l_1 + \frac{1}{2}$, $j_2 = l_2 + \frac{1}{2}$, j runs from $|j_1 - j_2| = l$ to $j_1 + j_2 = l' + 1$. When $j_1 = l_1 - \frac{1}{2}$, $j_2 = l_2 - \frac{1}{2}$, j runs from $|j_1 - j_2| = l$ to $j_1 + j_2 = l' - 1$. The two remaining cases are $j_1 = l_1 \pm \frac{1}{2}$, $j_2 = l_2 \pm \frac{1}{2}$. Of these cases $|j_1 - j_2| = l + 1$ in one case, and is $|l - 1|$ in the other case; $j_1 + j_2 = l'$ in both cases. Thus the assortment of j values in j-j coupling is the following: $|l - 1|$ and $l' + 1$ occur once; l and l' occur 3 times; and each value from $l + 1$ to $l' - 1$ occurs 4 times. This is just the same distribution as found for L-S coupling. This distribution is therefore independent of the coupling scheme for two electrons; the results can be generalized as indicated in the first paragraph.

PROBLEMS

1. (a) Prove Eq. (12.9) in case l is an integer, s is a half integer.
(b) Prove Eq. (12.9) in case both l and s are half integers.

2. Show that the total number of electrons in a filled shell is $2n^2$, where n is the principal quantum number of that shell.

3. Two electrons with the same orbital momentum l can combine to give a maximum angular momentum $J = 2l + 1$. Show that if the electrons are equivalent, this value of J is excluded.

4. Show that by the exclusion principle a shell containing $2(2l + 1)$ equivalent electrons must be in a $^1S_0$ state.

5. The ground states of the successive elements Sr to Cd are the following: $^1S_0$, $^2D_{3/2}$, $^3F_2$, $^6D_{1/2}$, $^7S_3$, $^6S_{5/2}$, $^5F_5$, $^4F_{9/2}$, $^1S_0$, $^2S_{1/2}$, $^1S_0$. Using the rules (12.8), carry through an analysis like that of section 4 of the text, attempting to determine what are the corresponding electron configurations.

6. Suppose a doublet transition $l \to l' = l - 1$, in which the line $j = l + \frac{1}{2} \to j' = l' + \frac{1}{2}$ is labeled A, $j = l - \frac{1}{2} \to j' = l' + \frac{1}{2}$ is labeled B, and $j = l - \frac{1}{2} \to j' = l' - \frac{1}{2}$ is labeled C. Using the sum rules (12.10), show that the relative intensities are $A:B:C = (2l' + 1)(l + 1):1:$ $(2l + 1)l'$. Therefore although the compound doublet actually contains three lines, one of them (B) is very weak and appears as a "satellite" or a strong doublet.

7. The element $_{41}$Nb has five electrons outside the krypton configuration. The preceding element $_{40}$Zr with 4 outside electrons has as lowest spectral term $^3F_2$, indicating that two electrons are $(5s)$ and the other two electrons are $(4d)$. In the lowest term of Nb, is a ^6D term compatible with the assumption that two of the electrons are $(5s)$, and the remaining three are $(4d)$?

8. To see the effects of the exclusion principle, fill out the first part of Fig. 12.3 for the case of nonequivalent p electrons, from p^0 to p^4.

9. (a) Draw a diagram depicting the energy levels of a ^3P triplet in L-S coupling, and their behavior in weak and strong magnetic fields. The following procedure may be used:
- (i) With no external field, the triplet spacing is that of (11.18).
- (ii) In a weak magnetic field, the splitting of each level of the triplet is given by (11.28).
- (iii) in a strong magnetic field, use (12.14) and (12.17).

To connect the magnetic sublevels in a weak field with the corresponding sublevels in a strong field, the following rules are sufficient:
- (i) The total $M_J = M_S + M$ is the same for weak and strong fields.
- (ii) Levels of the same M_J never cross in going from weak to strong fields.

(b) Repeat this procedure on a $^3S_1$ level.

(c) Using the results of (a) and (b) show how the three weak-field Zeeman patterns $^3S_1 - {}^3P_0$, $^3S_1 - {}^3P_1$, $^3S_1 - {}^3P_2$ go over into a Paschen-Back pattern in a strong field. Show that the Paschen-Back pattern has the general features of a normal Zeeman pattern: a central line polarized parallel (π) to $\boldsymbol{B}$ and two equally spaced lines on either side, which are polarized perpendicular (σ) to $\boldsymbol{B}$. The side lines in this case are split into three narrowly spaced components. The selection rules for the Paschen-Back effect are (12.15) and (12.16), with the additional feature that $\Delta M = 0$ is a π line, $\Delta M = \pm 1$ are σ lines.

10. The theorem discussed in illustrative problem 3 makes it possible to deduce from Fig. 12.3 the J values allowed for equivalent electrons in j-j coupling. Find the J values for two equivalent $p_{3/2}$ electrons as follows: for two p electrons in L-S coupling the J values given by Fig. 12.3 are $J = 0^2, 1, 2^2$, where 0^2 means two different $J = 0$ states ($^1S_0$ and $^3P_0$), etc.

The two equivalent p-electrons can be $(p_{1/2})^2$, $p_{1/2}\, p_{3/2}$, or $(p_{3/2})^2$. In j-j coupling two equivalent $p_{1/2}$-electrons are like two equivalent $s_{1/2}$-electrons, which can make only a $^1S_0$ state. Since $p_{1/2}$ and $p_{3/2}$ are not equivalent, they are not limited by the exclusion principle and can form all the J values allowed by the vector model. Any of the J values found in $L\text{-}S$ coupling not included in $(p_{1/2})^2$ and $p_{1/2}\,p_{3/2}$ must be attributed to $(p_{3/2})^2$.

(a) Show in this way that two equivalent $p_{3/2}$-electrons can have $J = 0, 2$ only.

(b) Extend the procedure to show that $(p_{3/2})^3$ has $J = \frac{3}{2}$ only.

(c) Show that $(p_{3/2})^4$ has $J = 0$ only.

(d) Show that two equivalent $d_{5/2}$-electrons have $J = 0, 2, 4$. For this purpose, note that in $j\text{-}j$ coupling, the J values of $(d_{3/2})^2$ and $(p_{3/2})^2$ are the same.

Part III

FURTHER APPLICATIONS OF THE THEORY

Atomic physics *per se* is in a sense a closed field: nobody feels any doubt that the electronic properties of individual atoms can be entirely explained by the principles discussed in Part II. On the other hand, the theory of quantum mechanics ought to apply to a wide range of natural phenomena, in spite of being specifically invented to explain the isolated atom. Part III (Chapters 13–14) surveys a few of these applications.

It is fair to say that the major activity in modern physics has been along lines that involve extension and application of the principles of quantum mechanics. One of these lines is the study of macroscopic matter, which requires in particular the development of a quantum statistical mechanics. The study of nuclear physics has also received great emphasis: it has the intriguing feature that although the general principles of quantum mechanics seem to apply, the specific details of nuclear forces and nuclear structure remain yet largely unknown.

Chapter 13

MODERN DEVELOPMENTS

Electron spin and the exclusion principle complete the list of basic physical concepts discovered in the realm of atomic physics. There still remain some complex optical spectra to unravel, but these now appear mainly as difficult exercises in the application of principles already discussed. No one expects new, fundamental insights into the principles of physics to come from such studies. Recent development of atomic physics has therefore consisted in application and extension of its ideas and methods to further fields, notably to the study of the atomic nucleus. On the theoretical side the notions of relativistic invariance, the uncertainty principle, wave functions, quantized angular momentum and intrinsic spin, associated magnetic moments, and the exclusion principle have all been taken over quite successfully into nuclear physics. On the experimental side many of the techniques originally developed for atomic studies have proved useful in nuclear studies as well. The atom today is well enough understood to serve as a laboratory for investigation of the less well-explored nucleus. This is an example of a process frequently repeated in the development of physics: a subject originally investigated for its own sake becomes so well analyzed that it can serve in turn as a powerful tool in further investigations.

We cannot hope to give a detailed account here of all the modern physics that is based ultimately on experience gained in atomic physics. A few selected examples are presented to show some applications of atomic techniques that have been of recent interest.

13.1. Isotopic mass and "atomic" energy

The techniques of deflecting charged particles in electric and magnetic fields first found application in atomic physics to the measurement of e/m, the specific charge on the electron. The enormous value of this specific charge as compared with that of ions was an important fact in establishing the independent existence of the electron as a subunit of the atom. The techniques are also applicable to determination of the ionic or hence nuclear masses, since the ionic charges q are known. We have discussed in Chapter 3 the principles of the mass spectrograph, an instrument for the precision measurement of nuclear masses. With the mass doublet method, accuracy to 5 or 6 significant figures is not unusual.

Such measurements reveal that most elements have several *isotopes*, in which the nuclei have the same charge $+Ze$, but different masses. These masses are close to integer values in amu, so that we can specify the different isotopes by mass numbers A. The different isotopes of an element all have identical electronic structures, so that we can ignore their differences in discussing problems of atomic physics. For nuclear physics, however, we must consider the isotopic differences as an essential fact.

The first problem is the source of the isotopic mass differences. For nuclei observed in nature, the ratio of A/Z varies from 2.0 among light elements to about 2.5 among the heaviest elements. An exception is the "ordinary" or lightest isotope of hydrogen, which has $A = Z = 1$. It is natural to assume that this hydrogen nucleus with a charge of one unit $(+e)$ and mass close to 1 amu is one of the building blocks of heavier nuclei. It is called the *proton*. If nuclei consisted exclusively of protons, we should find that $Z = A$ for all nuclei. Hence all nuclei heavier than ordinary hydrogen have other constituents besides protons. We could, for example, postulate that heavier nuclei contain A protons and $(A - Z)$ electrons, so that the total mass will be A amu and the total charge $+Ze$. Considerations of quantum mechanical principles like those of Chapter 10, problem 3, indicate that so small a volume as the nucleus could not ordinarily contain an electron. It is therefore necessary to postulate the existence of a second nuclear particle, the *neutron*. The neutron also has a mass of 1 amu and generally resembles the proton, except that it has no electric charge. Abundant experimental evidence now supports the existence of the neutron. No other particles like these *nucleons* (a generic term to include neutron and proton) appear in nuclei, so that there is no doubt that an isotope of mass number A and charge number Z contains Z protons and $A - Z = N$ neutrons. The rule that $Z/A \lesssim \frac{1}{2}$ means that nuclei generally have about equal numbers of neutrons and protons, with an increasing preponderance of neutrons for heavier elements.

As Eq. (3.26) indicates, the masses of isotopes derived from precision mass spectroscopy are not exactly integers in amu. Actually, a nucleus of mass number A has a somewhat smaller mass than the total of its constituent neutrons and protons. These mass defects provide direct experimental proof of the mass-energy relation (8.44), $E = Mc^2$. Consider, for example, the nucleus of heavy hydrogen (deuterium), $_1\text{H}^2$, which consists of a neutron and a proton bound together. This deuteron (neutron plus proton) normally resides in a ground state of lowest energy. The energy is quantized and hence has a definite, discrete value U_0. Since the system is bound, U_0 is negative. The corresponding binding energy $B_0 = -U_0 = |U_0|$ is the minimum energy necessary to split the deuteron into a free neutron and a free proton. We can make these statements without knowing the details of the specific nuclear forces holding the deuteron together.

If we use $E = Mc^2$ for the rest-mass energies of the nucleons, the total energy of the deuteron is

$$E_d = M_n c^2 + M_p c^2 - B_0 \qquad (13.1)$$

where M_n, M_p are the neutron and proton masses, respectively. For a deuteron at rest we should have the inverse relationship for the deuteron mass,

$$M_d = E_d/c^2 = M_n + M_p - B_0/c^2 \qquad (13.1a)$$

Thus the deuteron should have a mass defect of B_0/c^2. Direct measurement of the ionization potential by the photoelectric effect shows that $B_0 = 2.23$ mev. The corresponding mass defect is $M_n + M_p - M_d = 0.00239$ amu. Within experimental error the ratio of these two quantities is just equal to $c^2 = 9.0 \times 10^{20}$ (cm/sec)^2, thus providing direct proof for the equivalence (8.45) of mass and energy. Of course a similar reduction in the mass of an atom occurs because of the binding energies B_i of the electrons, but this reduction is generally too small to measure directly as a mass defect. The conversion factor from mass to energy is

$$1 \text{ amu} = 931 \text{ mev} \qquad (13.2)$$

The deviations of nuclear masses from exact integral values in amu are expressible by means of the *packing fraction*,

$$f = \frac{M - A}{A} \qquad (13.3)$$

Here M is the actual nuclear mass in amu, and A is the nearest integer. Since f is generally on the order of 10^{-4}, it is customary to quote values of $10^4 f$. Figure 13.1 presents a curve of this quantity, smoothed over a number of minor fluctuations. The packing fraction is positive for the lightest and heaviest isotopes and is negative for the middle-weight nuclei, from $A \approx 20$ to $A \approx 160$.

We can use the curve of Fig. 13.1 to see where the atomic bomb derives its energy. The U^{235} nucleus that absorbs a neutron and undergoes fission is most likely to split into two fragments of mass numbers approximately 95 and 140. The packing fractions from Fig. 13.1 are roughly $+5.5 \times 10^{-4}$ for the uranium, and -6.0×10^{-4} for $A = 95$, -3.0×10^{-4} for $A = 140$. Applying (13.3), we have for the mass difference of the uranium and its fission products

$$M_U - M_{95} - M_{140} = (Af)_U - (Af)_{95} - (Af)_{140}$$
$$\approx 0.23 \text{ amu} \approx 2.1 \times 10^2 \text{ mev} \qquad (13.4)$$

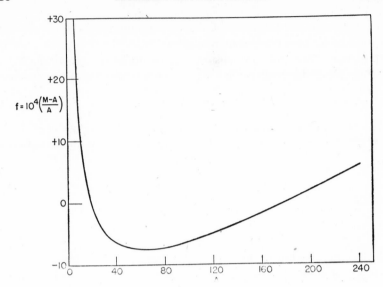

Fig. 13.1. Packing fraction as a function of atomic number A. The curve shown is an average, in which many irregularities have been smoothed out.

Therefore each uranium atom on fission liberates something on the order of 200 mev. The energy release per unit weight of fuel in this process roughly is 1 mev per amu.

The energy release in nuclear fission is enormous by comparison with chemical explosions. A chemical reaction releases energies on the order of a few ev per molecule, which is the characteristic magnitude of molecular binding energies. Thus the energy release per unit weight of fuel is on the order of a million times greater for nuclear fission than for any chemical reaction. Through a peculiar misnomer, this nuclear energy has acquired the popular designation of "atomic energy." Strictly speaking, true atomic energy is that available from electron configurations, conventionally known as chemical energy.

13.2. Nuclear spins and magnetic moments

The part of atomic quantum mechanics that deals with angular momentum should be directly transferable to nuclear systems. Although the exact nature of nuclear forces still remains a mystery, it is impossible for any forces internal to the nucleus to affect the rotational properties of the system as a whole. In the language of quantum mechanics we say that the total nuclear angular momentum I (in units of $\hbar$) is a good quantum number. The projection I_z along a particular axis is also a good quantum number. The general arguments showing that any quantized angular momentum can have only integral or half-integral values are identical in application to atomic or nuclear systems. Experiments show that the spins of both the proton and neutron are $\frac{1}{2}$. The spin I of a heavier nucleus is therefore integral or half-integral according as A is even or odd. In fact, $I = 0$ for all "even-even" nuclei in which N and Z are both even.

If the spin of a nucleus is $I = 0$, it will have no magnetic moment. Essentially this is because the magnetic moment is a vector quantity that must be associated with some "natural" vector of the nucleus, i.e., with the angular momentum. For $I = 0$ this natural vector vanishes, and so also must the magnetic moment. See illustrative problem 1 of Chapter 12. All nuclei with $I > 0$ will generally have magnetic moments. There are many such nuclei, since $I \geq \frac{1}{2}$ for odd A. The natural unit in which to measure these magnetic moments is the *nuclear magneton*,

$$\mu_N = e\hbar/2Mc \qquad (13.5)$$

where M is the mass of a nucleon. This definition is slightly ambiguous because of the mass difference of neutron and proton, but that difference of less than 0.1 % is of little importance here.

Nuclear magnetic moments are not integral or half-integral multiples of μ_N, as was the case in atomic systems. For example, the magnetic moment of the proton is $\mu_p = 2.79\mu_N$, instead of the value $\mu_p = \mu_N$ that would be expected if the proton were exactly like the electron. The magnetic moment of the neutron is $\mu_n = -1.91\,\mu_N$, which corresponds to a particle of negative charge, even though the neutron is electrically neutral. The magnetic moments of the proton and neutron indicate a compound structure for these particles, but there is at present no satisfactory understanding of this structure. Similar irrational values of the magnetic moment occur for heavier nuclei.

13.3. Hyperfine splitting

A number of methods for determining the nuclear magnetic moment and spin involve atomic principles. One method is to measure the hyperfine structure of atomic spectra. Hyperfine structure of spectral lines has been known since around 1900, soon after the development of the interferometer. In many elements the lines of the multiplet spectra, when viewed under the high resolving power of the interferometer, show further subdivision into a number of narrowly spaced components. This hyperfine spacing is generally on the order of a few tenths of wave numbers (cm^{-1}). The fine structure spacing, in comparison, is frequently on the order of 100 wave numbers. The fine structure splitting shows great variation throughout the periodic table, increasing from less than a wave number in the lightest elements to almost 10,000 wave numbers in the heaviest. The hyperfine structure shows no such variation.

The discovery of isotopes with different nuclear masses for the same element seems at first sight to provide a simple explanation for hyperfine structure. The correction for the motion of the nucleus and electron about their common center of gravity (section 9.7) would be different for different isotopes. Thus the spectrum from a natural element would be a superposition of the slightly different spectra of each isotope present. This would appear as a single spectrum with isotope hyperfine structure.

The solution of the hyperfine structure problem is a particularly simple example of the scientific method as applied in physics. By extremely precise and systematic observation, a certain regularly occurring phenomenon is discovered. A simple hypothesis is put forward to explain it, based on a mechanical model that is consistent with all other known features of the system. It next becomes necessary to verify or disprove the hypothesis by deducing its logical consequences and subjecting them to experimental test. If hyperfine structure is due solely to isotope mixtures, two obvious implications are that all lines of a single spectrum should show the same hyperfine structure, and that elements with only a single isotope should have no hyperfine structure. Experiment contradicts both these conclusions, so that we must seek another hypothesis. Another possible cause of hyperfine structure is a small magnetic moment associated with the nucleus. This hypothesis proves to be in such satisfactory agreement with experiment that we cannot doubt its validity. Characteristically, the second hypothesis does not entirely replace the earlier one, but rather complements it. The isotope effect is also undoubtedly present, but it is overshadowed by the nuclear moment effect. The name "hyperfine structure" has come to refer only to the nuclear moment effect.

If both the nucleus and the atomic electrons have magnetic moments, there will be a certain energy of interaction between them. This will make the energy of the total system somewhat different from that of the electrons alone. The difference will be small when measured in atomic units, since the magnetic moment of the nucleus is smaller than electronic moments by a factor on the order of $m/M \approx 10^{-3}$. Quantum mechanically, we must specify the energy levels of the total system not only by J for electrons but also by F, the quantum number of total angular momentum. Then F is defined from the rule for vector addition in quantum mechanics,

$$F = I + J$$
$$F = (I + J), (I + J - 1), \cdots, |J - I|$$

$$(13.6)$$

Each atomic energy level of angular momentum J accordingly splits into a number of levels with the same J but different F. There are $(2I + 1)$ or $(2J + 1)$ such levels, whichever number is smaller.

The pattern of the hyperfine structure can be determined if we know the exact law of interaction of the magnetic moments μ_I and μ_J. We obtain a simple plausibility argument for this law by returning to the old Bohr atom picture. The electron revolves in a circular orbit with the nucleus at its center. Classically, the magnetic field at the center of such a current loop is parallel to the orbital angular momentum L and in the opposite direction because the electron is negatively charged. Generalizing from this, we may expect that the induction at the nucleus due to the wave-mechanical motion of electrons with a total angular momentum J is

$$B_J = -AJ \tag{13.7}$$

where the coefficient A is independent of the orientation of J. The interaction energy with μ_I is

$$\Delta E = -\mu_I \cdot B_J = A' \cos (I, J) \tag{13.8}$$

Here A' is proportional to the magnitude of μ_I. The values of $\cos (I, J)$ allowed by quantum mechanics are as given by (11.17),

$$- \cos (I, J) = \frac{F(F + 1) - I(I + 1) - J(J + 1)}{2\sqrt{J(J + 1)} \sqrt{I(I + 1)}} \tag{13.9}$$

Since I and J are constant for a given set of hyperfine levels, we can write

$$\Delta E_F = A''[F(F + 1) - I(I + 1) - J(J + 1)] \tag{13.10}$$

The selection rules on F for optical spectra are the same as those for J, and indeed for any angular momentum,

$$\Delta F = 0, \pm1 \tag{13.11}$$

The only exception is l, for which $\Delta l = 0$ is excluded. From the observed hyperfine structure of the emission lines, we can infer the splittings ΔE_F of the original levels with the aid of (13.11). According to (13.10) the intervals between successive hyperfine levels are

$$\Delta E_F - \Delta E_{F-1} = A''2F \tag{13.12}$$

Thus the hyperfine intervals form a regularly increasing sequence, as illustrated in Fig. 13.2. The interval rule (13.12) and the relations leading up to it are exactly analogous to the arguments for the fine structure in section 11.4.

The coefficient A in (13.7) is in principle calculable from the electronic wave functions. Unfortunately, we cannot compute its value with high precision for atoms much heavier than hydrogen, because it is difficult to account accurately for the effects of the core. The algebraic sign of A follows, however, simply from vector model addition of the various l and s vectors of the individual electrons that combine to form J. Thus for I and $J > \frac{1}{2}$, the sign of the nuclear moment μ_I is found simply by observing whether the hyperfine splittings are in the order of Fig. 13.2 or inverted. The value of I comes from counting the number of hyperfine components of a level with large J; if $J > I$, this number is just $(2I + 1)$. If I or $J = \frac{1}{2}$, however, there are only two hyperfine components, and neither the sign of μ_I nor the magnitude of I is obtainable by such direct means. A determination is in principle possible from the relative intensities of the two lines, but in practice it is difficult to measure the intensities with sufficient accuracy and reliability. In no case do hyperfine measurements give a precise value for the magnitude of μ_I. They are most useful for determining the value of I and the sign of μ_I.

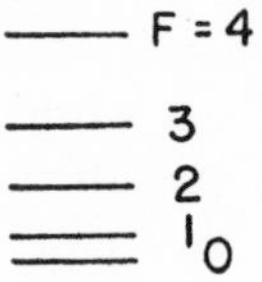

F = 4

3

2

1 **0**

Fig. 13.2. Hyperfine level structure for $J = I = 2$.

13.4. Molecular beam measurements of μ_I

Techniques first used in atomic physics have also provided the basis for a method of making precise measurements of μ_I. The molecular beam procedure of Rabi and collaborators represents a further development of the atomic beam methods of Stern and Gerlach. In order to measure directly the rather small nuclear magnetic moment in an atomic system, it is necessary that the much larger electronic moments vanish entirely. This is certain to be true only if $J = 0$, for if there is no angular momentum vector associated with the electron, there must also be no dipole moment vector. The condition $J = 0$ can be satisfied for a much wider variety of elements in molecules than in atoms, so that molecular beams are used for measurement of μ_I.

The molecular beam experiments do not use the inhomogeneous fields to determine μ_I directly. The fields provide instead a standard system; deviations of the molecular beam from this standard give the value of μ_I. The scheme of the apparatus is as shown in Fig. 13.3. The molecules emerge with thermal velocities from an oven O and pass

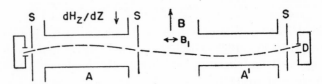

Fig. 13.3. Scheme of molecular beam experiment.

through a defining slit system S to a detector D. Along the path are two magnets A and A' that produce inhomogeneous magnetic fields such that

$$\left(\frac{dH_z}{dz}\right)_A = -\left(\frac{dH_z}{dz}\right)_{A'}$$ (13.13)

Thus a nucleus with constant component of μ_I or hence I along the z-axis will suffer equal and opposite deflections in magnets A and A', according to (3.30c). A molecule that leaves the oven with a small component of velocity in the z-direction will be deflected back to pass through the central slit S and will eventually reach the detector D. By proper adjustment of the apparatus, the beam current reading at the detector is essentially the same with the magnets A and A' both on or both off.

The detection of the beam when magnets A and A' are on depends on the fact that the z-component of μ_I remains constant throughout the path. If this component is somehow changed in the region between A and A', the deflections in the two magnets will no longer compensate, and the beam will not reach the detector. This change occurs in the following way: the space between A and A' contains a known homogeneous induction B in the z-direction. The energy of the nucleus in this induction is

$$E = -\mu_N B M_I(\mu_I/\mu_N)$$ (13.14)

where μ_N is the nuclear magneton (13.5), μ_I is the magnitude of the actual nuclear magnetic moment, and M_I is the z-component of the nuclear spin. The fact that M_I can assume only integral or half integral values is demonstrated in the original Stern-Gerlach experiment. The value of M_I can change on the emission or absorption of electromagnetic radiation. The selection rules on M_I are the usual ones for a magnetic quantum number, namely, $\Delta M_I = \pm 1$ for radiation polarized in the x- or y-direction and $\Delta M_I = 0$ for radiation polarized in the z-direction.

The energy change corresponding to $\Delta M_I = \pm 1$ is

$$|\Delta E| = \hbar\omega = \mu_N B \left|\frac{\mu_I}{\mu_N}\right|$$ (13.15)

Only the absolute magnitude of ΔE is determined, since $\pm \Delta E$ correspond to absorption and emission of a photon of angular frequency $\omega = E/\hbar$. In this case the photons are provided by a small oscillating magnetic induction B_1 in the xy-plane, which varies as $\cos \omega_1 t$. The frequency $\nu = \omega_1/2\pi$ is on the order of a few megacycles, so that the wavelength of the corresponding radiation is on the order of 100 meters. This radio-frequency region is far removed from the optical region, the original birthplace of the light quantum. Quantum mechanical principles should hold for all frequencies, however; they find verification for radio frequencies by the success of the molecular beam experiments.

A combination of all these details will yield a precision measurement of $|\mu_I|$. When the fields A, A', B, and B_1 are all on, the molecular beam will in general reach the detector, unless it happens that $\omega_1 = \omega$. In this case M_I of at least some molecules changes between A and A', so that the intensity reaching the detector diminishes. In practice it is easiest to keep ω_1 fixed and to vary the magnitude of B until the beam current passes through a minimum at B_0. The value of $|\mu_I|$ then follows from (13.15),

$$\left| \frac{\mu_I}{\mu_N} \right| = \frac{\hbar \omega_1}{B_0 \mu_N} \tag{13.16}$$

A typical transmission curve is shown in Fig. 13.4 for the measurement of F^{19}, where $|\mu_I| = 2.629\ \mu_N$.

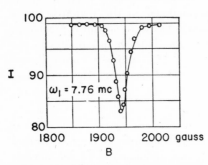

Fig. 13.4. Molecular beam resonance of F¹⁹ in NaF. The beam intensity I is in arbitrary units. (Rabi, Millman, Kusch, and Zacharias, *Phys. Rev.*, **55**, 526 (1939)).

This method can also be used to measure the proton magnetic moment. The present value is $\mu_p = +2.793$ nuclear magnetons. A similar procedure was first used by Alvarez and Bloch (1940) to measure the magnetic moment of the neutron. Two magnetized iron blocks stand in place of the inhomogeneous magnetic fields of the usual molecular beam experiment. Their magnetization is in the same direction as the intermediate uniform induction B, which we take as the z-direction. Such iron blocks act as polarizers for the neutrons, transmitting preferentially those neutrons with one value of M_I. When the intermediate induction B_0 and the frequency of the perpendicular field ω_1 satisfy the critical condition (13.16), the neutrons make transitions to the other possible value of M_I. The second iron block then discriminates against them, and a decrease in beam intensity results. The neutron magnetic moment measured by this method is -1.913 nuclear magnetons.

It is convenient to express nuclear as well as electronic magnetic moments in terms of g factors. The intrinsic moments of the neutron and proton are

$$\mathbf{\mu}_p = g_p \mu_N \mathbf{s}, \qquad g_p = 5.585$$

$$\mathbf{\mu}_n = g_n \mu_N \mathbf{s}, \qquad g_n = -3.826 \tag{13.17}$$

As in the electron case, the g factors are twice the measured μ_z because the z-component of s is of magnitude $\frac{1}{2}$.

13.5. The nuclear shell model

Chapter 12 discusses how to build up the chemical periodic table by adding successive electrons in accordance with the exclusion principle. The electrons occupy shells defined by different values of n, the principal quantum number. X-ray studies show that subshells exist in accordance with the different values of the quantum numbers l and $j = l \pm \frac{1}{2}$. A filled or "closed" shell generally does not contribute to the chemical or optical properties of an atom. This is also true to some extent of closed subshells. For instance, the failure of noble gases to form chemical compounds indicates the p-subshells are tightly closed.

Actually, there are two sets of forces among the electrons in atoms: the Coulomb force binding each electron to the central nucleus of charge $+Ze$, and the forces of mutual repulsion between pairs of electrons of charge $-e$. The quantum numbers n refer only to the central forces, and the assignment of n values is somewhat perturbed by the forces between electrons. The existence of well-defined shells indicates, however, that this perturbation is relatively small and can be neglected to a certain approximation. This is in agreement with the fact that the nuclear Coulomb force is in general much larger than that betweeen electron pairs.

The proton and neutron both have spin $\frac{1}{2}$, and like the electron obey the exclusion principle. At first sight, however, there appears to be no reason to expect shell structure in nuclei. There is no strong central force like that yielding the quantum number n in the atomic case. The entire binding energy of a nucleus comes from forces between pairs or groups of nucleons. Even if we somehow assign quantum numbers n to each nuclear orbit, we would expect the forces between nucleon pairs to mix different n values rather indiscriminately for any set of nucleons. Well-defined shells would not appear under such circumstances.

It has therefore been a recent development of great interest to discover that, in spite of all the learned arguments to the contrary, nuclei do appear to display a certain shell structure. We may attempt to understand the origin of the shells by introducing a fictitious central potential and neglecting all the interactions between nucleon pairs. That is, we somehow regard each nucleon as moving in an average field of force due to all the other nucleons, which field behaves like a central force and in which no specific pair forces are distinguishable. This model is of course a drastic oversimplification and cannot be rigorously correct. We use it at present merely on a tentative basis as being the simplest model that fits the facts, even though it appears inconsistent with other present knowledge about nucleon forces.

For the fictitious potential a number of different shapes are possible, but the most plausible choices all lead to essentially similar results. The simplest potential to treat is that of the three-dimensional harmonic oscillator. The energy levels of this potential are as shown in Fig. 13.5.

They have a principal quantum number n and an orbital angular momentum l, just as in the atomic case. For a pure oscillator these levels are equally spaced, and the higher levels become increasingly degenerate. The rule for the degeneracy is that all orbits with the same N have the same energy, where

$$N = 2n + l \qquad (13.18)$$

———— 1i, 2g, 3d, 4s

———— 1h, 2f, 3p

———— 1g, 2d, 3s

———— 1f, 2p

———— 1d, 2s

———— 1p

———— 1s

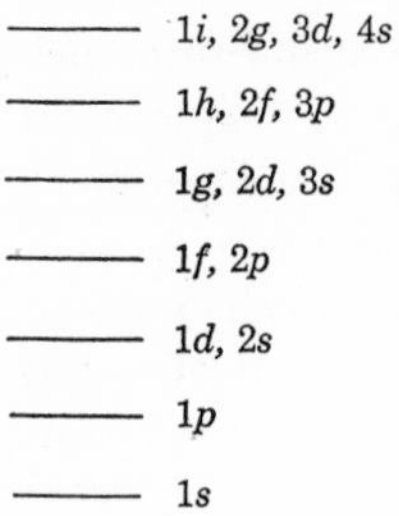

Fig. 13.5. Energy levels of a 3-dimensional harmonic oscillator.

Here $l = 0, 1, 2, \cdots$, and $n = 1, 2, 3, \cdots$, so that $N = 2, 3, 4, \cdots$.

We can hardly expect the fictitious potential to be a perfect oscillator potential, and there is accordingly a splitting of the degenerate levels. Observations show that in any set of levels of given N, the levels of smallest n and largest l lie lowest. As in the electron case, we may next look for a splitting of the levels of given l according to $j = l \pm \frac{1}{2}$. In atomic levels this splitting, due to coupling of the orbital momentum l and particle spin s, is relatively small. In nuclear levels, on the contrary, this spin-orbit splitting appears to be of dominant importance. It approaches the spacing between levels of different N and frequently exceeds the splitting between levels of the same N.

There is at present no good theoretical basis for the model discussed above. Its validity as a description of the lowest energy levels of nuclei rests on a large amount of empirical evidence. Certain isotopes show properties of exceptional stability and are therefore analogous to the noble gases in the atomic case. Such isotopes occur whenever either N or Z is one of the "magic numbers" 2, 8, 14, 20, 28, 50, 82, 126. These numbers must represent the closing of shells or subshells; since there are two kinds of nuclear particles, each type forms shells of its own that behave as if they were relatively independent of the other type of particle. The existence of these shells is support for strong spin-orbit level splitting. All the prominent magic numbers above 8 (except 20) are due to an orbit from the N energy level group that has been lowered by spin-orbit splitting until it lies in the neighborhood of the $(N - 1)$ level group. The energy level order is shown in Fig. 13.6. It should be emphasized that this order is qualitative only, and that there may be a good deal of crossing and recrossing of levels within a single shell, especially among the higher shells. The most definite feature of the level order is the existence of the closed shells.

Note that the spin-orbit splitting not only depresses the level of higher

j but also raises that of lower j. There is accordingly some tendency in the upper shells for the states $g_{7/2}$ and $h_{9/2}$ not to be the lowest in their shells but to be in competition with the $d_{5/2}$ and $f_{7/2}$ levels for the lowest position. At present, however, no very strong support can be given to many such finer details of the level order.

The spins and magnetic moments of nuclei constitute a large class of data that contribute direct and detailed information on the level order. We have discussed some methods for measuring these quantities in the preceding section. It is found that all even-even (N even, Z even) nuclei have spin zero. This suggests that the neutrons and protons tend to "pair off" in such a way that the pairs all have zero total angular

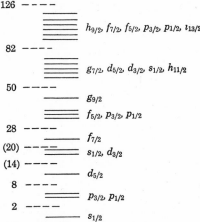

Fig. 13.6. Energy levels with l and j splitting. The levels in the bracketed group fill generally in the order indicated, but with many irregularities. The "magic numbers" are indicated; those in parentheses are not so well defined as the others.

momentum. In an even-odd nucleus we should therefore expect the odd nucleon to be the source of the entire spin and magnetic moment. On this hypothesis we get direct information about the orbits by measuring the spins of even-odd nuclei. This information is one of the principal sources of the detailed level order indicated in Fig. 13.6.

Each value of j is associated with two values of l in single-particle orbits. The two choices of l are distinguishable by measurements of the magnetic moment. By applying formulas (11.22) we obtain the g_j factor. The total magnetic moment in units of μ_N is conventionally taken to be the maximum z-component of $\mathbf{\mu}$:

$$\mu_j = g_j j = g_l \frac{j(j+1) + l(l+1) - s(s+1)}{2(j+1)}$$
$$+ g_s \frac{j(j+1) + s(s+1) - l(l+1)}{2(j+1)} \quad (13.19)$$

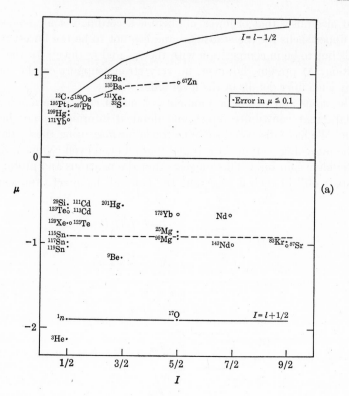

(a)

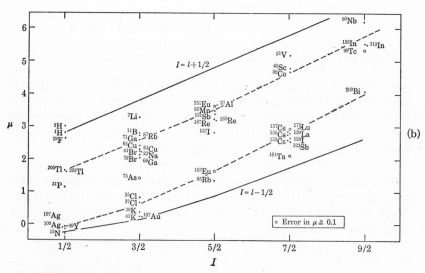

(b)

Fig. 13.7. Magnetic moments of even-odd nuclei and Schmidt limits: (a) odd neutron nuclei; (b) odd proton nuclei. (From P. F. A. Klinkenberg, *Revs. Modern Phys.* **24**, 63 (1953)).

Here $g_l = 1$ for the proton and $g_l = 0$ for the uncharged neutron; $g_s = g_p$ and g_n as given in (13.17). Using $s = \frac{1}{2}$, we can write the two cases $j = l + \frac{1}{2}$ and $j = l - \frac{1}{2}$ separately,

$$\mu_{j=l+\frac{1}{2}} = g_l l + \tfrac{1}{2} g_s$$

$$\mu_{j=l-\frac{1}{2}} = g_l \frac{(l + 1)(2l - 1)}{(2l + 1)} - \frac{1}{2} g_s \frac{2l - 1}{2l + 1} \qquad (13.20)$$

These formulas appear as continuous curves in Fig. 13.7, although of course they apply only for half-integral values of j. They represent the ideal one-particle case and are called the Schmidt limits, after their first proponent (1937). In Fig. 13.7 are also plotted the magnetic moments of known nuclei. Two features of this plot are clear: first, the measured moments usually are close enough to one Schmidt limit to permit a confident assignment of l; second, there are marked deviations from the Schmidt limits.

These deviations have not yet been entirely explained, but it seems probable that they represent a failure of the extreme one-particle model. The extreme assumption is probably unjustified that in an even-odd nucleus all the nucleons but one pair off to give zero angular momentum and zero contribution to the magnetic moment. One must allow in the nuclear ground states admixtures of 3-, 5-, $\cdots$, $(2n + 1)$-particle states. These states should certainly be present, according to the arguments above regarding the absence of a real central potential and the existence of strong forces between adjacent nucleons. The remarkable feature of the shell model is not that there should be deviations from the extreme one-particle picture, but that this picture turns out to be at all a reasonable first approximation.

Although many properties of nuclei support this general shell structure, there are also many details like the magnetic moments that need further clarification. The nuclear shell model is at present a still developing and most interesting extension of ideas originating in atomic physics.

13.6. The Lamb shift and electrodynamics

One of the present uses of atomic physics is to provide a laboratory for the investigation of finer details than those involved in earlier studies. In hyperfine structure, for example, the atom provides the magnetic field by which the spin of the nucleus is determined. Another interesting instance of the atom as a laboratory has recently occurred in the measurement of small corrections to the quantum theory of radiation. There is a large body of theoretical understanding related to the quantum mechanical treatment of the electromagnetic field, in particular to the properties of electromagnetic radiation. Although the subject of quantum electrodynamics is well beyond the scope of the present text, we can attempt to describe some of its problems and the light thrown upon them by atomic measurements.

The Schroedinger equation for atomic energy levels is more properly replaced by the Dirac equation, which correctly takes into account the electron spin and consequent fine structure. The general level structure is the same as for the Schroedinger equation. Both these equations are based on a definite approximation, however; they neglect the possibility of radiation by the atom. The different wave functions truly correspond to *stationary states*, for which the energy is exactly known and the life-time is infinite. This unrealistic picture is corrected in first approximation by introducing electromagnetic radiation. By virtue of its inter-action with the electromagnetic field, the electron can radiate energy and jump from one level to another. Thus an excited state of an atom is no longer infinitely stable but will decay by photon emission in an average time τ. Correspondingly, the excited energy level is no longer infinitely sharp but has a certain half-width $\Gamma = \hbar/\tau$.

If the interaction with the electromagnetic field alters the energy levels from the ideal Dirac equation by giving them half-widths Γ, it is reason-able to ask whether this interaction might not have some additional small effects on the positions of the energy levels. Strong evidence for an affirmative answer was provided by the work of Lamb and Retherford (1947); their measurements related to the $2S$ and $2P$ levels of hydrogen. In the hydrogen atom the effect of electron spin is to remove the de-generacy between energy levels of the same n but different j values. Levels of the same n, j but different l remain degenerate, however. For example, the $2^2S_{1/2}$ and $2^2P_{1/2}$ levels of hydrogen have the same term values, while the $2^2P_{3/2}$ level is higher by 0.365 cm^{-1}. This conclusion is based on the simple theory without correction for the effects of radi-ation. The measurements show that actually the $2^2S_{1/2}$ level is some 0.035 cm^{-1} higher than the $2^2P_{1/2}$ level. The discovery of this "Lamb shift" has greatly stimulated theoretical studies of quantum electro-dynamics, which have resulted in successful calculations of this effect and its magnitude. The observed situation is as indicated in Fig. 13.8.

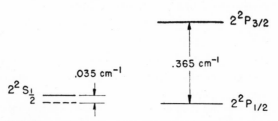

Fig. 13.8. Separation of $n = 2$ levels of hydrogen. The S level position is shown as measured; the dotted line is the S level predic-tion by the simple theory neglecting the radiation field.

It is of interest to note the atomic principles involved in the experiment. The ground state of hydrogen is 10.2 ev below the $n = 2$ levels. Both the $2P$ states decay by photon emission into the ground state in about 10^{-9} second. The $2S$ level is metastable, however, for selection rules forbid a transition with $\Delta l = 0$, so that the $2S$-$1S$ transition does not occur. A hydrogen atom in the $2S$ level can return to the $1S$ ground state only by collision with another atom or by simultaneous emission of two photons, to which the selection rule does not apply. Two-photon decay is much slower than one-photon emission and requires about 10^{-1} second to occur. Of course if the metastable hydrogen atom is taken from the $2S$ to one of the $2P$ states, it will decay very rapidly.

The experimental details of the measurement are similar to those of the molecular beam measurements. A beam of atomic hydrogen emerges from a thermal source. It passes through a perpendicular beam of electrons of energy somewhat exceeding 10.2 volts. These electrons excite a certain number of hydrogen atoms to the metastable $2S$ state by collision. From the electron bombardment the atoms pass to a region where a radio-frequency field of frequency ω is applied, and thence to a detector that responds to atoms in the metastable state. If there is an energy difference $2^2S_{1/2} - 2^2P_{1/2} = \Delta E$, then transitions from $2^2S_{1/2}$ to $2^2P_{1/2}$ will be induced by the radio-frequency field at the resonant frequency $\omega_0 = \Delta E/\hbar$. The metastable state will thus be destroyed. A measurement of the frequency ω_0 at which the beam current of metastable atoms decreases yields the value of ΔE.

In practice a slight modification is made by introducing a uniform magnetic induction B into the radio-frequency region. Induced transitions then occur between the Zeeman components of the $n = 2$ lines. This

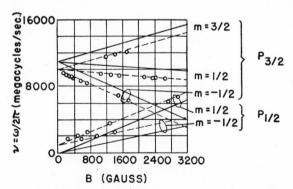

Fig. 13.9. Resonant ν versus B for $S_{1/2} - P_{3/2}$ and $S_{1/2} - P_{1/2}$ transitions. The m values of the P states are as listed; the m value of the S state is ½. The solid lines are calculated on the basis of no shift between $S_{1/2}$ and $P_{1/2}$ levels; the dotted lines are observed and correspond to the shift shown in Figure 13.8. (Lamb and Retherford, *Phys. Rev.*, **79**, 549 (1950)).

has the advantage that the resonant condition can be attained by varying the strength of B instead of the frequency ω. Also, a plot of the resonant values of ω verus B leads to a straight line that extrapolates to give an accurate value of ΔE.

Typical results of such measurements are shown in Fig. 13.9. The expected lines of ω_0 versus B assume that $\Delta E = 0$. The observed curves show a shift of $\Delta \omega = \Delta E/\hbar = 1057.8 \pm 0.1$ megacycles. The $2^2S_{1/2} - 2^2P_{1/2}$ curves do not tell whether ΔE is positive or negative, so that it is necessary to refer to the $2^2S_{1/2} - 2^2P_{3/2}$ curves. These show that the $2^2S_{1/2}$ level is shifted upwards relative to the $2^2P_{1/2}$.

This shift arises from interaction with the electromagnetic field, neglected in the simplest approximation. In quantum mechanics a charged particle like the electron interacts with the electromagnetic field by constantly emitting and reabsorbing photons. This holds true even of an electron at rest; each photon emitted is ultimately reabsorbed by the electron. These photons are not observed directly and are called virtual photons. The energy involved in this process of emission and reabsorption is part of what we measure as the rest-mass energy of the electron. Thus for an electron at rest the effects of the virtual quanta are not observable. For an electron in an atomic orbit, however, it turns out that the effects of the virtual quanta are slightly dependent on the type of orbit involved. This slight dependence is the cause of the Lamb shift. Quantitative calculations of this effect are in excellent agreement with experiment.

Another electrodynamic effect of this sort is a correction to the magnetic moment of the electron. The g factor in the simple Dirac theory is exactly $g = 2$, but with radiative corrections becomes

$$g = 2 \left(1 + \frac{\alpha}{2\pi} - 2.973 \frac{\alpha^2}{\pi^2} + \cdots \right) \tag{13.21}$$

where $\alpha = e^2/\hbar c = 1/137.04$ is the fine structure constant. This correction for the g value has also been verified by experiment.

SUMMARY

Atomic physics *per se* is now no longer in a stage of rapid development. Rather the concepts and methods that proved so fruitful in atomic physics have extended themselves to other fields, notably nuclear physics. A few examples of this extension are given.

The technique of deflecting charged particle beams in electric and magnetic fields, first applied to measurement of the specific charge of the electron, leads to accurate isotopic weights for nuclei. The high precision reveals mass defects ΔM that verify the mass-energy equivalence of relativity: $\Delta M = B/c^2$, where B is the binding energy of the nucleus. In this relation 1 amu = 931 mev. The mass defects account for the energy released in nuclear fission of uranium; in this fission a mass equivalent to about 200 mev is released as energy. This is really *nuclear* energy and is about 10^6 times as great as the energy release in chemical reactions, which is true *atomic* energy.

Atomic nuclei display angular momenta and magnetic moments that follow the same quantum mechanical rules as the corresponding atomic quantities. The neutron and proton both have spin $\frac{1}{2}$, like the electron. The unit in which to measure their magnetic moments is the nuclear magneton $\mu_N = e\hbar/2Mc \approx 5.5 \times 10^{-4} \mu_0$. The neutron and proton have anomalous magnetic moments, with $g_p = 5.58$ and $g_n = -3.82$. This indicates a compound structure for these particles, not now understood.

The hyperfine splittings of spectral lines, amounting to fractions of a wave number, are evidence for the existence of nuclear magnetic moments. Analysis of this structure parallels that for fine structure splitting in *L-S* coupling, with *J*, *I*, and *F* replacing *L*, *S*, and *J*. Here *I* is the nuclear spin and *F* is the total angular momentum of the atom, electrons plus nucleus. The selection rules on *F* for photon emission are the same as on *J*: $\Delta F = \Delta M_F = 0, \pm 1$. For a term with sufficiently large *J* the number of hyperfine structure lines is just $(2I + 1)$, which provides a method of determining nuclear spin. The hyperfine structure also determines the sign of the nuclear magnetic moment μ_I but does not give the magnitude of μ_I accurately.

For precision measurement of the magnitude of μ_I the molecular beam method has proved useful. This is an extension of technique of deflecting neutral atomic beams in an inhomogeneous magnetic induction. In this method the beam passes successively through two inhomogeneous inductions, so arranged that the deflections in each field are equal and opposite. When this perfect cancellation occurs, the beam is recorded in a detector. In the region between the inhomogeneous inductions, an oscillating induction causes changes $\Delta M = \pm 1$ in the *z*-component of the nuclear spin. This destroys the equality of the deflections in the two inhomogeneous fields, and the beam no longer gets through the apparatus to the detector. This drop in beam intensity occurs for a critical frequency ω_1, from which follows a precise value of the magnitude of μ_I. This experiment also verifies the validity of the quantum mechanical relation $E = h\nu$ for radio frequencies.

Another beam technique with radiofrequency excitation reveals that in hydrogen the $2S_{1/2}$ term is at a frequency ν some 1058 megacycles higher than the $2P_{1/2}$ term. In the simplest quantum theory where we neglect interaction with the electromagnetic field, the $2S_{1/2}$ and $2P_{1/2}$ levels are degenerate. We may ascribe the shift to the emission and reabsorption of virtual photons. The measurements have stimulated refinements in the theory, and the two are now in good agreement.

REFERENCES

J. Chadwick, *Proc. Roy. Soc.*, **136,** 692 (1932).

Haxel, Jensen, and Suess, *Phys. Rev.*, **75,** 1766 (1949).

W. E. Lamb, Jr., and R. C. Retherford, *Phys. Rev.*, **79,** 549 (1950).

J. Mattauch and S. Fluegge, *Nuclear Physics Tables*, Interscience, New York (1946).

M. G. Mayer, *Phys. Rev.*, **75,** 1969 (1949).

Rabi, Millman, Kusch, and Zacharias, *Phys. Rev.*, **55,** 526 (1939).

ILLUSTRATIVE PROBLEMS

1. Like atoms, nuclei have discrete, quantized excited levels from which they can decay to the ground state by emission of a photon. These nuclear photons are called gamma (γ) rays.

(a) If Cd^{111} emits a γ ray of energy $h\nu = 0.24$ mev, what is the recoil energy imparted to the nucleus? What is the effect of this recoil on the frequency of the γ ray?

(b) If the mean lifetime of the excited state of Cd^{111} in part (a) is $\tau = 8 \times 10^{-8}$ sec, what is the half-width or intrinsic energy spread Γ of the excited level?

(c) Comparing (a) and (b), what can you say about the possibility of using this γ ray for a resonance radiation experiment: i.e., using a Cd^{111} source of γ rays to excite the 0.24 mev level of other Cd^{111} nuclei, which would then re-emit this resonance radiation? Neglect Doppler effects from thermal motion of the nuclei.

Solution. (a) The photon momentum is $p = h\nu/c$; the nuclear recoil energy (the nonrelativistic approximation is sufficient here) is $\Delta E = p^2/2M = (h\nu)^2/2Mc^2$. Using $h\nu = 0.24$ mev, $M = A$ amu, and the conversion factor (13.2), we have $\Delta E = (0.24)^2/2 \times 111 \times 931 \approx 3 \times 10^{-7}$ mev $= 0.3$ ev. If the energy difference of the nuclear levels is E, the energy of the emitted γ ray is $h\nu = E - \Delta E$. The ΔE represents a Doppler shift of the photon frequency due to motion of the source.

(b) The uncertainty relation gives $\Gamma\tau = \hbar \approx \frac{2}{3} \times 10^{-15}$ ev sec. Thus for $\tau = 8 \times 10^{-8}$ sec, $\Gamma \approx 10^{-8}$ ev.

(c) Since $\Delta E \gg \Gamma$, it will be impossible to produce the resonance excitation or hence re-emission of resonance radiation, if we neglect Doppler effects. This result holds in general for nuclear γ radiation.

2. In Chapter 11 we considered the $^2S_{1/2}$ level to be single and to have no fine structure, although a member of a doublet system. If the nucleus of the atom has $I \neq 0$, what is the multiplicity of the $^2S_{1/2}$ level? In a transition from a single hyperfine component of $^2P_{1/2}$, what are the relative intensities of transitions to the various hyperfine components of $^2S_{1/2}$?

Solution. For $J = \frac{1}{2}$ and $I \neq 0$ the total spin F has two values, $F = I - \frac{1}{2}$ and $F = I + \frac{1}{2}$. The $^2S_{1/2}$ terms thus split into two hyperfine components. For hyperfine transitions the sum rules (12.10) hold if we replace the statistical weight $(2J + 1)$ by the corresponding statistical weight $(2F + 1)$. Thus for transitions to the two hyperfine components of $^2S_{1/2}$, the intensity ratio is $(2F + 1)/(2F' + 1) = 2I/2I + 2 = I/I + 1$. Observation of such alternating intensities is another way of determining nuclear spin.

PROBLEMS

1. The recoil effects considered in illustrative problem 1 also occur for photon emission by the atomic electrons.

(a) Compute the recoil energy ΔE of a Cd^{111} atom that emits an optical photon of wave number $k = 4.4 \times 10^4 \text{ cm}^{-1}$.

(b) If the mean life of this emission is $\tau = 10^{-6}$ sec, what is the natural energy spread Γ of the spectrum line?

(c) Would the resonance radiation experiment be possible in this case?

(d) Is this recoil of any physical importance? Compare ΔE with the average thermal energy per degree of freedom, $\frac{1}{2}kT$. Contrast this comparison with $\Delta E/\frac{1}{2}kT$ for illustrative problem 1.

2. Calculate the order of magnitude of the total binding energy of the electrons in a heavy atom, for example Pb. Is this binding energy within the range directly measurable as a mass difference? If so, why has it never been measured directly? Use as an approximation for the binding energy the formula $B = RhcZ_{eff}^2/n^2$, with $n = 1$, and sum (integrate) over all Z_{eff} from 1 to Z.

3. In general we gain nuclear energy whenever the packing fractions of the end products in a process are lower than the packing fractions of the original nuclei. Figure 13.1 therefore indicates that we should be able to gain nuclear energy not only by fission of heavy nuclei but by fusion of light ones. As an example, consider the fusion of two deuterons, $_1H^2$ to make an α particle $_2H^4$. The mass of the H^2 atom is 2.01474 amu, of an He^4 atom is 4.00388 amu. How much energy is released in the fusion, $_1H^2 + _1H^2 \rightarrow _2He^4$? Does this total energy release depend on whether the reaction goes directly or through a number of other intermediate nuclei? What is the energy release per unit mass of fuel, and how does it compare with the corresponding figure for uranium fission? This principle is the source of energy in stars.

4. Lithium has two isotopes of atomic masses 6 and 7. From the ionization potential determine the isotope hyperfine splitting of the atomic ground state. What difficulty is there in calculating the isotope splitting for a level caused by two or more optical electrons?

5. In nuclear ground states there frequently appears to be considerable j-j coupling, as opposed to the atomic case. The only cases resembling good L-S coupling are found among the light nuclei. Consider the two nuclei Li^6 and N^{14}, which both have $I = 1$. Their magnetic moments are $\mu = 0.822 \, \mu_N(Li^6)$ and $\mu = 0.404\mu_N(N^{14})$. Compare the computed μ for these nuclei for L-S versus j-j coupling: the states consist in each case of a neutron and a proton outside of (or lacking from) a closed shell; in L-S coupling the states would be $^3S_1$ for both nuclei, in j-j coupling $(p_{3/2}p_{3/2})_1$ for Li^6 and $(p_{1/2}p_{1/2})_1$ for N^{14}.

6. Each line of the ^2S-^2P resonance doublet in Na splits into a hyperfine structure. The total number of lines in the fully resolved hyperfine pattern is 10. Find the number of hyperfine components of each doublet line, and show that the nuclear spin of Na is $I \geq \frac{3}{2}$.

7. On a purely empirical basis it has been suggested [Schawlow and Townes, *Phys. Rev.*, **82,** 268 (1951)] that the deviations of nuclear magnetic moments from the Schmidt limits are in rough agreement with the following rule. Consider two nuclei, one with an odd number of protons Z_o and even number of neutrons N_e, the other with an odd number of neutrons N_o and even number of protons Z_e. Consider only cases where the spins I of the nuclei are the same and $N_o = Z_o$, even though $N_e \neq Z_e$ in general. Then if the displacement of each magnetic moment is measured in units of the distance between the appropriate Schmidt limits for the spin I, this relative displacement is approximately the same for the odd neutron as for the odd proton nucleus. This is a rule of thumb for predicting the order of magnitude of some unmeasured nuclear moments.

(a) How well does this rule check all the cases available for comparison in Fig. 13.7?

(b) In a molecular beam experiment with fixed frequency $\nu_1 = 8.3$ megacycles, through what range of B would you expect to have to sweep to find resonances with the magnetic moments of Ne^{21}, $Mo^{95, \, 97}$, $Ru^{99, \, 101}$?

Chapter 14

QUANTUM STATISTICAL MECHANICS

The discussions of previous chapters have shown how quantum mechanics is absolutely essential to an understanding of microscopic phenomena, which involve individual atoms. The connecting link between microscopic and macroscopic processes is Boltzmann's principle, as mentioned in Chapter 1, and the mathematical apparatus of statistical mechanics. Frequently the averaging processes of statistical mechanics tend to smooth out the quantum mechanical discontinuities, so that classical (as opposed to quantum) mechanics is quite adequate to describe the behavior of bulk matter. There are some cases, however, particularly at low temperatures, where quantum mechanical effects have a profound influence on large-scale processes. These cases represent total mysteries to classical kinetic theory. Historically they were the problems that led to the invention of the quantum, but for logical development we have found it convenient to postpone their discussion until now.

For this discussion we must repeat some of the development of statistical mechanics, paying attention throughout to quantum mechanical restrictions for the microscopic system. This turns out to be not much more difficult than for classical statistical mechanics. Quantum statistics allows us to explain satisfactorily the classical puzzles of the black body radiation spectrum and the failure of the law of Dulong and Petit for specific heats of solids. We also sketch the application to conduction electrons in metals.

14.1. Black Body Radiation

Any substance at a temperature $T > 0°K$ will radiate electromagnetic energy. From a quantum mechanical point of view, this radiation originates in the emission of individual photons by various atoms and molecules of the substance. Of course photon emission cannot occur unless the atom or molecule is already in an excited state. The necessary excitation energy comes from collisions of atoms and molecules in which energy of thermal motion (kinetic) transfers to energy of electronic excitation. The excited electronic states return rapidly to ground states with the emission of radiation. If the substance is a solid, we must understand "collision" of the atoms in a rather figurative sense, but the basic mechanism still remains the transfer of energy of thermal motion to electronic excitation.

Each emitted photon has a definite characteristic energy, and the spectrum will consist of an enormous collection of individual lines. For a complex mechanical system like a solid, however, these lines will be so numerous and so closely spaced that their distribution in frequency will appear continuous. This is especially true if the measurements are made with low resolving power. In this case the spectral distribution of intensity as a function ν or λ depends only on the temperature T of the substance if the radiating atoms are in equilibrium with a heat source at temperature T. A black body is the idealized case in which there is no dependence of the spectrum on the quantized energy levels of the atoms. Its properties are independent of constituent materials or surface conditions. The radiation spectrum follows entirely from the properties of the electromagnetic field (radiation) in equilibrium at temperature T.

Another way of defining a black body is to say that it absorbs every photon falling upon it. If it did not absorb every photon, it could not remain in equilibrium with the radiation field. Thus a good practical approach to a black body is a closed oven with a small aperture. Radiation falling on the aperture is almost certain to be absorbed after multiple internal reflections on the oven walls, so that the aperture behaves like a black body. Measurements of the black body spectrum with such an apparatus are shown in Fig. 14.1.

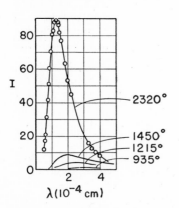

Fig. 14.1. Black body spectrum at various temperatures T (°K).

To interpret this spectrum, consider a radiation field in thermal equilibrium. We employ a mathematical artifice that is convenient in many applications, that of quantizing in a large box. We suppose the radiation to be contained in a large box of finite volume V with perfectly reflecting sides; after completing the solution of our problem with this restriction, we let the volume V become infinitely large. It always turns out that if we apply this technique correctly, the final step $V \to \infty$ does not alter the physical conclusions. The wave equation for photons in a box has a solution exactly similar to that for a particle in a box, except that the rest mass of the photons is zero. We accordingly recast Eqs. (10.23)–(10.25) to eliminate m_0, obtaining with the use of (10.6),

$$k_x = p_x/\hbar = 2\pi n_x/D_x$$
$$k_y = p_y/\hbar = 2\pi n_y/D_y \qquad (14.1)$$
$$k_z = p_z/\hbar = 2\pi n_z/D_z$$

Here p_x, p_y, p_z are the momentum components of the photon; k_x, k_y, k_z are corresponding wave numbers; D_x, D_y, D_z are the dimensions of the rectangular box; and n_x, n_y, $n_z = 0$, ± 1, ± 2, $\cdots$ are quantum numbers. Each set of quantum numbers corresponds to a physically distinct wave function of the photons in the box. Here we include details that were not of interest in the previous discussion of the box (section 10.2): we distinguish positive and negative values of n_j and include $n_j = 0$. The values of n_j are strictly quantized; but in the limit as $V \to \infty$, a small momentum change Δp_j represents a large quantum number change Δn_j. In this limit we can with negligible error replace the difference Δn_j by the differential dn_j. The number of different configurations in a given range of quantum numbers is then

$$dn' = dn_x \, dn_y \, dn_z$$

$$= D_x \, D_y \, D_z \, dp_x \, dp_y \, dp_z/(2\pi\hbar)^3 \qquad (14.2a)$$

$$= V p^2 \, dp \, d\Omega_p/(2\pi\hbar)^3$$

In the last line of (14.2a) we have transformed dp from rectangular to spherical coordinates: $p^2 \, dp \, d\Omega_p$ corresponds to a momentum vector with magnitude between p and $p + dp$, pointing into a solid angle $d\Omega_p$.

If we consider all states in the range $p^2 \, dp \, d\Omega_p$ as having the same energy, within the accuracy of our measurement, there are dn' degenerate states at this energy. The number dn' is therefore a statistical weight factor of the type discussed in Chapter 12. This factor appears in all quantum statistical considerations, and is a cornerstone of quantum statistical mechanics. In making sums over all microscopic states to obtain macroscopic quantities, we must take account of such statistical weights.

The statistical factor dn' is common to all types of particles quantized in the mathematical large box. For any particular type of particle we must also include any statistical weight factors peculiar to the particle. For photons there is an additional factor of 2, which corresponds to the two possible directions of polarization for each photon of frequency ν. The total number of photons in the range $dp \, d\Omega_p$ is therefore

$$dn = 2 \, dn' = 2V p^2 \, dp \, d\Omega_p/(2\pi\hbar)^3 \qquad (14.2b)$$

The photons in thermal equilibrium in this enclosure are like an ideal gas, to which the Boltzmann factor (1.9) applies. Consider photons of a specific frequency ν: at temperature T the relative probabilities for the presence of $0, 1, 2, \cdots n, \cdots$ photons are

$$p_0 : p_1 : p_2 : \cdots : p_n : \cdots$$

$$= C_0 : C_0 e^{-h\nu/kT} : C_0 e^{-2h\nu/kT} : \cdots : C_0 e^{-nh\nu/kT} : \cdots \qquad (14.3)$$

Here C_0 is a constant factor that Boltzmann's principle does not determine, and in the exponent $nh\nu$ is the energy of the system when n photons of frequency ν are present. The average number of photons present is

$$\bar{n} = \frac{\sum\limits_{n=0}^{\infty} n p_n}{\sum\limits_{n=0}^{\infty} p_n} \qquad (14.4)$$

To evaluate (14.4), we note that $p_n = C_0 y^n$, where $y = e^{-h\nu/kT}$, so that

$$\bar{n} = \frac{\sum\limits_{n=0}^{\infty} n y^n}{\sum\limits_{n=0}^{\infty} y^n} \qquad (14.5)$$

It is a mathematical identity that for $x < 1$,

$$\sum_{n=0}^{\infty} x^n = 1 + x + x^2 + \cdots = \frac{1}{1-x} \qquad (14.6)$$

$$\sum_{n=0}^{\infty} n x^n = x \sum_{n=0}^{\infty} n x^{n-1} = x \frac{d}{dx} \sum_{n=0}^{\infty} x^n = \frac{x}{(1-x)^2} \qquad (14.7)$$

Therefore

$$\bar{n}(\nu) = \frac{x}{1-x} = \left(\frac{1}{x} - 1 \right)^{-1} = (e^{h\nu/kT} - 1)^{-1} \qquad (14.8)$$

Equation (14.8) gives the average number of photons of frequency ν in the box. The total number in the frequency range ν to $\nu + d\nu$ follows by multiplication with the statistical weight factor dn, expressed in terms of frequency. For this purpose we note that the photon momentum is $p = h/\lambda = h\nu/c$, so that

$$dn_\nu = 2V \, d\Omega \, \nu^2 \, d\nu / c^3 \qquad (14.9)$$

We obtain the distribution of photon energies in the box by including a factor $h\nu$, the energy per photon:

$$dE = h\nu \bar{n}(\nu) \, dn_\nu = \frac{2V \, d\Omega \, h}{c^3} \frac{\nu^3 \, d\nu}{(e^{h\nu/kT} - 1)} \qquad (14.10)$$

The final factor in (14.10) is Planck's law for the frequency distribution of radiation in thermal equilibrium. This formula is in excellent agreement with measured curves, as in Fig. 14.1. The figure shows curves as a function of wavelength; we can convert (14.10) by substituting $\nu = c/\lambda$. Either as a function of ν or of λ, the distribution factor in (14.10) goes to zero as $\nu, \lambda \to 0, \infty$, and passes through a maximum between these limits. Planck's law was the first successful deduction of this qualitative behavior and provided the first introduction of the quantum. If the energy of the radiation does not come in discrete units $h\nu$, it is impossible to make the spectral distribution converge for large ν or small λ.

In the original deduction of this law, Planck proceeded by classical reasoning throughout until the single step at which the quantum hypothesis $E = h\nu$ became necessary. We have given here a completely quantum mechanical derivation, which has the advantages of brevity and simplicity. It is of at least historical interest to note that Planck's constant h can be evaluated from measurements on the black body spectrum alone. From (14.10) we can show that the wavelength λ_{max} at which the spectrum has its intensity maximum is

$$\lambda_{max} = hc/4.965kT = b/T \qquad (14.11)$$

Thus by measuring λ_{max} as a function of T we determine hc/k and h if k and c are known.

Another quantity capable of measurement that also determines h is the total intensity of radiation from a black body. Figure 14.2 shows the aperture in an oven that serves as a black body. The total energy density (energy per unit volume) just inside the aperture is u. This density consists of photons going in all directions with equal probability. Thus half the density will be moving inward and not escape from the oven at all. The other half of the intensity is moving outward with an average velocity $c \, \overline{\cos \theta}$, where $\overline{\cos \theta}$ is the average value over a uniform distribution of outward directions. This average value is

$$\overline{\cos \theta} = \frac{\displaystyle\int_0^{\pi/2} \cos \theta \, d(\cos \theta)}{\displaystyle\int_0^{\pi/2} d(\cos \theta)} = \frac{1}{2}$$

Thus the total intensity of radiation from the aperture in energy/cm^2 sec is

$$I = (u/2)(c/2) = uc/4 \qquad (14.12)$$

To find the total energy density, we integrate (14.10) over all directions,

$\displaystyle\int d\Omega = 4\pi$, and over all frequencies, obtaining

$$u = \int \frac{dE}{V} = \frac{8\pi h}{c^3} \int_0^\infty \frac{\nu^3 \, d\nu}{e^{h\nu/kT} - 1}$$

$$= \frac{8\pi}{(hc)^3} k^4 T^4 \int_0^\infty \frac{y^3 \, dy}{e^y - 1} \qquad (14.13)$$

$$= \left(\frac{8\pi^5}{15} \frac{k^4}{(hc)^3} \right) T^4 = aT^4$$

Thus

$$I = \frac{ac}{4}T^4 = \sigma T^4 \qquad (14.14)$$

The dependence of I or hence u on T^4 can be predicted by purely thermo-dynamical reasoning, but to evaluate the coefficient σ requires a detailed theory.

It is of interest to note that in all our discussion it has never been necessary to specify V, the volume of the large box, used for quantizing the radiation. We can therefore discard this artificial limitation and let $V \to \infty$ or to any arbitrary value.

Radiation measurements determine σ and hence h if k and c are known. Or if neither k nor h is well known, determination of both σ and b allows us to find k and h independently, as discussed in Chapter 1.

14.2. Specific heats of solids

The method of treatment of black body radiation finds immediate application to the problem of the specific heat of solids. A crystalline solid contains atoms packed in a regular array. The nuclei have equilibrium positions at the points of a three-dimensional geometric lattice. The simplest is the cubic lattice, illustrated in Fig. 1.2, and we shall use this as our model. The nuclei are not quite rigidly bound to the lattice points, but can execute harmonic vibrations about the lattice points as equilibrium positions. When the vibrations of all the nuclei are in phase, they constitute a standing wave, like those observed in a string under tension. In a standing wave the displacements of the individual nuclei bear a constant geometric relation to each other. The absolute magnitude of any displacement varies periodically with a frequency ν. This frequency is characteristic of the particular standing wave.

Mathematically, any standing wave is equivalent to the sum of two traveling waves of the same frequency, moving in opposite directions. Let the two traveling waves be (see section 9.4)

$$\varphi_1 = A \sin 2\pi(\nu t - x/\lambda)$$

$$\varphi_2 = A \sin 2\pi(\nu t + x/\lambda)$$

then their sum is

$$\Phi = \varphi_1 + \varphi_2$$
$$= 2A \sin (2\pi\nu t) \cos (2\pi x/\lambda) \qquad (14.15)$$

This is the equation of a standing wave. Furthermore, any vibration of the nuclei in the crystal, no matter how complicated and irregular it may appear, is representable by a sum of standing waves. Hence we may consider the vibrations of a solid to consist of a large number of traveling elastic waves. These waves have characteristic wavelengths λ and frequencies ν. They are responsible for the propagation of sound through the solid with velocity c', so that $\lambda\nu = c'$.

The general principles of wave mechanics imply that the wave-particle duality is a universal aspect of nature. Thus we should expect to define the corpuscular equivalents of these sound waves by the de Broglie relations $p = h/\lambda$, $E = h\nu$. These sound wave particles are called *phonons*. We may now take over bodily the discussion of the preceding section. The number of degenerate phonon states in a range $p^2 \, dp \, d\Omega_p$ is

$$dn' = Vp^2 \, dp \, d\Omega_p/(2\pi\hbar)^3 \qquad (14.16)$$

where in this case V appears as the actual volume of solid. If we integrate over all $d\Omega_p$ and convert to frequencies,

$$dn' = \frac{4\pi V}{c'^3} \nu^2 \, d\nu \qquad (14.17)$$

This is the number of degenerate modes for phonons of a single polarization. Actually, the phonons can have three polarizations, two transverse and one longitudinal. The velocity associated with transverse polarization is not generally identical with that for longitudinal polarization, but we ignore this difference, which is not essential to our considerations. With three polarizations, the number of degenerate phonon states between ν and $\nu + d\nu$ becomes

$$dn = 3 \, dn' = \frac{12\pi V}{c'^3} \nu^2 \, d\nu \qquad (14.18)$$

There is one important difference from the previous case of the photons in a box. A mole of a solid with a total of N_0 atoms can have only $3N_0$ independent modes of vibration, corresponding to the three independent directions of vibration for each nucleus. Therefore there must be a maximum frequency ν_0 such that

$$3N_0 = \int_0^{\nu_0} dn = 4\pi V(\nu_0/c')^3 \qquad (14.19)$$

The value of $\bar{n}(\nu)$ is computed in the same way as before, leading to (14.8). The total internal energy of vibration for one mole of the solid is therefore

$$U = \int_0^{\nu_0} h\nu\bar{n}(\nu) \, dn = \frac{12\pi Vh}{c'^3} \int_0^{\nu_0} \frac{\nu^3 \, d\nu}{e^{h\nu/kT} - 1} \qquad (14.20)$$

Substituting $y = h\nu/kT$, $y_0 = h\nu_0/kT$, and using (14.19) to eliminate V (notice that again the volume of quantization in the box drops out of the final result), we have

$$U = 3RT \frac{3}{y_0^3} \int_0^{y_0} \frac{y^3 \, dy}{e^y - 1} = 3RT \, D(y_0) \qquad (14.21)$$

where $N_0 k = R$, the gas constant.

To obtain the molar specific heat of the solid from (14.21), we should take dU/dT. Unfortunately, we cannot give the function $D(y_0)$ in analytic form suitable for taking the derivative with respect to T. Analytic approximations to $D(y_0)$ are feasible, however, for the limiting cases $y_0 \to 0$, $y_0 \to \infty$, which are of most physical interest. As $y_0 \to 0$, we put $e^y \approx 1 + y$ and obtain $D(y_0) \approx 1$; and as $y_0 \to \infty$, we can put

$$\int_0^{y_0} \to \int_0^{\infty} = \frac{\pi^4}{15}$$

as in (14.13). Thus

$$C_V = \frac{\partial U}{\partial T} \to 3R, \qquad T \gg \theta$$

$$\to \frac{12}{5} \pi^4 R \left(\frac{T}{\theta}\right)^3 = 2.3 \times 10^2 R \left(\frac{T}{\theta}\right)^3 \qquad T \ll \theta \qquad (14.22)$$

where $\theta = h\nu_0/k$ is the "Debye temperature" of the solid, named after the originator of this theory of specific heats.

Equation (14.22) indicates that at high enough temperatures all solids should approach Dulong and Petit's law, $C_v = 3R$. This is in agreement with observation. On the other hand, as $T \to 0$, the specific heats of all solids fall to zero. The value of C_v follows a T^3 law for low temperatures on the order of θ, a characteristic temperature of each solid. For most elements the values of θ range over about $100°$–$400°$ on the absolute scale. The diamond crystal is an exception, with $\theta \approx 2000°K$. This accounts for the fact that the specific heat of diamond falls particularly short of Dulong and Petit's law at ordinary temperatures.

Figure 14.3 compares the observed specific heat of silver with that calculated from the Debye formula (14.21). The agreement is quite good, especially in view of the fact that (14.19) is a crude approximation: the frequency distribution in a real crystal is always more complicated than assumed in (14.18). On this account the agreement of the simple Debye theory with experiment is not always so good as in Fig. 14.3. There can be no doubt, however, that this quantum mechanical explanation for the behavior of specific heats is in principle correct.

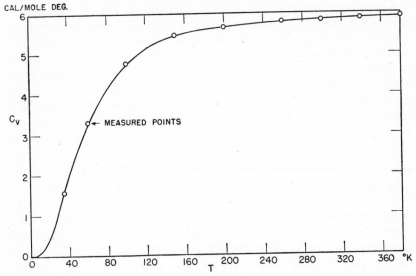

Fig. 14.3. Specific heat curve of silver.

This is the classic example of a macroscopic phenomenon that is strongly dependent on the microscopic restrictions of quantum mechanics.

We can see the physical implications of the limiting cases $T \rightarrow 0$ and $T \rightarrow \infty$ more clearly by considering what happens to $\bar{n}(\nu)$, the average number of phonons (photons) present in the system at temperature T. When $T \rightarrow \infty$ in (14.8), we can put $e^{h\nu/kT} \approx 1 + h\nu/kT$, so that

$$\bar{n}_\nu \approx \frac{kT}{h\nu} \gg 1, \qquad T \rightarrow \infty \qquad (14.23)$$

This is just the result we would get by the classical procedure of assigning the equipartition energy kT to each vibrational degree of freedom and dividing it into arbitrary units $h\nu$. On the other hand, when $T \rightarrow 0$ the average number of phonons present is

$$\bar{n}_\nu \approx e^{-h\nu/kT} \ll \frac{kT}{h\nu} \ll 1, \qquad T \rightarrow 0 \qquad (14.24)$$

This is a decidedly nonclassical result, in which the average number of phonons present is much smaller than the number necessary to provide the equipartition energy kT. The quantity $e^{-h\nu/kT}$ is just the Boltzmann factor for an energy $E = h\nu$, and its appearance is intimately related with the quantum hypothesis that phonon (photon) energy comes only in discrete units $E = h\nu$. If continuous energy distribution were allowed, as in the classical case, the exponent in $e^{-E/kT}$ would automatically adjust so that the average value of E is kT.

This discussion provides a good example of the correspondence principle referred to in Chapter 9. Under conditions where the quantum numbers are large, quantum mechanics yields essentially classical results. Specifically quantum effects dominate only when the quantum numbers become small and it is no longer a good approximation to replace integers by average nonintegral values. Thus when $\bar{n}_\nu \gg 1$ as in (14.23), classical conditions prevail, and Dulong and Petit's law holds. On the other hand, when the temperature becomes so low that $h\nu \gtrsim kT$, the equipartition energy, we must count individual quanta one by one. In this case classical averages are not sufficient; in particular the specific heat deviates markedly from the classical value.

14.3. Specific heats of gases

As discussed in Chapter 2, the specific heats of gases contain three components, related to thermal energy in translational, rotational and vibrational motion of the molecules. The translational specific heat of $\frac{3}{2}R$ per mole does not show quantum mechanical effects, but the other specific heats have the same general property as that of solids. At sufficiently high temperatures where kT is much larger than the quanta associated with rotation and vibration of the molecule, the corresponding specific heats have their classical values. As the temperature decreases, first the vibrational and then the rotational motion is quenched. We are finally left with only translational motion and a corresponding specific heat $\frac{3}{2}R$. As an example Fig. 14.4 shows the specific heat of H_2 gas as a function of temperature.

We consider briefly the simplest case of diatomic molecules. Their vibration relative to each other approximates that of a harmonic oscillator with a natural frequency on the general order of $\nu = 10^4/\text{sec}$. The energy levels of a harmonic oscillator in quantum mechanics are (Chapter 10)

$$E_n = (n + \tfrac{1}{2})h\nu \qquad\qquad n = 0, 1, 2, \cdots \qquad (14.25)$$

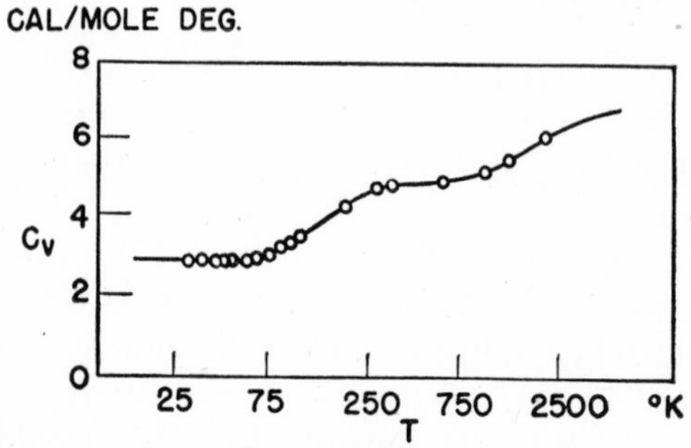

Fig. 14.4. Specific heat of hydrogen gas.

Here $\frac{1}{2}h\nu$ is the "zero-point energy" possessed by the oscillator even in its lowest state. At any temperature T, the average quantum number of excitation is

$$\bar{n} = \frac{\sum_0^\infty n e^{-En/kT}}{\sum_0^\infty e^{-En/kT}} = (e^{h\nu/kT} - 1)^{-1} \tag{14.26}$$

as in (14.8). Note that the extra $\frac{1}{2}h\nu$ is a constant factor and makes no difference in the derivation of $\bar{n}$. It also has no effect on the average vibrational energy of the molecule. Even at absolute zero, the oscillator will retain its $\frac{1}{2}h\nu$ of zero-point energy. We may therefore measure all vibrational energies from this $E_0 = \frac{1}{2}h\nu$ as a new reference point; the net available energy of an oscillator in an excited state E_n is then $E_n - E_0 = (n + \frac{1}{2})h\nu - \frac{1}{2}h\nu = nh\nu$. The average available vibrational energy per molecule is therefore

$$\bar{E} = \bar{n}h\nu = h\nu(e^{h\nu/kT} - 1)^{-1} \tag{14.27}$$

The vibrational heat per mole is

$$C_v = N_0 \frac{\partial \bar{E}}{\partial T} = R \left(\frac{\theta'}{T}\right)^2 e^{\theta'/T}(e^{\theta'/T} - 1)^{-2} \tag{14.28}$$

where $\theta' = h\nu/k$ and $R = N_0 k$. Here θ' is similar to the Debye temperature of (14.22), except that ν is the classical frequency of the gas molecule vibrations.

The behavior of (14.28) as a function of T is qualitatively the same as specific heat curve of a solid. Using the same approximations as for (14.23) and (14.24), we have

$$C_v \to R, \qquad\qquad T \to \infty$$
$$C_v \to R(\theta'/T)^2 e^{-\theta'/T} \to 0, \quad T \to 0 \tag{14.28a}$$

Thus at high temperatures the specific heat goes to the classical value of R per mole of one-dimensional oscillators; and at low temperatures $T \ll \theta'$, the vibrational specific heat falls to zero. For more complicated molecules with several independent modes of vibration the vibrational specific heat is a sum of terms like (14.28), each term corresponding to a classical vibration frequency of the molecule.

The similarity of the C_v curves for molecular vibration and for solids is of course not accidental. It arises from the fact that the average quantum number $\bar{n}$ is the same for the oscillator (14.26) as for the phonons or photons in a box. In the case of the solid the oscillator and phonon field pictures are just two slightly different ways of looking at the same thing. We could surely represent the solid as a sum of coupled oscillators, like a gigantic molecule. If we quantize the oscillators directly, we regard the thermal energy of the solid as residing in the excitation of the many individual atomic oscillators. On the other hand, if we first analyze the classical motions of these oscillators into a number of standing waves and then quantize this wave motion, the thermal energy resides in the phonons or quanta of this wave motion. We employed the second procedure in the previous section, but the two are mathematically equivalent. They differ only in the point at which quantization is introduced into the classical treatment.

This duality in the possible types of treatment carries over also to the case of photons, where we obtain the same expression (14.8) for $\bar{n}$. This implies that we can consider the electromagnetic field not only as decomposed into photons, but equivalently as comprising a set of oscillators of characteristic frequency ν. The presence of $n = 0, 1, 2, \cdots$ photons of frequency ν corresponds to the existence of the oscillator in its nth state of energy, $E_n = (n + \frac{1}{2})h\nu$. This concept of the field oscillators proves useful in some applications, particularly in dealing with the detailed quantum mechanics of the electromagnetic field. Frequently it appears in the derivation of the black body formula; for this reason the energies in Eq. (6.1) contain the extra $\frac{1}{2}h\nu$ of zero-point energy.

The zero-point energy of electromagnetic field oscillators is actually a source of some conceptual embarrassment. In this case, unlike that of a vibrating solid, there is no finite upper limit to the possible frequencies ν. This means that in a vacuum where no photons are present, the total energy of the equivalent field oscillators is

$$E = \int_0^\infty \tfrac{1}{2}h\nu \, d\nu = \infty \tag{14.29}$$

Thus we are led to the absurd conclusion that a vacuum has infinite energy, in comparison with which the finite energy of any real photon must be negligible. We can get around this difficulty by essentially the same method as used in discussing the molecular specific heat: since the zero-point energy is unavailable, we may as well measure energies from the zero-point energy as a new origin. That is, we define the divergent integral (14.29) to give us the zero point of our energy measurements. This procedure turns out to have no drawbacks for the present case: infinite energy never reappears or causes trouble in any applications. The general sort of difficulty represented by (14.29)—the appearance of divergent integrals and the necessity for removing them by "renormalization" of our measurements—appears rather frequently in the most advanced applications of modern quantum theory. In some cases it is possible to remove the divergences by special procedures, as above; but some divergences remain and there is at present no general assurance that they can be circumvented.

The rotational specific heat of a diatomic molecule comes from considering the quantized energy levels of a rigid rotator. When the molecule is not oscillating too strongly, it approximates a rigid rotator. The moment of inertia about the axis joining the atoms is zero, but the moment of inertia about a direction perpendicular to this axis has the value I. If the frequency of rotation is ω, the angular momentum and energy of rotation are

$$L = I\omega, \qquad E = \tfrac{1}{2}I\omega^2 = L^2/2I \qquad (14.30)$$

Classically these quantities may have any value; but quantum mechanics restricts them to $L^2 = l(l + 1)\hbar^2$. Hence the energy levels of the rotator in wave mechanics are

$$E_l = l(l + 1)\hbar^2/2I, \qquad\qquad l = 0, 1, 2, \cdots \qquad (14.31)$$

We obtain the average rotational C_v at temperature T energy by the same procedure as above, except that we must insert a statistical weight factor $(2l + 1)$ for the lth energy level. This factor is the degree of degeneracy of a given level due to the different possible values of $m = L_z/\hbar$, as discussed in Chapter 12. The average rotational energy per molecule is therefore

$$\bar{E} = \frac{\hbar^2}{2I} \sum_{l=0}^{\infty} \frac{l(l + 1)(2l + 1)e^{-l(l+1)\hbar^2/2IkT}}{\sum_{l=0}^{\infty} (2l + 1)e^{-l(l+1)\hbar^2/2IkT}} \qquad (14.32)$$

The specific heat derived from this expression has qualitatively the same features as the other specific heats. If the characteristic temperature is $\theta'' = (\hbar^2/2Ik)$, the rotational C_v per mole is

$$
\begin{aligned}
C_v &\to R, & T &\gg \theta'' \\
C_v &\to 0, & T &\ll \theta''
\end{aligned}
\qquad (14.33)
$$

For diatomic molecules the characteristic θ'' is generally an order of magnitude (factor of 10) smaller than θ'. We are therefore able to assign a C_v jump at lower temperature to rotational motion and a second jump at higher temperature to vibrational motion, as in Fig. 14.4.

14.4. Fermi-Dirac and Bose-Einstein statistics

Although we obtained the energy distribution (14.10) for photons of zero rest mass in an enclosure of volume V, we can make the same derivation apply exactly to material particles. The basic Eqs. (14.1) that lead to the statistical weight dn' do not involve the rest mass of the particles, so that we can take over dn' directly, provided that we use the original form (14.2) in terms of particle momenta. The form (14.9) is a special case valid only for rest mass equal to zero. In order to take over the factor $\bar{n}$ to the case of material particles, we must make a couple of modifications. One is the trivial change of substituting $W/h = \nu$ for the argument of $\bar{n}(\nu)$, where W is an energy associated with the particle. For the sake of generality we put

$$W = E + E_0 \tag{14.34}$$

where E is the energy we wish to consider (for example $E = p^2/2m$, the nonrelativistic kinetic energy of a particle of rest mass m) and E_0 is any residual energy like zero-point energies. The second step in taking over $\bar{n}$ from the photon case is more fundamental and is in the nature of a physical assumption. The occupation numbers $n = 0, 1, 2, \cdots$ indicate the number of photons of a given frequency present in the enclosure. The fact that n may take any arbitrarily large value means that any number of photons of a given energy may be present. For quantization in a large box, each energy corresponds to a given set of quantum numbers. Hence to apply $\bar{n}$ to material particles, we must assume that the particles are of such a nature that any number of them can be present in the box with identical quantum numbers.

This assumption is just the opposite of the exclusion principle, which allows at most one particle in a system with a given set of quantum numbers. In a system of identical particles, the individual members cannot differ in their intrinsic properties. But particles satisfying the exclusion principle must have different quantum numbers and in this sense must be "distinguishable." For the case of photons in a box, however, even the external quantum numbers can be the same for several particles, which are then totally indistinguishable under any measurement. Thus we can call particles "distinguishable" or "indistinguishable" according to the way in which they fill up the states of an external system, remembering that, of course, the particles are always identical with respect to their intrinsic properties.

In applying the law (14.10) to material particles, it is thus of paramount importance to know whether the particles are distinguishable or indistinguishable. Distinguishable particles like the electron are said to have Fermi-Dirac statistics; indistinguishable particles like photons are said to have Bose-Einstein statistics. If the material particles we are considering have Bose-Einstein statistics, their energy distribution follows (14.10),

$$dE = E\bar{n}(E)\, dn = \frac{SV\, d\Omega_p\, Ep^2\, dp}{(2\pi\hbar)^3} \left(\frac{e^{E/kT}}{A} - 1 \right)^{-1} \tag{14.35}$$

Here $A = e^{-E_0/kT}$ and S is a statistical factor for the particular particles concerned: $S = 2$ for photons with two polarizations, $S = 1$ for simple, monatomic molecules with total intrinsic angular momentum $F = 0$. We have used the earliest form (14.2) of the statistical factor dn'.

The number distribution of Bose-Einstein gas molecules corresponding to (14.35) is

$$dN = \frac{V \, d\Omega_p \, p^2 \, dp}{(2\pi\hbar)^3} \left(\frac{e^{E/kT}}{A} - 1 \right)^{-1} \tag{14.36}$$

Our previous experience with specific heats leads us to expect that for sufficiently high T, (14.36) should approach the Maxwell-Boltzmann distribution (2.23) of classical kinetic theory. We can verify this expectation in the following manner: suppose that the constant $A \ll 1$, so that the term -1 is negligible in the denominators of (14.35) and (14.36), and

$$dN \approx \frac{V \, d\Omega_p \, p^2 \, dp}{(2\pi\hbar)^3} \, A e^{-E/kT} \tag{14.37}$$

If the total number of gas molecules per cm^3 is n_0, then with $p = mv$,

$$n_0 = \frac{1}{V} \int dN \approx A4\pi \left(\frac{m}{2\pi\hbar} \right)^3 \int_0^\infty v^2 \, dv \, e^{-mv^2/2kT}$$
$$\approx A4\pi \left(\frac{m}{2\pi\hbar} \right)^3 \frac{\sqrt{\pi}}{4} \left(\frac{2kT}{m} \right)^{3/2} \tag{14.38}$$

or hence

$$A \approx n_0 (2\pi\hbar^2/mkT)^{3/2} \tag{14.39}$$

The integrand in (14.38) is just the Maxwell-Boltzmann distribution (2.23). The condition that (14.37) be a good approximation is that $A \ll 1$, and (14.39) shows that this is in fact true for $T \to \infty$ or $n_0 \to 0$. Thus classical statistics appear as a limiting case of Bose-Einstein statistics for high temperatures and low densities. These are just the conditions for ideal gas behavior. Thus a classical ideal gas has Maxwell-Boltzmann statistics; the Bose-Einstein and Fermi-Dirac statistics represent deviations from ideal gas behavior.

If the particles are like electrons and display Fermi-Dirac statistics, we must find a new expression for $\bar{n}$ appropriate to this case. For any given energy state W available to the particles, there are only two possibilities: either there are no particles present in that state, or there is one particle present. The ratio of probabilities for these two conditions is $p_0 : p_1 = 1 : e^{-W/kT}$ by the Boltzmann principle. The average number of particles in the state is equal to the absolute probability of finding one particle present:

$$\bar{n}(w) = \frac{p_1}{p_0 + p_1} = \frac{e^{-W/kT}}{1 + e^{-W/kT}} = (e^{W/kT} + 1)^{-1} \qquad (14.40)$$

This resembles (14.8) with the important difference that the -1 is replaced by $+1$. The number distribution for Fermi-Dirac statistics is accordingly

$$dN = \frac{SV \, d\Omega_p \, p^2 \, dp}{(2\pi\hbar)^3} \left(\frac{e^{E/kT}}{A} + 1 \right)^{-1} \qquad (14.41)$$

This distribution also goes to the classical Maxwell-Boltzmann distribution as $T \to \infty$. The argument is exactly the same as for the Bose-Einstein case: when $A \to 0$, it does not matter whether the negligible term is $+1$ or -1. The general conclusion is that the classical distribution is the limiting form of all quantum mechanical distributions as $T \to \infty$. This example illustrates the universality of the correspondence principle.

It is only at low temperatures that the quantum statistical distributions differ appreciably from classical statistics and from each other. For Bose-Einstein statistics the effect of $T \to 0$ is to concentrate all the particles at a single energy; we then say that the gas is *degenerate*. In practice this degeneracy is confused by other phenomena such as the deviation of the gas molecules from ideal, pointlike behavior (finite size). For the Fermi-Dirac case, however, an interesting and distinctive result occurs. Suppose that as $T \to 0$ the constant $A \to \infty$ in the form $A = e^{E_0/kT}$, where E_0 is a constant. Then the $\bar{n}$ factor in (14.41) becomes

$$[e^{(E-E_0)/kT} + 1]^{-1} = 1 \quad \text{for} \quad E < E_0 \Big\} \qquad T \to 0 \qquad (14.42)$$
$$= 0 \quad \text{for} \quad E > E_0 \Big\}$$

We can evaluate the constant E_0 by requiring (14.41) to fit a given density n_0 of particles per cm^3:

$$n_0 = \frac{1}{V} \int dN = \frac{4\pi S}{(2\pi\hbar)^3} \int_0^{p_0} p^2 \, dp = \frac{4\pi}{3} S \left(\frac{p_0}{2\pi\hbar} \right)^3 \qquad (14.43)$$

where the cutoff momentum p_0 corresponds to the cutoff energy E_0.

The Fermi-Dirac distribution function dN/V is plotted in Fig. 14.5 for $T = 0$ and for an elevated temperature. The change in shape of the distribution is relatively slight for ordinary temperatures and affects mostly the high energy particles.

14.5. "Electron gas" in metals

In a crystalline solid most of the electrons are tightly bound to nuclei at the lattice points. If the solid is a good conductor of electricity, however, the outermost electrons of each atom are relatively free to wander from one lattice position to the next. These electrons are responsible for the conduction of electricity. If we make the simplifying though not entirely realistic assumption that the conduction electrons are completely free to move without interference through the solid, we can treat them as an ideal "electron gas." By comparing the expected properties of this electron gas with observations on metals, we can show that the assumption of freely moving conduction electrons is a reasonable first approximation.

There are two points of interest that lead us to consider the electron gas. The first is that it follows the exclusion principle and hence Fermi-Dirac statistics. These are peculiarly quantum-mechanical restrictions that do not exist for a classical gas. In the second place, the small mass of the electrons means that they go over from quantum mechanical to classical behavior at very high temperatures. According to (14.39) the condition for classical behavior of a gas is that $n_0(2\pi\hbar^2/mkT)^{3/2} \gg 1$. The temperature T at which this condition obtains is obviously in inverse proportion to m. Thus we can expect the electron gas to show quantum mechanical behavior up to temperatures several thousand times that at which ordinary gases display quantum effects. In fact, the energy distribution of the electron gas in metals still has distinctly nonclassical features at the highest attainable temperatures. The $T > 0$ curve of Fig. 14.5 corresponds to an electron gas at about 2000°K.

To evaluate the Fermi-distribution functions for electrons in a metal, we assume a certain number g of conduction electrons per atom, expecting that g will generally be on the order of 1. For electrons the statistical weight factor is $S = 2$, because of the two possible orientations of electron spin, $m_s = \pm\frac{1}{2}$. Then for a metal of density ρ and atomic weight A, Eq. (14.43) becomes

$$n_0 = \frac{gN_0\rho}{A} = \frac{8\pi}{3}\left(\frac{p_0}{2\pi\hbar}\right)^3 \tag{14.43a}$$

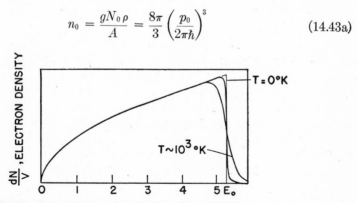

Fig. 14.5. Fermi-Dirac distribution of conduction electrons in a metal. E_0 is in ev units.

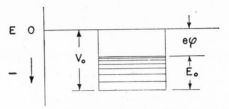

Fig. 14.6. Conduction electrons in a metal, regarded as a potential well.

$$E_0 = \frac{p_0^2}{2m} = \left(\frac{3gN_0\rho}{8\pi A}\right)^{2/3}\frac{4\pi^2\hbar^2}{2m} = 26\left(\frac{g\rho}{A}\right)^{2/3} \text{ ev} \quad (14.43b)$$

For metals $(g\rho/A)^{2/3}$ is on the order of $\frac{1}{3}$, so that the maximum energy is on the order of 10 ev above the lowest possible energy for the conduction electrons. The conduction electrons normally remain bound in the metal, and it requires an additional energy $e\varphi$ to liberate any electrons. We therefore draw an energy diagram of the conduction electrons as in Fig. 14.6. The metal appears to the conduction electrons as a sort of potential energy well. The top of the well is at energy $E = 0$, where an electron can escape from the metal; the bottom of the well is at energy $-V_0$. The electrons fill up all the energy states in the well to a level E_0 above the bottom. These highest electrons have energy $E_0 - V_0 = -e\varphi$, where $e\varphi$ is the minimum energy necessary to liberate any electron from the metal. Thus the potential depth inside the metal is

$$V_0 = E_0 + e\varphi \qquad (14.44)$$

Since both E_0 and $e\varphi$ are on the order of 5–10 ev, V_0 is of order 10–20 ev. This discussion and Fig. 14.6 apply to the electron distribution at $T = 0°\text{K}$, but are substantially valid in general because the distribution of Fig. 14.5 varies so little with temperature.

It is of interest to look for direct confirmation of the potential V_0, since this would provide indirect evidence for this model of the conduction electrons in a metal. In particular, establishment of a value $V_0 > e\varphi$ would lend support to the Fermi-Dirac statistical treatment of the electron gas. A direct measure of the potential V_0 appears in the experiments of Davisson and Germer (Chapter 9). If the potential is really present in the interior of a metal, an electron of kinetic energy eV outside the metal should have a kinetic energy $e(V + V_0)$ inside the metal. Here V is the accelerating potential applied to produce the bombarding electron beam. By de Broglie's hypothesis (9.26), the wavelengths of the corresponding electron wave inside and outside the crystal should be in the ratio

$$\frac{\lambda_o}{\lambda_i} = \frac{p_i}{p_o} = \sqrt{1 + \frac{V_0}{V}} = n \qquad (14.45)$$

Here n is the effective refractive index of the metal crystal as seen by an electron wave entering from the outside region, where we take $n = 1$.

If $V \gg V_0$, the refractive index of the crystal does not differ much from $n = 1$, and we may apply Bragg's law directly as in Chapter 9 to obtain verification of de Broglie's hypothesis. If V is of the same magnitude as V_0, however, n becomes appreciably greater than unity. In this case the electron wave not only undergoes Bragg reflection inside the crystal, but also suffers observable refraction at the crystal surface. In the simplest case where the Bragg planes are parallel to the crystal surface, Bragg's law becomes

$$j\lambda = 2d \sqrt{n^2 - \cos^2 \theta} \tag{14.46}$$

where θ is the apparent reflection angle observed in the laboratory system. This equation reduces to the usual (5.12) when $n = 1$.

Interpretation of the electron diffraction measurements with (14.46) allows a determination of the effective index of refraction n, and from this an evaluation of V_0 by (14.45). Measurements on nickel reveal that $V_0 \approx 17$ v, and for zinc $V_0 = 15$ v. These potentials are considerably larger than the respective work functions $\varphi = 4.6$ v and 4.2 v of these metals. The experiment thus provides direct support for the Fermi-Dirac distribution of electrons in a metal.

At temperatures above $T = 0$ there will be a few electrons with energies $E > E_0$, so that thermionic emission of electrons from the metal can occur. We have estimated the thermionic current in Chapter 2 for the classical Maxwell-Boltzmann distribution; it turns out that Fermi-Dirac statistics give a similar result. We repeat for the present case the arguments that led to (2.26). The electrons that escape from the metal surface, taken perpendicular to the x-direction, must have a kinetic energy of at least $eV_0 = p^2/2m$ as measured from the bottom of the Fermi well. The y-, z-components of their velocities are parallel to the metal surface and of no consequence for emission, so that we integrate over all values of the corresponding momenta. The rate of emission of electrons is also proportional to v_x, the speed with which electrons approach the surface. Writing (14.41) in Cartesian coordinates, we have for the emission rate

$$j = \int v_x \frac{dN}{V} = \frac{2}{(2\pi\hbar)^3} \int v_x \, dp_x \, dp_y \, dp_z \left(\frac{e^{E/kT}}{A} + 1 \right)^{-1} \tag{14.47}$$

Since $E \geq eV_0 \gg kT$ for emission, we can neglect the term 1 in the parentheses, and the last factor becomes just $Ae^{-E/kT} = e^{(E-E_0)/kT}$. The integrations now proceed as for (2.26): the integral over all p_y values gives a factor $(2\pi mkT)^{1/2}$, as does the integral over all p_z. Integrating over p_x from $\sqrt{2m\epsilon V_0}$ to ∞ gives a factor $kTe^{(E_0-\epsilon V_0)/kT} = kTe^{-\epsilon\varphi/kT}$. Thus the rate of emission of electrons per cm² of surface is

$$j = \frac{mk^2}{2\pi^2\hbar^3} T^2 e^{-\epsilon\varphi/kT} \tag{14.48}$$

The electric current density is $J = \epsilon j$, where here ϵ is the electron charge to distinguish it from the mathematical symbol e.

The expression (14.48) is similar in form to the classical Eq. (2.26). The dominant factor $e^{-e\varphi/kT}$ appears in each case. The principal difference is the temperature dependence T^2 in (14.48) as opposed to $T^{1/2}$ in (2.26). Because of the dominance of the exponential factor, it has not been possible so far to distinguish experimentally between these two formulas. We conclude, therefore, that the Fermi-Dirac electron gas gives practically classical results for thermionic emission, even though the electron distribution still retains the nonclassical form of Fig. 14.5. This is because we have restricted ourselves for this process to the small fraction of electrons in the high-energy "tail" of the distribution. This tail evidently behaves in a classical fashion, although the bulk of the distribution does not.

To find nonclassical properties of this electron gas, we must consider a phenomenon that involves the bulk of the electrons rather than the high energy part. One such phenomenon is the specific heat C_v, already discussed for several other cases in preceding sections. Our general experience with previous cases indicates that quantum mechanical effects make $C_v \to 0$ for $T \ll \theta$, some characteristic temperature. We have also seen that the characteristic temperature for electrons is enormously high because of their small mass. Thus we anticipate that C_v for electrons will be very small.

The procedure for obtaining C_v is as before: using (14.41), we compute the internal energy of the electrons at some finite temperature T, $U = \int E \, dN$. Then $C_v = \partial U/\partial T$. The mathematical operations cannot be carried out in closed form, but after some algebra we obtain the approximate result for the specific heat per mole of conduction electrons

$$C_v \approx R \frac{mkT}{4\hbar^2} \left(\frac{3N_0 \, g\rho}{8\pi A}\right)^{-2/3} \approx R \frac{5kT}{E_0} \tag{14.49}$$

At room temperature $kT \approx \frac{1}{40}$ ev, while we have seen that metals have $E_0 \approx 10$ ev. Thus $C_v \approx 10^{-2}R$ per mole of electron gas at room temperature. On a classical basis we should have had to assign the usual $C_v = \frac{3}{2}R$ per mole to the electrons as a monatomic gas; the specific heat of solids would then have been $\frac{3}{2}R + 3R = \frac{9}{2}R$ on inclusion of the atomic vibrations as in section 14.2 above. Even at temperatures high enough to give a good approach to the law of Dulong and Petit for the atomic vibrations, there is no experimental evidence for an additional $\frac{3}{2}R$ due to the electrons. The absence of this specific heat term is further evidence for the necessity of quantum statistics for the electron gas.

The electron specific heat is difficult to observe at ordinary temperatures because of its small magnitude relative to the C_v of lattice vibrations. Equation (14.49) has the feature, however, that it holds down to $T = 0$. Thus at very low temperatures C_v (lattice) $\sim T^3$ and C_v (electron) $\sim T$, so that the electron specific heat will exceed the lattice specific heat as $T \rightarrow 0$. The electron specific heat with its characteristic linear T dependence is actually observed at temperatures a few degrees above absolute zero.

SUMMARY

Classical statistical mechanics forms the connection between microscopic and macroscopic phenomena. Quantum statistical mechanics involves a reworking of some details of this connection in order to introduce quantum mechanical restrictions into the microscopic phenomena. These restrictions do not appreciably affect the large-scale behavior of matter as long as the equipartition energy kT is large compared with the energy differences of the quantum states concerned. As $T \rightarrow 0$ this condition fails, and quantum effects become important.

Black body radiation is a case where quantum effects are always of importance. The statistical weight factor of photons in an enclosure is $dn = SV \, d\Omega \, p^2 \, dp/(2\pi\hbar)^3$ with $S = 2$ for two directions of polarization: a similar statistical weight factor is common to all free waves or particles in quantum mechanics. The average number of photons present with frequency ν is $\bar{n}(\nu) = (e^{h\nu/kT} - 1)^{-1}$. Only a quantum mechanical treatment is which $h\nu$ assumes a fixed value and does not go to zero with kT is capable of explaining the shape of the black body spectrum, which goes to zero as $\nu \rightarrow 0$ and as $\nu \rightarrow \infty$.

The elastic vibrations of crystalline solids provide another type of wave motion that can be quantized; the corresponding quanta are phonons. By cutting off the phonon frequencies at a maximum ν_0 characteristic of the solid, we obtain an expression for the internal energy and hence specific heat of the solid. These formulas contain a parameter $\theta = h\nu_0/k$, the Debye temperature, which is characteristic of the solid. For $T > \theta$, the specific heat C_v approaches the classical value of $3R$ per mole; for $T \ll \theta$, $C_v \rightarrow 0$ as $(T/\theta)^3$. Thus quantum mechanics accounts for the deviations from the law of Dulong and Petit.

Similar considerations apply to the specific heats of gas molecules, both rotational and vibrational. At sufficiently low temperatures

$C_v \rightarrow 0$ for both types of motion. For diatomic molecules C_v (rotational) $\rightarrow R$, the classical value, at moderate temperatures; and at higher temperatures C_v (vibrational) $\rightarrow R$ also.

The similarity of the vibrational specific heat of a molecule with the phonon and photon energy formulas suggests that the phonon and photon fields are equivalent to a number of harmonic oscillators. This is physically true for the phonon case and proves to be a useful concept for the photons as well.

The phonon and photon cases represent a type of statistics in which the particles are indistinguishable from each other. This is the Bose-Einstein statistics, in which any number of particles can have the same quantum numbers. If on the other hand the particles are quantized according to the exclusion principle they must be strictly distinguishable, and no two particles can have identical quantum numbers. This is the Fermi-Dirac statistics, for which

$$\bar{n} = \left(\frac{e^{E/kT}}{A} + 1 \right)^{-1}.$$

The Fermi-Dirac statistics apply to the "electron gas" of conduction electrons in a metal. Because of the light mass of the electrons, the corresponding distribution dN changes only slightly over all available temperatures and always resembles its form at $T = 0$. This form is a distribution from $E = 0$ up to a certain maximum $E_0 \approx 10$ ev for most metals. The top of this distribution is still below the energy for escape from the metal by the amount of the work function $e\varphi$, which is on the order of 5 ev. The conduction electrons therefore seem to find themselves in a potential well in the metal of depth $V_0 \approx 15$ ev. The real existence of this potential V_0 is found in the Davisson-Germer experiments on diffraction and refraction of electrons by metal crystals. The specific heat associated with the electron gas at room temperature is, contrary to classical predictions, negligible in comparison with the specific heat of the lattice vibrations. Only as $T \rightarrow 0$ does the electron specific heat predominate. The thermionic emission law on the quantum mechanical model has a factor T^2 instead of $T^{1/2}$ as in the classical case. This difference is not significant because of the dominant $e^{-e\varphi/kT}$ term in both formulas.

REFERENCES

M. Born, *Atomic Physics*, Hafner, New York (1952).

C. J. Davisson and L. H. Germer, *Proc. Nat. Acad. Sci.*, **14**, 1619 (1928).

A. Eucken, *Handbuch der Experimentalphysik*, Vol. 8, Akademische Verlagsgesellschaft M. b. H., Leipzig (1929).

J. C. Slater, *Introduction to Chemical Physics*, McGraw-Hill, New York (1939).

H. S. Taylor and S. Glasstone, *A Treatise on Physical Chemistry*, Vol. 1, Van Nostrand, New York (1942).

ILLUSTRATIVE PROBLEMS

1. Quantum mechanics has the feature of reversibility. For any detailed process there exists a corresponding reverse process, described by the same basic formulas (matrix elements). The only difference between the forward and reverse formulas is the various statistical weight factors involved. Hence if we have a formula for the rate at which an atom radiates photons in going from state n to state n', we can deduce the rate at which it goes from n' to n by absorbing photons, merely by considering statistical factors. This procedure is sometimes called the method of *detailed balancing*.

Consider a photoelectric effect in which an electron in an atom goes from state n' to state n by absorbing a photon of frequency $\nu_{nn'}$. This is the reverse of the emission process described by emission formula (10.85). Obtain a quantitative formula for the photoabsorption from (10.85) and the principle of detailed balancing.

Solution. In order to use the principle of detailed balancing, we must write the expression for radiative emission (10.85) in a form that exhibits the statistical weight factor (14.9) for the emitted photon. Accordingly we write for the emission rate

$$\frac{1}{\tau_{n \to n'}} = \frac{1}{\tau_e} = |M|^2 \left(\frac{8\pi V \nu^2 \, d\nu}{c^3} \right) \tag{14.50}$$

The second factor in Eq. (14.50) is the statistical weight factor; the remaining quantity $|M|^2$ is a matrix element that is the same for the transitions $n \to n'$ and $n' \to n$. Thus the rate for the absorption process is

$$\frac{1}{\tau_{n' \to n}} = \frac{1}{\tau_a} = |M|^2 \left| \frac{E'}{E_0} \right|^2 \tag{14.51}$$

Here $|E'|$ is the magnitude of the electric vector of the light ray inducing the photoelectric absorption, and $|E_0|$ is the amplitude of this vector for the emitted photon in (10.85). In Eq. (14.51) the factor $|M|^2$ just comes from detailed balancing, as discussed above; and since the absorption rate must obviously be proportional to the intensity of the incident light beam, we have to add a factor $|E'/E_0|^2$.

The value of $|E_0|^2$ is given by (6.4) as $|E_0|^2 = 2\pi h\nu/V$, where V is the same mathematical large box as in the statistical weight factor (14.2b). Substituting this factor into Eqs. (14.50) and (14.51), we have

$$\frac{1}{\tau_a} = \frac{1}{\tau_e} \frac{|E'|^2}{2\pi \, d\nu} \frac{c^3}{8\pi h\nu^3} \tag{14.52}$$

Just as in the derivation of (6.4), we must in quantum mechanics separate the electric vector of a light wave $E \cos \omega t$ into two parts, positive and negative frequencies, $E \cos \omega t = \frac{1}{2}Ee^{i\omega t} + \frac{1}{2}Ee^{-i\omega t}$. Only one frequency participates in any quantum mechanical transition, so that the factor E' appearing in Eq. (14.52) is actually $E/2$, where E is the classical amplitude of the light wave. The energy density of this light wave is $|E|^2/8\pi = \rho(\nu) \, d\nu = |E'|^2/2\pi$ where $\rho(\nu)$ is the energy density per unit frequency range of the incident beam. Thus

$$\frac{1}{\tau_a} = \frac{1}{\tau_e} \frac{|E'|^2}{2\pi \, d\nu} \frac{c^3}{8\pi h\nu^3}$$

$$= \rho(\nu) \frac{c^3}{8\pi h\nu^3} \frac{1}{\tau_e}$$

$$= \rho(\nu) \frac{2\pi}{3} \frac{\alpha c}{\hbar} (|\langle x \rangle|^2 + |\langle y \rangle|^2 + |\langle z \rangle|^2)$$

2. Show that the average energy of a quantized rotator goes to the classical value for large kT.

Solution. When $kT \to \infty$ it is a sufficient approximation to replace the sums by integrals in Eq. (14.32). If we let $l(l+1) = y$, then $2l + 1 = dy$, and

$$\bar{E} = \frac{\hbar^2}{2I} \frac{\displaystyle\int_0^\infty y \, dy \, e^{-y\hbar^2/2IkT}}{\displaystyle\int_0^\infty dy \, e^{-y\hbar^2/2IkT}} = \frac{\hbar^2}{2I} \left(\frac{2IkT}{\hbar^2}\right)^2 \times \left(\frac{2IkT}{\hbar^2}\right)^{-1} = kT$$

the classical value for the rotation of a diatomic molecule.

3. Suppose that we had some sort of intermediate statistics in which the maximum number of particles in a system that could have all quantum numbers the same was N. Find the average occupation number $\bar{n}(E)$ for particles of energy E in equilibrium at temperature T. Electrons have two spin orientations, so that we might try to satisfy the exclusion principle by taking $N = 2$. Would this be correct?

Solution. Let $y = e^{-E/kT}$. Then

$$\bar{n} = \frac{\sum\limits_{n=0}^{N} ny^n}{\sum\limits_{n=0}^{N} y^n} = y \frac{d}{dy} \log \left(\sum_0^N y^n \right)$$

$$= y \frac{d}{dy} [\log (1 - y^{N+1}) - \log (1 - y)]$$

$$= y \left[\frac{1}{1 - y} - \frac{(N + 1)y^N}{1 - y^{N+1}} \right]$$

For $N = 1$ we get $\bar{n} = y/(1 + y) = (e^{E/kT} + 1)^{-1}$, the Fermi-Dirac case. For $N \to \infty$ the term in $(N + 1)y^N \to 0$, since $y < 1$, and we have

$$\bar{n} = y/(1 - y) = (e^{E/kT} - 1)^{-1}$$

the Bose-Einstein case.

To treat electrons as a case with $N = 2$ would be correct only if the two spin states were indistinguishable. This would imply that the electrons can convert freely from $m_s = +\frac{1}{2}$ to $m_s = -\frac{1}{2}$ states. The conservation of angular momentum, however, requires that the total z-component of the electron spin be a constant: $\sum m_{s_i} = $ const where the sum runs over all conduction electrons in the solid. This condition means that the electrons are not free to convert their spins, so that the $N = 2$ case is not correct. We should use $N = 1$ with a statistical factor $S = 2$ for the electron spin.

Particles obeying such intermediate statistics appear not to be mathematically inconsistent, but none are now known.

PROBLEMS

1. Obtain dn/dE for relativistic particles; show how this expression goes over in limiting cases to that for (a) nonrelativistic particles; (b) particles of zero rest mass.

2. Derive (14.11).

3. The specific heat of copper as a function of absolute temperature in °K is as follows (E. H. and E. Griffiths, *Proc. Roy. Soc.*, **90**, 557 (1914):

T (°K):	23.5	50	90	130	170	210	250	290	390
C_v (cal/mole):	0.22	1.32	3.46	4.73	5.16	5.40	5.58	5.67	5.85

Using $R = 1.985$ cal/mole and the curve of Fig. 14.3 for the Debye function, determine the Debye temperature of copper.

4. Calculate the specific heat C_v of a black box full of radiation at temperature T. Why has this specific heat no upper limit, as contrasted with the case for solids?

5. The velocity of sound and observed Debye temperature for various substances are

Substance	Al	Fe	Ag	Cd	Pt	Pb
$c'(10^5$ cm/sec)	3.4	3.5	1.8	1.6	1.9	.75
$\theta(°K)$	398	420	215	160	225	88

Compute the expected Debye temperature from c' and compare with the observed θ. Here c' is an average effective velocity over all polarizations of the phonons.

6. Use as a general principle the fact that quantum mechanical effects are of significance for macroscopic phenomena only when kT is on the order of the spacing of individual quantum levels for the system. Compute the approximate temperature at which the translational specific heat of He gas will show quantum effects when the gas fills a 1-liter container 10 cm on a side. What can you deduce in general about the possibility of observing such effects in gases?

7. From the data given in section 14.5 on E_0 for nickel and zinc, compute the number of free electrons g per atom of these metals.

8. Besides conduction electrons in metals, another and cruder application of the Fermi well is to neutrons and protons in nuclei. Are Fermi-Dirac statistics appropriate to these particles? Take the binding energy of the most loosely bound nucleon in a nucleus to be $B_0 = 8$ mev, and take the nuclear Fermi well to be a sphere of radius $R = r_0 A^{1/3}$, where $A = N + Z$ and N is the number of neutrons, Z the number of protons in the nucleus; take $r_0 = 1.2 \times 10^{-13}$ cm. What is the depth V_0 of the well? What is the average binding energy per particle? (Assume $N \approx Z \approx A/2$.)

9. Using the observed values of θ in problem 5, find the approximate temperatures at which the expected C_v (electrons) $> C_v$ (lattice) for Al, Ag, Pt, Pb. Use $E_0 \approx 10$ ev.

10. The sum $f = \sum_i S_i e^{-E_i/kT}$ of the Boltzmann factor over all states of a quantum mechanical system is called the partition function. Here S_i is a statistical weight factor. The partition function is a useful device in statistical applications, particularly to thermodynamic quantities.

Show that the average energy and specific heat are

$$\bar{E} = kT^2 \frac{\partial}{\partial T} \ln f$$

$$C_v = \frac{\partial \bar{E}}{\partial T} = \frac{2\bar{E}}{T} + kT^2 \frac{\partial^2 \ln f}{\partial T^2}.$$

For the diatomic molecule, show that $f = f_t f_r f_v$, where the f's are separate partition functions for translation, rotation, and vibration; show that therefore $\bar{E} = \bar{E}_t + \bar{E}_r + \bar{E}_v$, $C_v = C_v(t) + C_v(r) + C_v(v)$. Write the f_t, f_r, f_v explicitly.

Appendix I

MATHEMATICAL SYMBOLS AND NOTATION

$\rightarrow$ approaches; in diagrams, indicates direction of increasing co-ordinate

$\sim$ proportional to

$\approx$ approximately equal to

$\neq$ not equal to

$\equiv$ identical with

$>$ greater than

$\gg$ much greater than

$\geq$ greater than or equal to

$\gtrsim$ greater than or approximately equal to

$<$ less than

$\ll$ much less than

$\leq$ less than or equal to

$\lesssim$ less than or approximately equal to

∞ infinity

$n! = n(n-1)(n-2) \cdots 3 \cdot 2 \cdot 1$ for $n = $ integer

$$= \int_0^\infty x^n e^{-x}\, dx \text{ in general}$$

$\sin x = x - x^3/6 + \cdots + (-1)^n x^{2n+1}/(2n+1)! + \cdots$

$\cos x = 1 - x^2/2 + \cdots + (-1)^n x^{2n}/(2n)! + \cdots$

$e^x = 1 - x + x^2/2 - x^3/6 + \cdots + (-1)^n x^n/n! + \cdots$

$\dfrac{1}{1-x} = 1 + x + x^2 + x^3 \cdots$

$1/\sqrt{1-x^2} = 1 + x^2/2 + \frac{3}{8}x^4 + \cdots$

$i = $ imaginary unit, $i^2 = -1$

$z = x + iy$, complex number

$z^* = x - iy$, complex conjugate

$Re(z) = x = \frac{1}{2}(z + z^*)$, real part of a complex number

$Im(z) = y = \frac{1}{2}i(z^* - z)$, imaginary part of a complex number

$|z| = \sqrt{x^2 + y^2} = (zz^*)^{1/2}$, absolute value or magnitude

$e^{iz} = \cos z + i \sin z$, imaginary exponential

i, j, k, unit vectors in the x-, y-, z- directions

$A = A_x i + A_y j + A_z k$, vector with components (A_x, A_y, A_z)

$| A |$ or $A = \sqrt{A_x^2 + A_y^2 + A_z^2}$, magnitude or length of vector A

$A \cdot B = A_x B_x + A_y B_y + A_z B_z = AB \cos \theta$, scalar (dot) product

$A \times B = i(A_y B_z - A_z B_y) + j(A_z B_x - A_x B_z) + k(A_x B_y - A_y B_x)$,

vector (cross) product

$A \times (B \times C) = B(A \cdot C) - C(A \cdot B)$, vector identity

$\nabla = i\, \partial/\partial_x + j\, \partial/\partial_y + k\, \partial/\partial_z$, vector derivative operator

$\nabla = \nabla \cdot \nabla = \partial^2/\partial_x^2 + \partial^2/\partial_y^2 + \partial^2/\partial_z^2$, Laplacian

SOME PROPERTIES OF THE ELEMENTS

Z = atomic number

A = atomic weight on chemical scale

ρ = density. At 20°C if solid at this temperature, otherwise liquid at boiling point

mp = melting point in °C

bp = boiling point in °C

V_1 = first ionization potential in volts for free atoms

Element	Symbol	Z	A	ρ	mp	bp	V_i
Actinium	Ac	89	227				
Aluminum	Al	13	26.97	2.70	660	1800	5.98
Americium	Am	95	(243)				
Antimony (Stibium)	Sb	51	121.76	6.69	630	1380	8.64
Argon	A	18	39.94	1.40	−186	−189	15.76
Arsenic	As	33	74.91	5.73	sublimes	615	10
Astatine	At	85	211				
Barium	Ba	56	137.36	3.5	850	1140	5.21
Beryllium	Be	4	9.02	1.8	1350	1510	9.32
Bismuth	Bi	83	209.00	9.78	270	1450	8
Boron	B	5	10.82	1.73–2.54	2300	2550	8.30
Bromine	Br	35	79.92	2.93	−7.2	58.8	11.84
Cadmium	Cd	48	112.41	8.65	320	770	8.99
Calcium	Ca	20	40.08	1.55	810	1200	6.11
Carbon	C	6	12.01	1.88–3.51	>3500	4200(?)	11.26
Cerium	Ce	58	140.13	6.7–6.9	640	1400	6.91
Cesium	Cs	55	132.91	1.87	28.5	670	3.89
Chlorine	Cl	17	35.46	1.56	−102	−34	13.01
Chromium	Cr	24	52.01	7.0	1620	2200	6.76
Cobalt	Co	27	58.94	8.9	1480	3000	7.86
Columbium	Cb	(see Niobium)					
Copper	Cu	29	63.57	8.94	1080	2300	7.72
Curium	Cm	96	(224)				
Dysprosium	Dy	66	162.46				6.82
Erbium	Er	68	167.2	4.77(?)			

Element	Sym-bol	Z	A	ρ	mp	bp	V_i
Europium	Eu	63	152.0				5.67
Fluorine	Fl	9	19.00	1.11	−223	−187	17.42
Francium	Fr	87	223				
Gadolinium	Gd	64	156.9				6.16
Gallium	Ga	31	69.72	5.91	29.8	1800	6.00
Germanium	Ge	32	72.60	5.36	960	2700 (sub)	8.13
Gold	Au	79	197.2	19.32	1060	2600	9.22
(Aurum)							
Hafnium	Hf	72	178.6	13.3	2000 (?)	3200	5.5
Helium	He	2	4.003	.15		−269	24.58
Holmium	Ho	67	164.94				
Hydrogen	H	1	1.008	.07	−259	−253	13.60
Indium	In	49	114.76	7.3	155	1450	5.79
Iodine	I	53	126.92	4.93	sublimes	184	10.44
Iridium	Ir	77	193.1	22.42	2400	4500	9.2
Iron	Fe	26	55.85	7.87	1535	3000	7.90
(Ferrum)							
Krypton	Kr	36	83.7	2.16	−157	−153	14.00
Lanthanum	La	57	138.92	6.16	826	1800	5.61
Lead	Pb	82	207.2	11.3	327	1620	7.42
(Plumbum)							
Lithium	Li	3	6.94	0.53	186	1600	5.39
Lutecium	Lu	71	174.99				5.0
Magnesium	Mg	12	24.32	1.74	650	1110	7.64
Manganese	Mn	25	54.93	7.20	1260	1900	7.43
Mercury	Hg	80	200.61	13.55	−38.9	357	10.43
(Hydrargyrum)				(20°C)			
Molybdenum	Mo	42	95.95	10.2	2620	3700	7.18
Neodymium	Nd	60	144.27	6.95	840		6.31
Neon	Ne	10	20.18	1.20	−249	−246	21.56
Neptunium	Np	93	(237)				
Nickel	Ni	28	58.69	8.90	1460	2900	7.63
Niobium	Nb	41	92.91	8.5	2500	3500	6.88
Nitrogen	N	7	14.01	.81	−196	−210	14.54
Osmium	Os	76	190.2	22.48	2700	>5300	8.7
Oxygen	O	8	16.00	1.14	−218	−183	13.61
Palladium	Pd	46	106.7	11.8	1550	2400	8.33
Phosphorus	P	15	30.98	1.82−2.70	44.1	280	11.0
Platinum	Pt	78	195.23	21.4	1770	4300	8.96
Plutonium	Pu	94	(239)				
Polonium	Po	84	210				
Potassium	K	19	39.10	0.87	62.3	760	4.34
(Kalium)							
Praseodymium	Pr	59	140.92	6.5	940		(5.76)
Promethium	Pm	61	(147)				
Protactinium	Pa	91	231				
Radium	Ra	88	226.05	(5)	960	1150	5.28
Radon	Rn	86	222.0	4.4	−71	−62	10.75

Element	Symbol	Z	A	ρ	mp	bp	V_i
Rhenium	Re	75	186.31	20.5	3100		7.87
Rhodium	Rh	45	102.91	12.3	1990	>2500	7.7
Rubidium	Rb	37	85.48	1.53	38.5	700	4.18
Ruthenium	Ru	44	101.7	12.2	2450	4150	7.5
Samarium	Sm	62	150.43	7.7	1350		5.6
Scandium	Sc	21	45.10	2.5–3.0	1200	2400	6.56
Selenium	Se	34	78.96	4.3–4.8	200	690	9.75
Silicon	Si	14	28.06	2.42	1420	2600	8.15
Silver (Argentum)	Ag	47	107.88	10.50	960	1950	7.57
Sodium (Natrium)	Na	11	23.00	0.97	97.5	880	5.14
Strontium	Sr	38	87.63	2.6	800	1150	5.69
Sulfur	S	16	32.06	1.92–2.07	119–113	445	10.36
Tantalum	Ta	73	180.88	16.6	3000	$\gtrsim$4100	6
Technetium	Tc	43	(99)				7.45
Tellurium	Te	52	127.61	6.24	450	1390	9.01
Terbium	Tb	65	159.2				(6.74)
Thallium	Tl	81	204.39	11.85	300	1550	6.11
Thorium	Th	90	232.12	11.3	1850	>3000	
Thulium	Tm	69	169.4				
Tin (Stannum)	Sn	50	118.70	5.75–7.31	232	2260	7.33
Titanium	Ti	22	47.90	4.5	1800	>3000	6.33
Tungsten (Wolfram)	W	74	183.92	19.3	3370	5900	7.98
Uranium	U	92	238	18.7	1150		4
Vanadium	V	23	50.95	5.9	1710	3000	6.74
Xenon	Xe	54	131.3	3.3	−112	−107	12.13
Ytterbium	Yb	70	173.04		1800		6.2
Yttrium	Y	39	88.92	5.51	1490	2500	6.38
Zinc	Zn	30	65.38	7.14	420	910	9.39
Zirconium	Zr	40	91.22	6.4	1900	>2900	6.84

Appendix III

VALUES OF SOME PHYSICAL CONSTANTS

Reference: "Least-Squares Adjustments of the Atomic Constants, 1952," by J. W. M. DuMond and E. R. Cohen, *Revs. Modern Phys.* **25,** 691 (1953).

Symbol and Name

N_0, Avogadro's number:
$$6.02472 \pm 0.00036 \times 10^{23} \text{ g/mole}$$

c, velocity of light:
$$299{,}792.9 \pm 0.8 \times 10^5 \text{ cm/sec}$$

e, electronic charge:
$$4.80288 \pm 0.00021 \times 10^{-10} \text{ esu}$$

m, electron rest mass:
$$9.1085 \pm 0.0006 \times 10^{-28} \text{ g}$$

h, Planck's constant:
$$6.6252 \pm 0.0005 \times 10^{-27} \text{ erg sec}$$

$F = N_0 e$, Faraday constant:
$$96520.1 \pm 2.5 \text{ coulomb/g mole}$$

$\alpha = e^2/\hbar c$, fine structure constant:
$$7.29726 \pm 0.00008 \times 10^{-3}$$
α^{-1},
$$137.0377 \pm 0.0016$$

$r_0 = e^2/mc^2$, classical electron radius
$$2.81784 \pm 0.00010 \times 10^{-13} \text{ cm}$$

$\lambda_0 = h/mc$, Compton wavelength of electron:
$$2.42625 \pm 0.00006 \times 10^{-10} \text{ cm}$$

$a_0 = \hbar^2/me^2$, Bohr orbit radius:
$$5.29171 \pm 0.00006 \times 10^{-9} \text{ cm}$$

$R_\infty = mc^2\alpha^2/4\pi\hbar c$, Rydberg for infinite mass:
$$109{,}737.309 \pm 0.012 \text{ cm}^{-1}$$

M/m, proton to electron mass ratio:
$$1836.13 \pm 0.04$$

$R_H = R_\infty(1 - m/M)$, Rydberg for hydrogen:
$$109{,}677.576 \pm 0.012 \text{ cm}^{-1}$$
energy per electron volt:
$$1.60207 \pm 0.00007 \times 10^{-12} \text{ erg/ev}$$

mc^2, electron rest mass energy:
$$0.510984 \pm 0.000016 \text{ mev}$$
conversion from amu to ev
$$931.162 \pm 0.024 \text{ mev/amu}$$

$n_0 = N/V_0$, Loschmidt's number:
$$2.68713 \pm 0.00016 \times 10^{19}/\text{cm}^3$$

$k = R/N$,   Boltzmann's constant:
$$1.38042 \pm 0.00010 \times 10^{-16} \text{ erg/degree}$$

Appendix IV

EQUATIONS OF CLASSICAL ELECTROMAGNETISM

The units used throughout are absolute, unrationalized cgs units. This system includes two different sets of units, electrostatic units (esu) for electrical quantities and electromagnetic units (emu) for magnetic quantities. The units are specified in each equation below, using emu and esu as may be appropriate. Conversions to practical units are given in Appendix V.

1. *Definition of fields E and B.* The electric field E and magnetic induction B in any medium are defined in terms of the force F felt by a test charge q at any point in the medium. We may write $F = F_s + F_v$, where F_v depends on the velocity v of the test charge, and F_s is independent of this velocity. Then

$$E \text{ (esu)} = F_s \text{ (dynes)}/q \text{ (esu)} \qquad \text{(IV-1a)}$$

$$v \times B \text{ (emu)} = F_v \text{ (dynes)}/q \text{ (emu)} \qquad \text{(IV-1b)}$$

2. *Electrostatic potential V.* A conservative force in mechanics is always derivable from a potential, $F = -\nabla\varphi$, where φ is the potential. The electrostatic potential V is a function defined so that a charge q at any point has a mechanical potential $\varphi = qV$. The force equation and (IV-1a) then yield

$$E \text{ (esu)} = -\nabla V \text{ (esu)} \qquad \text{(IV-2a)}$$

The esu unit of V is the statvolt, and of E is the statvolt/cm. Forces of type (IV-1b) are not generally derivable from a potential, so that we define only the electrostatic potential.

3. *Field and potential of a point electric charge.* A point charge of magnitude q (esu) in empty space has an electrostatic field

$$E \text{ (esu)} = q \text{ (esu)}\mathbf{1}/r^2 \text{ (cm)} \qquad \text{(IV-3)}$$

where **1** is a unit vector pointing outwards in the direction of the radius r. The electrostatic potential of this point charge in empty space is

$$V \text{ (esu)} = q \text{ (esu)}/r \text{ (cm)} \qquad \text{(IV-4)}$$

These relations show that the esu unit of potential, the statvolt, equals one statcoulomb (esu unit of charge) per cm; and that the esu unit of electric field is the statvolt/cm = statcoulomb/cm^2.

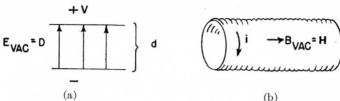

(a)   (b)

Fig. IV-1. Production in a vacuum of (a) a uniform electric
field, and (b) a uniform magnetic induction.

4. *Production of uniform fields.* A uniform electrostatic field E results in the interior of an idealized parallel-plate capacitor in which we neglect edge effects. The field is as shown in Fig. IV-1a; if the capacitor is in a vacuum, the magnitude of the field is

$$E_{vac}(\text{esu}) = V \text{ (esu)}/d \text{ (cm)} \tag{IV-5a}$$

where V is the potential or voltage difference across the capacitor, and d is the plate separation.

Similarly, the ideal model for producing a uniform magnetic induction B is the long solenoid shown in Fig. IV-1b, where end effects are neglected. If the solenoid is in a vacuum, the field in its interior is of magnitude

$$B_{vac}(\text{emu}) = 4\pi n \text{ (cm}^{-1})i \text{ (emu)} \tag{IV-5b}$$

where n is the number of turns per centimeter of the solenoid length, and i is the current. The emu unit of B is gauss, and the emu unit of i is abamperes = abcoulombs/sec.

5. *Definition of fields D and H.* Insertion of a material medium into the capacitor and solenoid of section 4 above alters the forces felt by a test charge, or hence alters E and B from the values they would have in free space. For many applications it is desirable to define auxiliary fields that depend only on the charge and current configurations producing them and not on any intervening material media. These abstract fields are the electric displacement D and the magnetic field H. These are more properly the fields produced by the capacitor and solenoid in Fig. IV-1. In cgs units they are identical with the values that E and B would have in vacuum; but they are defined to retain these values also in the presence of a material medium.

6. *Relation of E, B to D, H through ϵ, μ.* In a simple material medium E and D are parallel but of different magnitude; likewise, B and H are parallel but of different magnitude. They are thus related by constants of proportionality:

$$E \text{ (esu)} = D \text{ (esu)}/\epsilon \tag{IV-6a}$$

$$B \text{ (esu)} = \mu H \text{ (emu)} \tag{IV-6b}$$

The dielectric constant ϵ and magnetic permeability μ are constants characteristic of each particular medium. In the cgs system they are conveniently dimensionless numbers; D and H have the same units as E and B, respectively. For free space $\mu_0 = \epsilon_0 = 1$ in cgs units.

Note that there is a certain asymmetry in (IV-6a) and (IV-6b), which unfortunately carries over into the designation of E and H by the names "field," although they are not physically corresponding quantities. This asymmetry corresponds to a real physical phenomenon: for material media we generally find both μ and $\epsilon > 1$. This means that electric media generally tend to reduce, and magnetic media generally tend to increase the effects of the external charge and current distributions. Nonetheless, it is E and B that are physically comparable as specifying the force on a test charge, while D and H are physically comparable as the abstract (vacuum) fields produced by a given geometrical configuration of charges and currents, regardless of the intervening medium.

7. *Polarization P and magnetization M.* The physical cause of the difference between E, B and D, H in a medium is the polarization of that medium. The external fields D, H cause the charges and currents in the medium (originally distributed at random) to align themselves with the field. This is illustrated schematically in Fig. IV-2 for the electric case. The alignment of charge produces a secondary electric field P known as the polarization. The effective field E felt by a test charge in the medium is the sum of D and P. Since P generally opposes and reduces D, we write

$$E = D - 4\pi P \qquad (\text{IV-7a})$$

A numerical factor 4π occurs here; in the cgs system P has the same esu units as D and E.

For the magnetic case we have in a similar fashion

$$B = H + 4\pi M \qquad (\text{IV-7b})$$

where the magnetization M results from polarization of the medium. In this case a $+$ sign replaces the $-$ sign above, corresponding to the fact that the magnetization generally tends to be parallel to H and to increase it in forming B. The emu units of B, H, and M are identical.

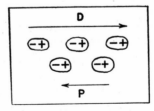

Fig. IV-2. Polarization produced in a dielectric medium.

8. *The susceptibility* χ. This is a dimensionless (in cgs) proportionality constant, defined for the electric and magnetic cases by

$$P = \chi_e E \qquad\qquad \text{(IV-8a)}$$

$$M = \chi_m H \qquad\qquad \text{(IV-8b)}$$

These definitions of χ_e and χ_m do not exactly correspond, because P and M are physically analogous quantities, while E and H are not. The asymmetry between electric and magnetic cases in (IV-6) and (IV-7) is thus preserved.

The constants of the medium χ_e and χ_m may be related to the previous constants ϵ and μ through (IV-6) to (IV-8):

$$\epsilon = 1 + 4\pi\chi_e \qquad\qquad \text{(IV-9a)}$$

$$\mu = 1 + 4\pi\chi_m \qquad\qquad \text{(IV-9b)}$$

These equations appear symmetrical, but it must be remembered that physically ϵ plays the same role as $1/\mu$. Therefore we again see that χ_e and χ_m are not strictly equivalent.

9. *Dipole moments* $\mathbf{\mu}$. An electric dipole moment is defined as follows: consider two equal point charges of opposite sign, separated by a distance d as shown in Fig. IV-3a. If the vector $\boldsymbol{d}$ is directed from the negative to the positive charge, the system represents an electric dipole moment

$$\mathbf{\mu}_e \text{ (esu)} = q \text{ (esu)} \boldsymbol{d} \text{ (cm)} \qquad\qquad \text{(IV-10a)}$$

In the idealized case we let $d \to 0$ and $q \to \infty$ in such a way that $\mathbf{\mu}$ remains constant. The ideal dipole thus displays no internal charge distribution.

The magnetic dipole moment is defined as indicated in Fig. IV-3b. A small loop of area A carries a current i. In the limit as the loop becomes infinitesimally small, we may regard A as a plane area. The magnetic dipole moment vector is perpendicular to A (defined by direction A), and is given by

$$\mathbf{\mu}_m \text{ (emu)} = i \text{ (emu)} A \text{ (cm}^2\text{)} \qquad\qquad \text{(IV-10b)}$$

when i is in the direction indicated. We may again idealize this by allowing $A \to 0$, $i \to \infty$ in such a way that $\mathbf{\mu}$ remains constant.

(a)   (b)

Fig. IV-3. (a) Electric dipole moment. (b) Magnetic dipole moment.

The polarization **P** and magnetization **M** are simply related to the induced dipole moment per unit volume of the material,

$$P \text{ (esu)} = n \text{ (cm}^{-3}) \; \mathbf{\mu}_e \text{ (esu)} \tag{IV-11a}$$

$$M \text{ (emu)} = n \text{ (cm}^{-3}) \; \mathbf{\mu}_m \text{ (emu)} \tag{IV-11b}$$

where n is the number of dipole moments were cm^3 of the substance.

10. *Dipoles in fields.* The potential energy of a dipole in a field **E** or **B** is

$$\varphi = -\mathbf{\mu}_e \cdot E \tag{IV-12a}$$

$$\varphi = -\mathbf{\mu}_m \cdot B \tag{IV-12b}$$

Taking the gradient $-\nabla\varphi$ of these potentials shows that the field exerts a torque on the dipole,

$$T = \mathbf{\mu}_e \times E \tag{IV-13a}$$

$$T = \mathbf{\mu}_m \times M \tag{IV-13b}$$

11. *Energy content of fields.* Electric and magnetic fields in space or in a material medium represent energy stored in the field during the process of its creation. This energy is regained in other forms upon collapse of the field: the recovery is perfect for fields in a vacuum, imperfect for material media (hysteresis). The energy densities or energy per unit volume associated with electric and magnetic fields are

$$u \text{ (erg/cm}^3) = (1/8\pi)E \cdot D \text{ (esu)} \tag{IV-14a}$$

$$u \text{ (erg/cm}^3) = (1/8\pi)B \cdot H \text{ (emu)} \tag{IV-14b}$$

12. *The light wave.* In classical electrodynamics the light ray is a combination of moving electric and magnetic fields. It is customary to describe it in terms of the fields **E** and **H**, respectively, although they are not physically equivalent quantities. The electric and magnetic vectors associated with a light wave of frequency ν and wavelength λ are

$$E = E_0 \sin 2\pi \; (\nu t - x/\lambda) \tag{IV-15a}$$

$$H = H_0 \sin 2\pi \; (\nu t - x/\lambda) \tag{IV-15b}$$

The vibrations of **E** and **H** are always in phase. The wave travels with a velocity

$$v = \nu\lambda \tag{IV-16}$$

The amplitude vectors E_0 and H_0 are perpendicular to each other and to the direction of the velocity **v**.

In empty space we have

$$v = q \text{ (esu)}/q \text{ (emu)} = c = 3 \times 10^{10} \text{ cm/sec} \tag{IV-17}$$

A schematic diagram of a light wave is shown in Fig. IV-4.

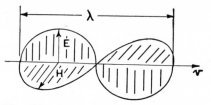

Fig. IV-4. Plane polarized light wave.

13. *Polarization of light.* The light wave of Fig. IV-4 has its vector E always in the same plane and is said to be plane-polarized. For any direction of v there are only two independent directions of plane polarization. If we take v to define a z-axis, we can take the independent planes of polarization to define x- and y-axes. Natural light is unpolarized, which means that it contains equal amounts of the two independent types of polarization. It can be made plane-polarized by various optical devices.

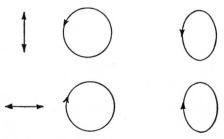

Fig. IV-5. Motion of the tip of the E-vector as seen looking into beams of plane, circularly, and elliptically polarized light.

Another type of polarization is circular polarization, in which the vectors E and H rotate uniformly with an angular frequency $\omega = 2\pi\nu$ about the axis of v as the light wave proceeds. Just as for plane polarization, there are two independent types of circular polarization— one clockwise and one counterclockwise. We may also consider natural light as composed of equal amounts of these two components. It is further possible to make elliptically polarized light, which is similar to circular polarization, except that the magnitudes of E and H depend on their directions. The motion of the E vector when viewed along the direction of v is shown in Fig. IV-5 for the two independent components of plane, circular and elliptic polarization.

14. *Energy flow and Poynting vector of a light wave.* A light wave carries energy in the direction of v at the rate uv, where u is the energy density in the associated fields. From (IV-14) this energy flow is

$$S \text{ (erg/cm}^2 \text{ sec)} = uv = \frac{v}{8\pi}(E \cdot D + B \cdot H) = \frac{v}{8\pi}(\epsilon E^2 + \mu H^2) \quad \text{(IV-18)}$$

The energy flow in the electric field equals that in the magnetic field; hence for light waves,

$$\epsilon E^2 = \mu H^2 = \sqrt{\mu\epsilon}EH \tag{IV-19}$$

The energy flow is accordingly

$$\boldsymbol{S} = \frac{v}{4\pi}(\epsilon E^2) = \frac{v}{4\pi}(\mu H^2) = \frac{v\sqrt{\mu\epsilon}}{4\pi}(\boldsymbol{E} \times \boldsymbol{H}) \tag{IV-20}$$

When a light wave impinges normal to the plane surface of a medium, $\boldsymbol{S}$, $\boldsymbol{E}$, and $\boldsymbol{H}$ are continuous across this surface. Therefore for all media

$$v\sqrt{\mu\epsilon} = \text{const} = c \tag{IV-21}$$

where c is the velocity of light in vacuum with $\mu = \epsilon = 1$. The energy flow in any medium is thus the Poynting vector

$$\boldsymbol{S} = \frac{c}{4\pi}\boldsymbol{E} \times \boldsymbol{H} \tag{IV-22}$$

15. *Intensity.* The intensity of a light wave is its average energy flow: at any fixed position the time average of S is

$$I = \frac{v}{4\pi}\epsilon E_0^2 \overline{\cos^2 \omega t} = \frac{v}{8\pi}\epsilon E_0^2 = \frac{v}{8\pi}\mu H_0^2 = \frac{c}{8\pi}E_0 H_0 \tag{IV-23}$$

where E_0, H_0 are the amplitudes of the E and H vectors.

16. *Refractive index.* In phenomenological optics, the refractive index of a medium is

$$n = c/v = \sqrt{\mu\epsilon} \approx \sqrt{\epsilon} \tag{IV-24}$$

by (IV-21). The last approximate form follows from the fact that $\mu \approx 1$ for most transparent media.

17. *Radiation by accelerated charge.* A classical accelerated charge q (esu) radiates energy in the form of light waves. The instantaneous rate of energy radiation is

$$dU/dt \text{ (erg/sec)} = \frac{2}{3}\frac{q^2 \text{ (esu) } a^2 \text{ (cm/sec}^2)}{c^3 \text{ (cm/sec)}} \tag{IV-25}$$

Here $a^2 = \boldsymbol{a}\cdot\boldsymbol{a}$ is the square of the magnitude of the acceleration. At great distances from the charge, the radiated light is transverse and is polarized according to the behavior of $\boldsymbol{a}$. An oscillating charge radiates plane-polarized light, a rotating charge radiates circularly or elliptically polarized light.

Appendix V

ELECTROMAGNETIC UNITS

The absolute, unrationalized cgs system of units is used throughout the text. Various reasons prompt this choice. The literature on atomic physics appears almost exclusively in these units, so that the student will be prepared to undertake collateral reading or further study without conversion of units. The great advantage of these units is that numerical factors are most frequently equal to unity, so that in examining a formula we can immediately concentrate on its physical implications without the encumbrance of inconvenient and physically insignificant numerical conversions. The major conversion factor involved is the vacuum velocity c of light. Since this is a universal constant of nature, it automatically fits into the physically meaningful part of each equation. In any case, the question of units should cease to be a serious problem for the student by the time he has completed a course in atomic physics. He should then be able to think in terms of atomic units— electron volts for energy, A for length (or perhaps some more natural unit like a_0, the Bohr radius), $\hbar$ for angular momentum, μ_0 for magnetic moments.

The cgs system involves two sets of units: electrostatic units (esu) and electromagnetic units (emu). The basic relation between them is (IV-17). At points in the text where confusion might arise, the charge in emu has been denoted with a prime (q', e') to distinguish it from charge in esu (q, e). For convenience in the early parts of the text, which treat macroscopic processes phenomenologically, we list equivalent quantities in the two cgs systems and in unrationalized practical units.

Quantity	Symbol	esu		practical	emu
Potential	V	1/300 statvolt	= 1 volt		= 10^8 abvolts
Charge	q	3×10^9 stat-coulombs	= 1 coulomb		= 10^{-1} abcoulomb
Electron charge	e	4.8×10^{-10} statcoulomb	= 1.6×10^{-19} coulomb		= 1.6×10^{-20} abcoluomb
Current	i	3×10^9 stat-amperes	= 1 ampere		= 10^{-1} abampere
Capacity	$C = q/V$	9×10^{11} cm	= 1 farad		= (not used)
Magnetic induction	B	(not used)	= 10^{-4} weber/m^2		= 1 gauss
Electric field	E	1 statvolt/cm	= 3×10^4 volt/m		= (not used)

Quantity	*Symbol*	*esu*	*practical*	*emu*
Magnetic field	H	(not used)	$= 10^3$ ampereturn /m	$= 1$ oersted
Electric displacement	D	1 statvolt/cm	$= \frac{1}{3} \times 10^5$ coulomb/m²	$=$ (not used)
Dielectric constant of free space	$\epsilon_0 = D/E$	1	$= \frac{1}{9} \times 10^{-9}$ farad/m	$= 1/c^2$
Magnetic permeability of free space	$\mu_0 = B/H$	$1/c^2$	$= 10^{-7}$ henry/m	$= 1$

The relation of practical to cgs units is essentially through the quantity of energy or work: $W = qV = 10^7$ ergs (esu) $= 1$ joule (practical) $= 10^7$ ergs (emu).

The units in the table above and throughout the text are unrationalized. So-called rationalized units follow if we multiply by $1/4\pi$ the equations giving D and H for any geometry of charges and currents. Thus the rationalized electric displacement of a point charge q in empty space is $D = q/(4\pi\epsilon_0 r^2)$. This provides an example of the numerical simplicity of cgs units in which $D = q/r^2$.

ANSWERS TO EVEN-NUMBERED PROBLEMS

Chapter 1

2. (a) 2.44×10^{-13} dyne;
(b) 5.20×10^{10} dynes ≈ 58 tons.

4. (a) 22 tubes;
(b) 1.05×10^{-11} mole, 3.08×10^{9} counts;
(c) 1.9×10^{11} yr.

6. (a) 7.15×10^{23}; (b) 6.08×10^{23}.

8. $\nu = 60/\text{sec}, 350\ g$.

10. 2.47×10^{-4}.

Chapter 2

2. (a) $81 \times 10^{4}\ \text{m}^2 \approx \frac{1}{4}$ sq mile;
(b) 1.86×10^{22} dyne;
(c) $2.29 \times 10^{12}\ \text{dyne/cm}^2 \approx 4Y$;
(d) 1.26×10^{7} cal $\approx \frac{1}{7}$ heat of formation.

4. (a) 5.42×10^{4} dyne/cm;
(b) 0.12 A; (c) 3.9%;
(d) $Y \approx 1.8 \times 10^{12}\ \text{dynes/cm}^2$.

6. (a) $1.066 \times 10^{-38}\ \text{g cm}^2$;
(b) $1.069 \times 10^{-38}\ \text{g cm}^2$;
(c) $\omega = 1.95 \times 10^{12}/\text{sec}$.

8. $n = D\sqrt{f/kT}$, 42.6 vibrations.

10. 7.64×10^{6}, 1.31×10^{-5} cm, 10^{-3} mm Hg.

Chapter 3

2. (a) $\boldsymbol{B}$ points up and out of page; inside capacitor plate is positive;
(b) $v = \left(\dfrac{cV}{dB}\right)\left(\dfrac{2R}{2R - x}\right); \qquad \dfrac{q}{m} = \left(\dfrac{2c}{xB}\right)v;$
(c) Since v depends only on x and fixed constants, the system acts as a velocity filter. All particles arriving at x have the same velocity. The filter selects not only v but q/m at the same time; to get different velocities for a fixed q/m requires a complicated (nonlinear) adjustment of fields.
(d) Selection of q/m means that the system functions as a mass spectrometer. The mass scale is parabolic rather than linear; this has the advantage of producing a relatively large separation

Δx for two particles of almost the same q/m when one operates near the peak of the parabola, given by $q/m = 4Vc^2/RdB^2$.

(e) $B = 500$ gausses;

(f) $v = 1.7 \times 10^7$ cm/sec, $V = 300$ volts.

4. The ions bend in a circular path of radius R; those incident at angle φ strike the plate at a distance $d = R \sin (\psi + \varphi)$ from the slit. To first order $\Delta d = R \sin (\psi + \varphi) - R \sin (\psi - \varphi) \approx 2R\phi \cos \psi$. This vanishes when $\psi = 90°$, and the ions complete a semicircle before striking the plate. The second order $\Delta^2 d = -\frac{1}{2}\varphi^2 R \sin \psi = -\frac{1}{2}\varphi^2 R$, when $\Delta d = 0$. The second-order effect smears the line on the side $d < R$; the line has a sharp outer edge at $d = R$, corresponding to $\varphi = 0$.

6. 0.17%; 29.4 m

8. (a) 4.15 mev; (b) 29.4 cm.

(c) 1.41×10^5 volts/cm, (d) $Z = 13$.

10. 0.14 cm.

Chapter 4

2. The axis A will precess about E with constant angular velocity $\omega = 0.5 \times 10^6$/sec, independent of γ.

4. $\delta = 2.6 \ 10^{-16}$ cm, $\alpha = r^3 = 1.25 \times 10^{-25}$ cm^3.

6. 7.05 amp.

8. 0.020 atm.

10. 9×10^6 scale divisions.

Chapter 5

2. 1.98×10^{-2} radians $= 1°8'$

4. (a) λ (A) $= 2.598/j$, $j = 1, 2, 3, \cdots$

(b) $j \le 5$. The first order is generally the most intense; in this case the reflection from all planes are coherent for the third order, which is therefore specially intense. Thus $j = 1, 3$, give stronger reflections than $j = 2, 4, 5$.

6. (a) (6, 2, 3) (b) $\frac{1}{3}$ A

(c) λ (A) $= 0.444/j$, $j = 1, 2, 3, \cdots$;

(d) $\Delta = 180° - 2\theta = 96°$.

8. $j\lambda = 2d\sqrt{n^2 - \cos^2 \theta}$,

$\Delta\theta \approx 2(1 - n)/\sin 2\theta = 10^{-4}$ radians.

10. $\Delta = 2\theta = 8°$.

Chapter 6

2. V (kv) $= 6.15\ j/d$ (A), $V = 2.03, 4.06, 6.09$ kv.

4.

	V	$K\alpha_1$	$K\alpha_2$
Ag	25.5 kv	559 X.U.	563 X.U.
Cs	35.9	399	405
Pt	78.2	185	191
Pb	87.8	166	171
Dy	54.0	268	272

6. 818.93 ($L_{\text{III}} - M_{\text{I}}$), 844.92 ($L_{\text{III}} - M_{\text{II}}$), 903.11 ($L_{\text{III}} - M_{\text{III}}$), 943.49 ($L_{\text{III}} - M_{\text{IV}}$), 955.16 ($L_{\text{III}} - M_{\text{V}}$), 1068.59 ($L_{\text{II}} - M_{\text{I}}$), 1193.45 ($L_{\text{II}} - M_{\text{IV}}$), 1209.80 ($L_{\text{I}} - M_{\text{III}}$), 1250.72 ($L_{\text{I}} - M_{\text{IV}}$), 1262.46 ($L_{\text{I}} - M_{\text{V}}$). The transitions violating selection rules (6.17) are relatively weak. The allowed transition $L_{\text{I}} - M_{\text{II}}$ is observed but cannot be measured accurately because of proximity to the strong line at $k/R = 1150.71$ ($L_{\text{III}} - N_{\text{IV}}$). The calculated value for $L_{\text{I}} - M_{\text{II}}$ is $k/R = 1151.6$. See S. Idei, *Sci. Repts. Tohoku Imp. Univ.*, **19**, 559 (1930).

Chapter 7

2. (a) 1.06 ev, (b) 1.16×10^4 A;
    (c) 2.09 v; (d) 2090 A.

4. (a) 4.18 v; (b) 1.59 v; (c) 7810 A;
    (d) 20.9×10^5 m^{-1}; (e) 1.59 ev.
    (f) $p_2 = -0.29,\ p_3 = -0.32,\ p_4 = -0.30,\ p_5 = -0.29$.

6. (a) $\lambda_1 = 1S - 3P,\ \lambda_2 = 1S - 2P$,
    ($\lambda_4,\ \lambda_5$) $= 2S - 3P,\ 2P - 2S$;
    ($\lambda_3,\ \lambda_6$) $= 3D - 3P,\ 2P - 3D$. From the data given, the last pairs may be exchanged.
    (b) $1S = 4.096 \times 10^3$ cm^{-1},
    $2P = 2.402,\ 3P = 1.066,\ (2S, 3D) = (1.175, 1.525)$
    (c) 2.12 volts;
    (d) 3300 A. Note that it must be exactly this wavelength, since a photon cannot give up a fraction of its energy, as an electron can.

Chapter 8

2. $v = 2.25 \times 10^{10}$ cm/sec, $E = 0.78$ mev, $T = 0.27$ mev,
    $V = 681$ v

4. (a) $P = 0,\ E = 2m_0c^2/\sqrt{1 - v^2/c^2},\ T = E - 2m_0c^2$;
    (b) $v_1 = v_2' = 0,\ m_1 = m_2' = m_0,\ v_2 = v_1' = -2v/(1 + v^2/c^2)$,
    $m_2 = m_1' = m_0(1 + v^2/c^2)/(1 - v^2/c^2)$;

(c) $P_s = -2m_0 v/(1 - v^2/c^2)$, $E_s = 2m_0 c^2/(1 - v^2/c^2)$.

6. 3.7×10^{-33} g.

Chapter 9

2. $V = 0.21 \times 10^6$ v, $\lambda = 0.024$ A,
$\nu = 1.77 \times 10^{20}$/sec.

4. This would correspond to the Compton effect formula with $\lambda' = \infty$, which is impossible for finite λ.

6. (a) $\lambda_i = 1.22$ A; (b) $\lambda_r = 1.53$ A;
(c) $n_i/n_r = 1.25$; (d) $r = 39°$; (e) $V = 75$ v;
(f) Assume that the classical accelerating force is normal to the plane of the two grids.

8. (a) 122 v; (b) 102 A;
(c) Relative to H^1 the shift of the other atoms is toward higher frequency: in units of 10^{12}/sec, $\Delta\nu = 0.673, 0.897, 1.020, 1.122, 1.154$ for H^2, He^3, He^4, Li^6, Li^7, respectively.

10. constant $= 0.48$.

Chapter 10

2. $\Psi_{n00} = 1/r(2\pi R)^{-1/2} \sin (n\pi r/R)$. If $n = 0$, $\Psi^2 \equiv 0$, and there is no particle in the box.

4. (a) 0.47; (b) 0.05.

6. $\langle V_c \rangle = 2W$, $\langle T \rangle = -W$, just as in the classical case.

8. $P_l^{l-k} (\cos \theta)$ is a polynomial in $\sin \theta$ and $\cos \theta$ that contains only the powers k, $k - 2$, $\cdots$, 1 or 0 of $\cos \theta$.
(a) $k = 0$, $(\cos \theta)^0 = $ const, no node;
(b) $k = 1$, $\cos \theta = 0$ at $\theta = 90°$, the equatorial plane;
(c) $k = 2$, $\cos^2 \theta - $ const $= 0$, $\theta = \pm\theta_0$, a double cone;
(d) $k = 3$, $(\cos^2 \theta - $ const$) \cos \theta = 0$, $\theta = 0$, $\pm\theta_0'$, equatorial plane and double cone;
(e) $\theta_0 = \pm 55°$;
(f) $\theta_0' = \pm 41°, 90°$ $(m = 0)$; $\theta_0 = \pm 63°$ $(m = 1)$.

10. 7.7×10^{-8} ev.

Chapter 11

2. (a) $L = 2, S = 1, J = 3$; $L = 3, S = 3/2, J = 3/2$.
(b) 7; 4.
(c) $^3D_1$, $^3D_2$, $^3D_3$; $^4F_{3/2}$, $^4F_{5/2}$, $^4F_{7/2}$, $^4F_{9/2}$.

4. $S = 2, L = 2$; $S = 3/2, L = 2$; $S = 5/2, L = 2$.

6. The electron g's follow from (11.23) by substituting j, l, and $s = \frac{1}{2}$ for J, L, and S. Then $g_j = 1 \pm 1/(2l + 1)$ for $j = l \pm \frac{1}{2}$

8. $^1P_1$, $^1D_2$, $^1F_3$; $^3P_{012}$, $^3D_{123}$, $^3F_{234}$.

10. (a) Three components: $^2F_{5/2} - {}^2G_{7/2}$; $^2F_{7/2} - {}^2G_{7/2}$; $^2F_{7/2} - {}^2G_{9/2}$.
    (b) 18, 22, 24 components, respectively.

Chapter 12

2. For each l there are $(2l + 1)$ independent values of m; and $\sum_{l=0}^{n-1}(2l + 1) = n^2$. The additional factor 2 comes from the electron spin states, $s_z = \pm\frac{1}{2}$.

4. Every possible value of m and s_z must be present just once; thus $M = \sum m = 0$, $S_z = \sum s_z = 0$. But a state that has only zero for its M value must have $L = 0$; by a similar argument, $S = 0$. Thus $L + S = J = 0$, and only a $^1S_0$ state is possible.

6. $(A + B)/C = (l' + 1)/l'$, $(B + C)/A = l/(l + 1)$. Putting $B = 1$, and remembering that $l - l' = 1$, we get $A = (2l' + 1)(l + 1)$, $C = (2l + 1)l'$.

8. $p^0\ ^1S$,
   $p^1\ ^2P$,
   $p^2\ ^{1,3}SPD$,
   $p^3\ ^{2,2,4}PSPDPDF$,
   $p^4\ ^{1,1,3,3,3,5}SPDPSPDPDFSPDPDFDFG$.

10. (a) $(0^2, 1, 2^2) - 0 - (1,2) = (0,2)$, where $(1,2)$ are the J values of $(p_{1/2}, p_{3/2})$.
    (b) Figure 12.3 shows that p^3 has $J = (1/2), (3/2)^3, (5/2)$. For equivalent electrons $(p_{1/2})^3$ is impossible; $(p_{1/2})^2 p_{3/2}$ is $^1S_0 p_{3/2}$ with $J = 3/2$; and $p_{1/2}(p_{3/2})^2 = p_{1/2}(0,2)$ has $J = 1/2, 3/2, 5/2$. Thus for $(p_{3/2})^3$, $J = (1/2, 3/2^3, 5/2) - 3/2 - (1/2, 3/2, 5/2) = 3/2$.
    (c) $M = \sum m_j = 0$, so $J = 0$ by the argument of problem 4; that is, four equivalent $p_{3/2}$ electrons form a closed shell. The simplest way to obtain the result (b) is by subtracting one electron from this closed shell.
    (d) From Fig. 12.3, d^2 has $J = 0^2, 1, 2^3, 3, 4^2$. $(d_{3/2})^2$ has $J = 0, 2$ just as $(p_{3/2})^2$; $d_{3/2}d_{5/2}$ has $J = 1, 2, 3, 4$ Then $(d_{5/2})^2$ has $J = (0^2, 1, 2^3, 3, 4^2) - (0, 2) - (1, 2, 3, 4) = (0, 2, 4)$.

Chapter 13

2. $B_{tot} = 1/3\ RhcZ^3 \approx 4.5Z^3$ ev $= 2.3$ mev for Pb. Although energy (mass) differences of this magnitude are measured, one never measures B_{tot} directly, but only ΔB_{tot}. This quantity is in all cases too small a fraction of the total mass to be observed.

4. 7.0×10^{-5} ev. The center of gravity motion depends upon the coordinates of all the optical electrons and becomes very complicated for more than one optical electron.

6. $^2S_{1/2} - {}^2P_{3/2}$, four components; $^2S_{1/2} - {}^2P_{3/2}$, six components. The $^2P_{3/2}$ splits into four components, indicating that $2I + 1 \geq 4$.

Chapter 14

2. Put $\nu = c/\lambda$, $d\nu = -c\, d\lambda/\lambda^2$ in (14.10), obtaining $dE \sim x^{-5}\, dx$ $[e^{1/x} - 1]^{-1}$, where $x = \lambda kT/hc$. Maximize this expression with respect to x, and obtain $(5 - y) = 5e^{-y}$, where $y = 1/x$. This has the numerical solution $y = 4.965$, or $\lambda = hc/4.965\, kT$.

4. Equation (14.13) yields $C_v = d(uV)/dT = 4aVT^3$. The finite specific heat for solids depends on the existence of an upper cutoff frequency ν_0, so that $h\nu_0/kT \to 0$ as $T \to \infty$. The photons have no such cutoff.

6. By Eq. (10.26) the difference between the two lowest energies of a particle of mass M in a box of side D is $\Delta W = (\pi\hbar)^2/2MD^2 \approx 3.5 \times 10^{-31}$ erg for the present example. This corresponds to an absolute $T \approx 2 \times 10^{-15}$ °K, many orders of magnitude below the lowest attainable limit.

8. Since neutrons and protons have spin $\frac{1}{2}$, each type of particle satisfies Fermi-Dirac statistics with particles of the same kind. For an effective temperature $T = 0$, the maximum momentum P_0 of either type of nucleon is given by integrating (14.2b): $N = Z = A/2 = 2(\frac{4}{3}\pi R^3)(\frac{4}{3}\pi P_0^3)/(2\pi\hbar)^3$. The factor 2 is for the two spin directions of a nucleon. The corresponding maximum energy is $E_0 = P_0^2/2M \approx h^2/32Mr_0^2 \approx 34$ mev; $V_0 = E_0 + B_0 = 42$ mev. The average energy is $\bar{E} = \overline{P^2}/2M = \frac{3}{5}E_0 \approx 21$ mev, so $\bar{B} = V_0 - \bar{E} = 21$ mev.

10. $$\bar{E} = \frac{1}{f}\sum_i s_i E_i e^{-E_i kT} = \frac{1}{f}\left[-\frac{df}{d(1/kT)}\right] = kT^2 \frac{d}{dT}\ln f.$$

For a diatomic molecule, $S_i = S_t S_r S_v$ and $E_i = E_t + E_r + E_v$, so the exponential factors break up into products also: $\ln f = \ln f_t + \ln f_r + \ln f_v$; and since $\bar{E}$, C_v depend only on $\ln f$, $\bar{E} = \bar{E}_t + \bar{E}_r + \bar{E}_v$, etc. Here f_t is given by (2.23),

$$f_r = \sum_J (2J + 1)e^{-J(J+1)\hbar^2/2IkT}$$

$$f_v = \sum_n e^{-[n+(1/2)]h\nu/kT} = e^{-h\nu/2kT}(1 - e^{-h\nu/kT})^{-1}.$$

INDEX